Old to New_

Old to New_

Houses by Paul Archer Design

Paul Archer
with Phyllis Richardson

For my wife, Fiona, and our son, Thomas_

First published in Great Britain 2012

Written and edited by Paul Archer and Phyllis Richardson

Book design and layout: Peter Dawson, www.gradedesign.com

Paul Archer Publishing Limited (UK)
oldtonew@paularcherdesign.co.uk

British Library Cataloguing-in-Publication Data.
A catalogue record of this book is available from the British Library.

ISBN: 978-0-9573903-0-0

Printed and bound in the UK by Kingsbury Press.

www.paularcherdesign.co.uk

Contents_

Introduction_

I love old buildings, and I love modern architecture. When I was studying architecture, debate seemed polarised between those who thought old buildings were inherently superior, with their human scale and patina of age, and those who seemed to suggest that we needed a brave new world of fantastic light and hygiene. It struck me that buildings of all ages can be wonderful or they can be poor. They either improve our quality of life or they hinder our enjoyment of it.

Before setting up my own practice, I worked on many building types, and I realised early on that I have always enjoyed working on 'the home' in preference to other buildings. I've always felt a great affinity with Winston Churchill's comment that we first make our homes, and then it is our homes that make us. Our homes are the greatest expressions of ourselves as individuals, the most personal of spaces. How we organise these spaces affects how we gather as a family, how we interact as individuals, and is a reflection of larger changes in society.

What makes a great home? For me it is the successful integration of architecture, interiors and garden. It is a space that allows us to escape the pressures of the outside world and be ourselves. All homes are arranged in spaces that progress towards privacy, leading from the street through the public rooms, to the bedroom. There are many variations in how you structure this progression but get it wrong and your house won't work.

This book is about my work in adapting old, sometimes historic, sometimes beautiful buildings to work for today's families and individuals. Through projects involving a variety of houses and the different people and families who inhabit them, I've noticed certain trends in what people prefer today, as opposed to how people have lived in houses in the past. The most obvious movements have been in the emphasis on the kitchen as the primary focus for the modern house, and in the desire to integrate indoor and outdoor spaces. Also, there has been a rise in the enjoyment and importance of bathing spaces: their function has evolved from one of basic utility to one of pleasure and relaxation. These trends are not universal, but they do represent the way we want to live now, at least in Western society. Our old houses were built for past generations of families and for their social customs. However, I have often found that period houses can be amazingly flexible, and with a bit of creative thought can be successfully adapted to our modern lifestyle. The trick is to do this in a sensitive manner, without destroying what we love about our old buildings.

With this in mind, someone might look at my work and ask, 'Why modernism?' Of course, it is possible to alter and adapt our historic buildings in styles that match the original. Perhaps the most vocal advocate of this strategy is Prince Charles, who has demonstrated his preference for houses that mimic older traditions. But I think when you are talking about adding on to an older house, this kind of thinking can result in a missed opportunity. For me, adding a copy of a historic style to an original only dilutes the original. The Modernist movement has given us a whole new understanding of space and light and, with new developments in efficient and energy-saving methods, the British are finally beginning to see the advantages that these advanced building techniques can bring to their homes.

Opposite: Ahmad House 2 (page 42).
Pp 2–3: Boucher House, completed 2011

For example, some very exciting advances have been realised in the use of glass. I've become known for working a lot with glass. My choice to use glass is a response to what clients want. I have been commissioned by many people who live in centuries-old buildings, and one of the principal complaints about nearly all of these houses is the lack of light. People who are adding on to old buildings that have small or few windows are usually keen to let in more light. In other words, it's not so much the glass that we are interested in, but the amount of natural light that can be brought inside. I've also explored advances in energy efficiency in my work. But in addition to using new techonologies, I have researched the materials and methods of the past, which sometimes present better solutions than more 'modern' approaches.

This book is a catalogue of my work with English houses. There are twenty-six projects, which represent a large portion, though not nearly all, of the houses we have worked on as an independent practice. These are organised chronologically, not by the date of the projects but by the age of the original houses we worked with. In this way it is possible to see the particular solutions we have applied to the different periods or 'types' of structures. In addition, there are four 'comment' sections, which present my thoughts on specific issues to do with renovating an existing house. 'Working with Old Buildings' describes our approach to old and new spaces and how we adapt old houses to a modern lifestyle. 'How to Green your Old House' talks about ways to make an old house or new extension energy efficient. 'Working with Glass' explains why and how I've chosen to use this material and the most recent advances in its manufacture. 'Cultural Shifts in House Design' talks about the trends in lifestyle and in clients' expectations that I have seen in working on English houses over the last twelve years. In all, this book is a celebration of my work, a way of showing how, as a practice, we have embraced the challenge of working with old houses, how we have added, renovated and, I feel, improved the experience of living in them.

Some general points about English period houses

As the projects in the book are arranged in order of the age of the original building, it is worth noting a few general characteristics of each period. English houses built in the seventeenth century came out of a form of construction that had been used since the Middle Ages. In these houses thick (2-foot/61cm) stone walls are common, with deep window reveals and small windows. Interiors tend to be dark, but will have large, open fireplaces.

The Georgian townhouse was a revolution in design, which was partly to do with the use of classical proportions, and because it introduced a very efficient form for high-density urban housing. The finely balanced relationship of house to street – the raised ground floor, the treatment of the threshold, the wrought-iron railings – allowed the houses to be packed close together while maintaining a sense of privacy. The sash window was probably invented in the previous century, but came into its own with these houses, as the use of brick allowed for thinner, stronger walls that could handle bigger window openings that brought in more light.

The Victorians didn't reinvent the Georgian townhouse, but they did introduce advances in technology. The railways and canals meant that materials could be moved around the country more easily. Bricks became the predominant building material, and the nine-inch wall became the standard. The Fire Acts of the late eighteenth century decreed that, to stop the spread of fire from one house to the next, floors had to span front to back rather side to side, and the wooden boxes for sash windows had to be hidden behind brick reveals.

The modern movement of the twentieth century did reinvent house design, but it took a long time for innovations to filter through. In the mainstream British market windows actually started to get smaller, and there is a belief that housing design actually went backwards. Some public housing made great advances, but many builders made homes with very poor-quality living spaces. The open-plan interior began to appear in mainstream housing in the 1960s and 1970s, but Britain really only awakened to the possibilities of modernism at the start of the twenty-first century.

Opposite: Cohen/Levin House (page 76).

Completion date: January 2001
Location: Keynsham, near Bristol
Materials: Glass and terra cotta

Old buildings and modern boundaries_

Wadham House 1
Jacobean farmhouse

Historic buildings sometimes pose surprising challenges. With the Wadham House the problem wasn't in maintaining the old building but with the fact that it had already been so neglected and stripped of its original elements, including ownership of the surrounding land. However, the seventeenth-century cottage itself was still very appealing. It had massive, two-foot-thick (61cm) stone walls, inglenook fireplaces and a characteristic pantile roof. What it needed was a way to make the most of its period features and transcend its spatial limitations.

Built as a farmhouse in 1620, the house was later sold to the Catholic church in the 1930s and used as a presbytery. It was bought by a builder in the 1980s. The house had once had a large garden with an old abbey wall forming one edge. However, the building had been sold by the church long ago, after which it was used for a variety of activities, including being occupied for some time by a school. Unfortunately, the church had retained ownership of the garden, leaving the house sitting on a very small plot. This is possibly why it was abandoned some time during the 1970s: it didn't function very well as a family home. The house then fell into a very poor state of repair before eventually being rescued by a builder in the mid 1980s. It was bought by my parents in 1987, during the time that I was at architecture school.

Despite signs of neglect, the house could have been fantastically cozy inside, with its exposed timber beams and a beautiful elm staircase. However, it was inherently dark and cold, even at the height of summer. What was left of the garden was basically a very strange L-shaped, corridor-like space. Last, but not least, of its problems was the fact that the main road from Bristol to Bath runs along the boundary, and this created a good deal of traffic noise.

At this time, my parents were still working though they had no children at home, so there weren't the same requirements as for a young family. But they wanted the house to be better suited to entertaining and special family events. Mostly, though, it had to work as a home for a couple.

This was a case of modernising the arrangement of spaces on the inside, so that they just worked better, with a strong, clearly defined design scheme. The second part of the task was to make the very limited outdoor

As the house is set in a medieval village, the outside of the extension takes a discreet approach. A new wall was built in Blue Lias stone matching the original house, with Bath stone copings matching the original window sills.

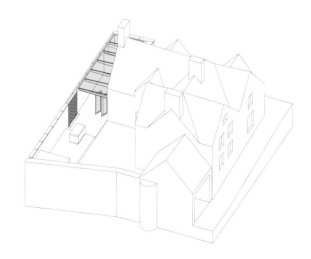

Red terra-cotta tiles were used to
clad the wall and floor. These are super
vitrified so can be used both inside and
out. The tiles on the wall just outside the
doors are stepped so that they jump in
and out of the wall line. Here there is no
rain-water pipe, and the rain water is
allowed to flow down this section of tiles
and collect in a water trough at the base
of the wall. A pump was installed so that
in summer the stored rain water can be
circulated back to the top of the wall and
allowed to flow back down the stepped
tile work. You soon realise when you
start working with an architecture
that flows between inside and out
that the acoustic environment outside
becomes far more significant to your
enjoyment of the space. Here the traffic
noise from the nearby road is, quite
literally, drowned out by the sound of
moving water.

space a pleasant and usable part of the house. Firstly, we moved the kitchen to the back of the house, and created a large new living space, which focused on the inglenook fire. A small utility room that sat in the corner of the original courtyard to the rear was demolished to give the garden a more coherent square form. Then we covered over the long, thin space between the north boundary wall and the new kitchen with structural glass. The utility space was repositioned at the back next to a small WC, and both are topped with the glass roof, which makes them much more interesting than your average utility rooms.

However, the idea behind the glass roof was not just to create a remarkable feature. It enabled us to add to the enclosed living space, but in a way that was very discreet and almost impossible to discern when viewed from the street. As much as I wanted the interior spaces to be more modern, I wanted the new and old to touch in as delicate a manner as possible.

So there are no industrial-looking attachments; the glass head detail is cut directly into the stonework. It's a dramatic intersection of periods and ideas, but not, I think, jarring or unsympathetic. Where we worked on the old structure, we did our best to keep to traditional materials. We found the stone quarry that had supplied the material for the original walls, and so were able to rebuild the boundary wall with the stone that matched the main building. For the coping stone we used the same stone that had been used for the sills of the house.

It could have been a case of making do with what was left of the old features and surrounding space of the house, but I really feel we were able to contribute something better by considering the small modern addition of the glass roof. Even on rainy days now there is something to enjoy in the architecture.

Having the glass cut directly into the old stone wall helps minimise the visual impact, making it much less obtrusive on the wall than standard lead flashing. The tile pattern of narrow and wider pieces is coordinated with the glass beams. The tiled stand-alone barbecue allows guests to gather around the chef in the open area of the garden.

Completion date: January 2006
Location: Clifton, Bristol
Materials: Zodiaq® reconstituted stone,
oak and white glass with aluminium edging

Get the balance right_

Harley House
Georgian terraced house

Period buildings have a lot of qualities that make them attractive to modern buyers. Harley House is a Georgian townhouse. It was built around 1760, and had had some modernisation but many of its features were still intact or at least recoverable. Mouldings and cornices had been preserved and the larger proportions of the first-floor rooms and tall windows were still in place, though the use had changed and everything needed work. The house also had an interesting and traceable history. It had been built by a wealthy Bristol merchant, Mr Harley, and originally had a primary position on the edge of the Bristol Downs, and a huge garden. Then the family sold off the garden to build the townhouses that now surround it. The house still had a lot of lovely Georgian character, but the question was how to make it a more useful modern family home while retaining the best historic features.

Harley House is a listed building, which means that it is protected from wholesale destruction or change. When you buy a listed building you are taking on quite a bit of responsibility; in effect, you are making an investment in our heritage for future generations. This is nearly always an ongoing job of constant maintenance, and can put a lot of people off. However, the clients here took this task very seriously, and nearly half of the budget was spent just looking after the old house, leaving only half for the updating and additions that would turn it into the family home they wanted.

Things had gone downhill for Harley House since its grand beginnings. The building of townhouses on the property left it with only a tiny, north-facing garden. In recent years, previous owners had updated and added modern services, but rather than working them into the structure or concealing them, these pipes and wires just ran across the plasterwork and mouldings. One of the strangest features of the house in the twentieth century was that the entrance led directly into the kitchen.

A lot of the first part of the work involved learning about the existing house—talking to experts about the best repair methods and untangling the web of twentieth-century pipes and wires. All of the services were re-run and hidden within a new vertical riser inserted into the old dumb waiter. We also added modern improvements in services, such as underfloor heating and effective lighting design that mimicked candlelight rather than harsh ceiling lights. Roof tiles were relaid and chimney breasts repaired.

The most remarkable change in the house came with moving the kitchen away from the entrance and reclaiming the first-floor *piano nobile* for the main living space. In most Georgian houses this front room on the first floor is the most important. It expands to the full width of the building, as the stairs are at the back, and has grander proportions than the lower or upper floors. This was true of Harley House. The first-floor rooms have taller ceilings, more ample fireplaces, intricate cornice detailing and, most importantly, large south-facing windows. We discovered, through cutting out part of the skirting boards, that the front room had originally been open to the room behind it. This evidence helped us to persuade the conservation officer to let us open it back up again so that we could put the large family kitchen at the back of the space. While you normally wouldn't put the family space so far away from the garden, here there was no private garden but there were great views to be had from the first floor out over the Downs.

Concrete roof tiles were replaced with slate according to conservation preferences. This was done to match the neighbours (but the roof was probably covered in pantiles originally). The original pantiles on the back roof slopes were relaid, all the chimney breasts and parapets were carefully repaired, and new lead flashing was used to replace the 'flashband', a sticky-backed lead substitute from the 1990s.

The starting point of the project was to ensure that the restoration of the original features of the house that were remaining was given priority. The hues of the new paintwork were determined by evidence of earlier colour schemes.

The lighting design was a very important part of the project. We have decided against the use of downlights in our work because they have been so overused in the last twenty years. 'Spotty' ceilings full of downlighters tend to say 'developer' rather than individual home to me. We preferred to mimic the effect of candlelight, which is much warmer and more intimate. For this we used lots of small point sources and wall lights.

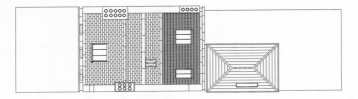

New Roof

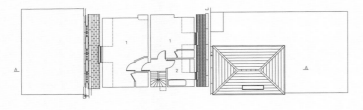

New Third Floor
1 Bedroom
2 Bathroom

New Second Floor
1 Bedroom
2 Dressing
3 Bathroom

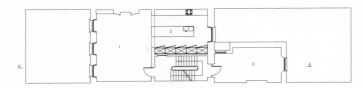

New First Floor
1 Living
2 Kitchen
3 Study

New Ground Floor
1 Living
2 Bedroom
3 Shower
4 Kitchen

New Basement
1 Bedroom
2 En-suite
3 Playroom
4 Utility

My favourite detail here is the kitchen
extractor fan. This is the exact proportion
of the original chimney breast that
we cut back to ceiling level. Two large
industrial-quality extractor fans are set
into the base of this, and a flush induction
hob is recessed into the Zodiaq® worktop.
The old smoke vent became the new
extract for cooking odours.

The garden, which had once been huge,
was almost non-existent when we came
to the project. Without a garden, the next
best thing was to move the family space
up onto a higher floor to get the views
over the park, and the best natural light.

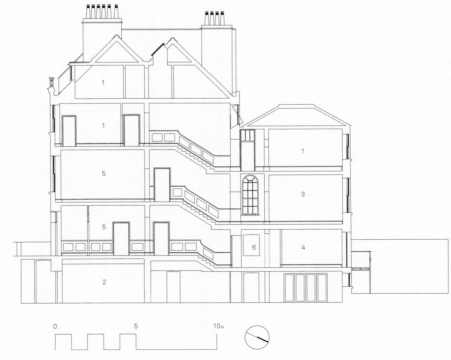

New Section

1　Bedroom
2　Guest bedroom
3　Study
4　Kitchen
5　Living
6　Shower room

The second-floor master suite uses lots of timber and dark tones to create a warm, private atmosphere. The clients specified separate 'his' and 'her' walk-in wardrobes.

The bath in the master suite was fitted with a block timber cover so that it could double as a bench, as the clients would most often be using the shower and liked the idea of having another surface.

The guest bathroom on the basement level (lower left) uses a series of etched-glass screens to let borrowed daylight through the space.

With the living spaces opened up on the first floor, we reconfigured the ground-floor space as a suite for the grandparents, with its own living room positioned at the front of the house near the entrance. The family now enter on the ground floor and proceed upstairs to their living room, kitchen and bedrooms. The master suite is situated above the first floor, with a spacious bedroom above the living room, and a large walk-in wardrobe and bath at the back. The children's rooms are on the floor above the master suite. The basement is a guest suite and games room with a fold-down bed. Some floors were still covered in beautiful parquet, and we managed to salvage enough pieces to re-use as a border around the carpet. This is a good trick if you don't have enough of the original parquet to relay the whole floor.

It seems to me that one of the things we enjoy most about listed buildings is the layering of history. Although I am convinced of the value and importance of modern methods and materials, imposing the latest design approach is not always the best solution (dogma can be a dangerous thing!). There are times when I feel it is better to copy sections of the original. In this project we did both with a very satisfying result. We began with a rather wonderful but well-worn period building that had awkward living spaces. It is now a fully functioning, multi-generational, modern home with carefully preserved eighteenth-century elements helping to frame a comfortable contemporary lifestyle.

Completion date: December 2009
Location: Islington, London
Materials: Zinc and limestone

Over and underground_

Rayner House
Georgian terraced house

The Rayner House is a beautiful, Grade II-listed townhouse in London, which was built as part of a classic Georgian terrace composition that treats a group of houses as one grand palace. This house forms the end wing, so we had the advantage of a side rather than a front entrance. The owners were a young family who had lived in the house for some time but were outgrowing their space. They wanted to get the main living spaces in the house working better, connect the house and garden, and then add some guest accommodation. Over the years they had put in applications for permission to extend the house, but these were all batted back to them by the planning authority due to conservation restrictions. We had to see if there was a more creative way to achieve the extra space the family needed while still adhering to planning guidelines.

The first challenge was to convince the clients to take down their relatively new conservatory (above) as it was dark, being on the north side of the building, and it had been set at too low a level to have a relationship with the garden.

Being part of a listed building, even the wobbly garden wall was protected and had to be retained. The glass pavement lights bring natural light into the basement spaces below, while at surface level they emphasise the linear flow of the garden.

Sitting on the same footprint as the original garage (below), the new garden room (opposite, left) faces south. The two panels above the stairwell sit behind the original garage doors and can be opened onto the street to allow large pieces of furniture to be brought inside.

The solution was influenced by the fact that there was some room for manoeuvre underground. Below the back garden were some vaulted spaces, which seemed to date from the same time that the house was built. These had been converted to use as a bathroom some time in the mid twentieth century and featured very strange mosaic tiles. This can't ever have been a pleasant space, as it was so dark, cold and damp. Still, it was something to work with.

The garden had to be designed as part of the whole but it also needed to be robust enough to handle things like a kids' game of football. There was a ruined garage at the far end of the garden, and this gave us good grounds to reinstate a structure of the same size. However, the first thing to do was to persuade the couple to replace the conservatory that they had put in only a few years before. This allowed us to access the garden directly from the ground-floor living room. The next key move was to convert the garage structure into a usable space and, most importantly, make it an extension of the house by connecting to it through spaces underneath the garden. We did this partly by using the original vaults, and partly by digging a new link tunnel. We had wanted this to be more than a tunnel but the local authority planners insisted that we leave enough ground to plant a substantial tree, which, I agree, does make a difference to the overall street scene.

We kept the basic form of the old garage and added a wide bay of about 600mm depth with three sliding, folding doors so that you can sit under shelter at the end of the garden and have a wide-open view back towards the house. This room can be used as part of the guest suite or as an outdoor family room. We put the guest room below the garden room on the basis that you need less light for sleeping. We converted the original vaults into the guest shower room and retained their arching forms.

The main challenge here was to get light down into the lower floor, and we accomplished this by inserting a line of four flush pavement lights. These are clear glass panes (about 2.5 by 0.75m) with a dot print on the upper surface. The printed detail provides a bit of modesty screening as well as a non-slip surface (essential for football). The stone pavers are set up on adjustable feet so the paving can lie perfectly flat, not having that drunken feel as it follows the fall of the ground level, while rain water runs through the joints and along the ground underneath.

The sections of pavement glass provide shafts of natural light, as well as variation and drama to the rooms below. These rooms have been thoroughly modernised and finished with high-quality materials to make them feel as open and unlike a basement as possible. A skylight in the roof of the new garden pavilion sits over the stairwell leading to the rooms below, allowing even more light to wash through both the ground- and lower-floor rooms. As the garden is north facing, the space outside the new pavilion has become a wonderful place to sit and enjoy the sun. I like the idea that when the doors are open on a summer evening the family can set up a dining table in the new space. But it did also occur to me that with the doors open, the width would make a good-size goal area!

The position of each of the roof lights coincides with the four steps in the basement ceiling. A fold-down bed in the guest room (above) can be put away and the room used as a gym with equipment (left).

Overleaf: the pavement lights become glowing floor tiles in the evening. The top face of the glass has been silk-screened with a dot pattern to create a non-slip surface.

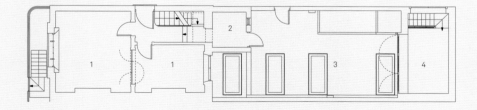

New Ground Floor
1 Reception
2 Cloaks
3 Garden
4 Garden room

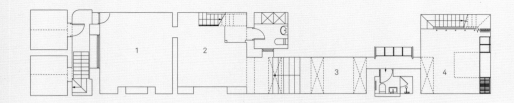

New Basement
1 Kitchen
2 Living
3 Family
4 Guest room

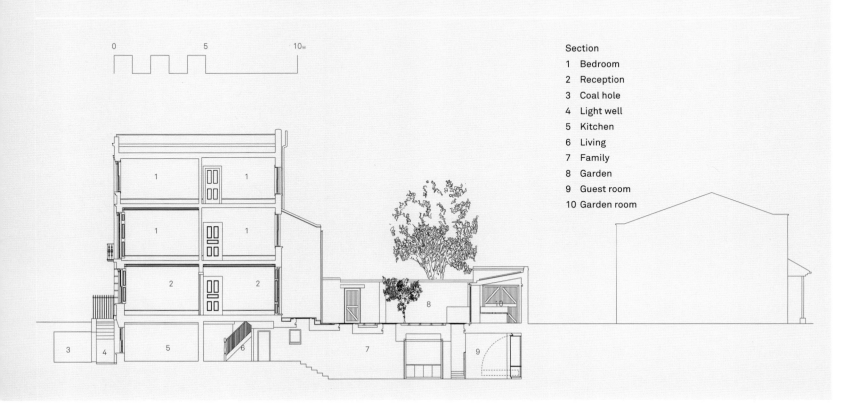

Section
1 Bedroom
2 Reception
3 Coal hole
4 Light well
5 Kitchen
6 Living
7 Family
8 Garden
9 Guest room
10 Garden room

Completion date: August 2009
Location: Islington, London
Materials: Black glass and granite

Restore, re-new, modernise_

Hunt House
Regency townhouse

I don't think anybody had lived at Hunt House for some time. The rooms had been laid out as bed-sits, probably in the interwar years. The interior was cold and damp: water was coming in from the roof above and from the earth below. Originally built as one of a group of four houses, it would have been surrounded by green countryside. By the time we saw it, the house was in a fairly dilapidated state, hardly having been touched by modern services. But as a result it still retained many of its period features. Despite the work it might need, a building of this kind is always a treat to work with because it still has so much of its original character. Our aim was to carefully restore the house and enable the enjoyment of the original features while adding a contemporary layer to turn it into a modern family home.

The shed volume to the left of the back door (above) was retained in the new structure. This addition was designed to keep to the same boundary as that original extension. The pivoting door opens to a covered outdoor space, which can be used as a shelter by outdoor smokers.

To start with we had to tackle the changes that had already been made to this house. Instead of being set up as a normal house, there were about three interconnected flats, one on each level, which all shared a common hall. There were individual kitchenettes, and lots of separate wiring and services. Luckily, all of the old woodwork was in place, though it needed careful mending, sanding and repainting. The main fireplaces, doors and shutters were also still in situ. We kept (and restored) almost all of these existing elements, something that we agreed with the clients at the very first meeting. But from there we needed to move forward with a scheme to rationalise the interior.

The clients were a creative couple with young children, and this needed to be a family home. Having lived in a converted warehouse flat, they were keen on open-plan living, but, on the other hand, they didn't want to lose the qualities of the old structure. They also wanted to have a connection to the garden for the children. Overall, they wanted whatever scheme we came up with to be 'green'.

This house had the typical arrangement with the street entrance on the middle level of three storeys, and the garden level with the lower floor. We wanted to create a direct flow from the front door down to the living area and out to the garden. We managed this by adding a small staircase that takes you down to the lower level directly from the entrance hall rather than the traditional dog-leg arrangement. From there your eye is drawn through the house out the original back doorway, into the glazed extension

and out to the garden. The new lower floor is divided into three distinct spaces: a reading room (also used for guest accommodation) at the front of the house; a TV room in the darker core of the ground floor; and the kitchen/dining area in the new, light-filled space facing onto the garden.

The extension was also a combination of old and new. There were a number of sheds, as well as a lean-to structure at the back. We got rid of all but one substantial structure, which we absorbed into the footprint of the new space. The modern, glazed room is now full of the light and greenery of the garden. By making the wall and the roof in glass we minimised the barrier between indoors and out, emphasising the connection instead. The new roof is part sedum, which looks great from the upper floor windows. In addition to the glass section at the rear we also added a long roof-light, which brings natural light to the inner rooms and signals a distinction between the historic building and the new extension.

Adding glass and allowing for passive solar gain is one way of making a house more efficient. The most basic energy-saving and cost-effective thing you can do to a house is to seal it from draughts as much as possible. Yet houses like this have to breathe, to keep moisture (damp) from building up. So the whole house has a heat recovery ventilation system (HRVS) that draws fresh air in (warming it through a heat exchanger) while drawing stale air out. The balance between old and new actually worked out really well and shows how a very bold modern design can sit well with an older building.

A very fine steel frame is built into the corner junction of the glass. This frame works with the glass wall to hold up the glass roof. A less imaginative engineer might have used a much larger steel, resulting in less transparency.

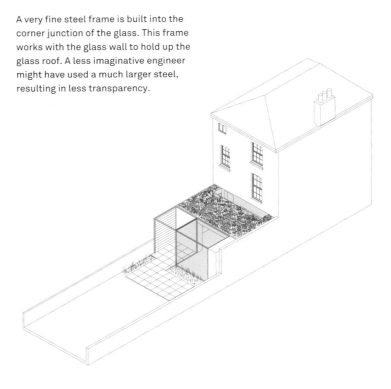

The idea was to bring the experience of the garden as close as possible to the indoors. Therefore, the planting has been taken right up to the glass to make eating in the dining space akin to sitting outside.

The floor is paved with large granite slabs that continue outdoors. The surface on the inside is honed to a smooth finish, while the outdoor slabs have been flamed for a non-slip finish. This is a great material for a kitchen because it is impermeable and very strong. We used super-sized slabs rather than standard pieces, so the space feels grander in proportion.

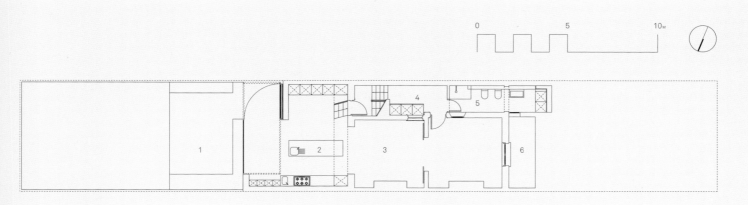

New Lower Ground Floor

1 Terrace / 2 Kitchen / 3 Living / 4 Hall / 5 Bathroom and utility room / 6 Light well

The family bath (below left) and the guest bath (below right) are clad in the same tiles, light grey to go along with the timber floor and dark grey to match the granite floor, which runs through from the kitchen.

The exterior colour was matched to one of the earliest colours discovered under the many layers of paint. We installed new double-glazed window units that have super-skinny glazing bars to mimic the proportions of the original Regency windows.

Completion date: April 2006
Location: Kensington, London
Materials: Turkish limestone and bog oak

Light-filled elegance underground_

Ahmad House 2
Regency terraced house

In the early nineteenth century, when it was built, this was a well-proportioned townhouse sitting on the outskirts of London. But then the city expanded, the house became part of the Royal Borough of Kensington and Chelsea, and fifty years after it went up, the entire terrace lost its back gardens in the construction of the new underground District Line. Consequently, the two-storey Regency house, our second project for Mr Ahmad, had no garden at the back and at the front there was only a small garden space that had become more a part of the streetscape. Our initial idea was to build upwards, so we applied for permission to add a new mansard roof, but, this being a notoriously strict conservation area, we were denied. So, since we couldn't go back because of the railway and we couldn't go up because of the planning authority, we decided to go down.

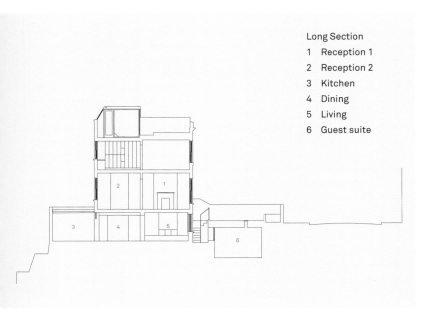

Long Section
1   Reception 1
2   Reception 2
3   Kitchen
4   Dining
5   Living
6   Guest suite

We left the light well between the front garden and the front of the house to bring light into this basement space below. The bifold windows can be folded back to create a wide opening (facing the house). Pavement lights were added to bring direct natural light into the room.

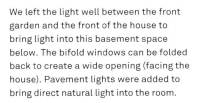

Digging down might seem like a dramatic building solution, but done in the right way, it can be very liberating in terms of space. Here, it wasn't necessary to go under the whole house, as there were already basement rooms that could be put to better use. Carving out a space beneath the paved front garden made sense, as it would be a lot easier to deal with than excavating under the actual house. The client wanted to give the house a more open and bespoke living space, while adding a guest room. He also had ideas about building a hammam in the new underground area, which would have been quite something, but in the end he decided to be sensible and dedicate rooms to more practical purposes.

Of course, we proceeded with some amount of caution. We carefully took apart the existing garden pavement, steps and railings (and replaced them afterwards). After some delicate negotiations with the neighbours, we then dug down about 4.5 metres, enough to create airy 2.4-metre ceilings for the new guest accommodation. The basement rooms under the house were then opened up and turned into primary living space – a sitting room with new fireplace, a dining room and, at the back, a new kitchen. The rest of the house, containing the formal living room on the ground floor and master bedroom and study on the first floor, needed only general repairs.

A big concern with basement rooms is obviously light, and we employed a range of solutions to ensure that the new underground guest quarters, as well as the basement living spaces, felt warm and bright. Firstly, we left the original light well between the garden and the main house so that the new

guest suite had natural light coming in. Then, when we re-laid the garden paving stones, we replaced several with glass to let some direct sunlight into the room from above. We added a continuous limestone floor that runs from the new space through to the living space. We even continued it on to form the hearth for the fireplace, and to the kitchen area. The pale colour of the stone bounces the light around and unifies the rooms. And the single material, with its natural variations, creates a very smooth, modern atmosphere.

We also made a set piece of the stair leading from the new underground space up to the ground floor. This had been a simple service stair, but now that the basement rooms were to be used as primary living spaces for the house we thought that the stairs should be more of an event. The treads are cantilevered out of the wall and the balustrade is made from a single piece of glass that runs from floor to ceiling. This maximises the light and also makes the living space feel as wide as possible.

This is the second project that we have carried out for this client, and it was a project for him alone, so it was very personal in terms of his taste and choices. For example, he sourced the particular limestone that was used on the floors and hearth in Turkey, and he chose the 'bog oak', a beautifully rich dark timber, for the kitchen, giving that space a more enclosed, cave-like quality. It is wonderful to have that amount of involvement from a client, to make the project a collaborative effort.

In a basement space, the use of glass increases the sense of openness. The living space here takes a light tone from the oak stair and limestone flooring, while the client chose the darker 'bog' oak for a cave-like kitchen experience. The darker timber also works well with the black-glass appliances and black-granite worktop.

The fireplace sits in the space of the original chimney breast with a new raised hearth that provides storage on either side of the fireplace. The lifted middle panel sits over a slotted vent. The black granite surround is the same material that was used for the kitchen countertops.

Working with old buildings_

Old buildings were made quite differently from modern ones. This might seem obvious, but the implications of the fact are often ignored, and many problems are stored up for the future. When upgrading an old house it is important to use appropriate construction technology, and it's important to know what you don't know in this area – if your building is listed, then it is a good idea to call in the experts and do the job properly. There are two main considerations in working on old houses: how to do the conservation work, and how to make any new work relate to the original building, even if a new addition is thoroughly modern in design and function.

The approach to architectural conservation work has evolved and been refined all through the twentieth century. In the early half of the century, conservation was carried out using modern materials. It soon became apparent that many of these kinds of repairs started to do more damage to the old structures than would be caused by natural wear and tear. For example, cement was often used to repair exterior degradation, but we now know that pointing some types of softer brick with a hard, impermeable, cement-based mortar causes the brickwork to erode more quickly. It is now generally understood that brick walls constructed with lime-based mortar lasted well because they were breathable and flexible. Moisture passes through the walls and the softer lime mortar allows the building to flex as moisture builds and then dries out again. Cement, however, is non-permeable, which means that after being re-pointed with cement, the bricks in any wall will crack from having to take on all of the movement and changes in moisture content.

We have also learned to appreciate the Victorians' strategy of building walls of one-brick thickness, which turns out to be perfect for the English climate. Throughout the winter months the walls slowly absorb increasing amounts of rain water, but the summer months usually give the wall enough time to dry out again before the onset of the next winter. If you put your hand on the inner face of a brick wall in the spring after a particularly wet winter, it is often damp to the touch; yet that same wall will be perfectly dry again by the end of a warm summer.

I'm a great believer that we should look after our architectural heritage, but I feel we should have the courage to build in a style of our own. As I've mentioned elsewhere in the book, modernism offers some wonderful new experiences and ways of living. But how do we avoid modern designs that, as Prince Charles once put it, appear as a 'monstrous carbuncle on the face of an old friend'? Our own work varies in terms of how we relate a new structure to an existing building, as every design has different constraints, but there are some consistent themes that can be identified.

Firstly, the form of a new extension ought to harmonise visually with the old building, though it shouldn't attempt to replicate its style. The most straightforward way to do this is to identify the main building lines of the existing structure and carry them through into the new. My old tutor at university would call these 'regulating' lines. However, the mass and form of the extension should be in sync. For example, if the back of the existing building has a stepped façade, then this can be echoed in the new structure, either by creating a stepped roofline that follows the line of the old façade, or perhaps by introducing a changing ceiling level that has a stepped form.

The success of this design strategy is affected by the way that you handle the junction between the new building and the old. Very often we choose to construct this junction in glass. It is important to consider that when you extend a room beyond the original boundary, you are making the existing area deeper in plan, so the back of the room becomes more distant from the windows, which are usually the main source of natural light. This is why we will try to add roof-lights at the point where the old and the new building meet, to get as much natural light back into the original space as possible.

This method also offers an opportunity to make a clear distinction between the old building and the new. For, when I say that the new building should 'harmonise' with the old, I do not mean that it should try to be an exact copy in style or materials. This has never been my way of thinking, or I would never have used glass in the ways that we have. I have always liked the approach of the SPAB (the Society for Protection of Ancient Buildings, of which William Morris was a co-founder). They encourage working in such a way that makes it possible to 'read' the building, that is, to be able to unpick its history. In this way a building is allowed to display all its different layers of history, and is not a confused build-up of additions that attempt to copy its 'original' style.

Secondly, as a further way of harmonising the structures, we try very hard to maintain a relationship between the proportions of new and old elements. We let the proportions of the old structure help determine the proportions of the new, and this works from the large-scale changes down to smaller details. One example of the former is Hunt House (pp. 34–41). Looking at the width of the house from the rear, we could see that it followed the common proportions for the period of having approximately one-third of the space devoted to the stairwell, with the other two-thirds given over to living space. In devising the extension we came up with a solution that involved having one-third of the structure set back (coinciding with the stairwell area) and two-thirds coming forward (mirroring the original living spaces). With regard to smaller details, it is very common that we will copy the existing house skirting heights or mouldings, albeit in a modern profile.

Thirdly, and just as importantly, the material of the new works should have something to do with the existing house. Again, this does not mean a slavish copying of the original, but that there is some sense of harmony. The Collins House (pp. 52–57) is a good example. Here, we used new aluminium flashings but we had them powder-coated in black to match the original black, cast-iron rain-water pipes. A lot of older buildings feature lead on their external roofs and flashing, but since lead is no longer used by most of Europe anymore due to its toxicity we try to avoid it. Instead, we use a lot of zinc for the new builds as it resembles the lead and doesn't look out of place next to the old buildings. Zinc also has the advantage of 'crisper' edges that look more refined.

After all of this discussion of adding a layer of new to our old buildings, it is important to point out that sometimes you have to know when to replicate a part of the original building, rather than putting in something new. This is a fine judgement, but a classic example is the decision to put back traditional timber sash windows if the originals have been replaced by modern variants. There is something about the proportions of the Victorian townhouse (in particular) that just don't work as well with modern replacement windows. In each case, it is important to know when it's best to follow the rules, or tradition, and when to break with it. The aim is to show respect for the original building, and strike some harmony of style, proportion and materials, while being able to create comfortable, modern living spaces.

Opposite: Harley House (page 18).

Completion date: January 2006
Location: Canonbury, London
Materials: Concrete and black aluminium

Connecting with outdoors_

Collins House
Early Victorian terraced house

Victorian houses occur in more variations than you might think. The Collins House is a nineteenth-century, double-fronted design that sits at the end of a terrace on a corner plot. In terms of plot size, this is fairly luxurious compared to most London terraced houses. However, though the house is wide, it is only one-room deep. There were usable basement rooms, which had windows that were open to light at the front, but the rear basement room faced a light well that was actually rather dark, as it came up against the raised garden. The ground sloped further upward, leaving the basement in the shadows, and the kitchen was stranded without any access to the garden just beyond it. So, although the house possessed a huge garden with a favourable south-facing aspect, it felt, and was, disconnected from the life of the house.

In addition to solving the problem of the dark basement rooms and access to the garden, there were other issues. The stairway split the main floors down the centre so that there were no large spaces for the family to enjoy. Although the clients had already invested a lot of time and energy in improving the garden, and wanted to have more use of it, they couldn't be sure how long they would be in this house, so their plans for reorganising were less ambitious than they might have been. For instance, we looked at a significant excavation of the garden across the full width of the house, which would have allowed the whole basement level open access and visual connection to the outdoors. However, it was decided that this was a disproportionate budget spend given the uncertainty of the clients' time here.

The original light well added no positive qualities to the house or garden.

Although this scheme is very modern, I wanted to connect the new and old through the use of materials. The original house has render on the lower level, and the upper walls are in London brick. Other key features are the black cast-iron pipework and painted timber. The new aluminium flashings are powder coated in black to match the old cast-iron elements. The concrete retaining walls are painted white on their vertical faces to correspond with the original render.

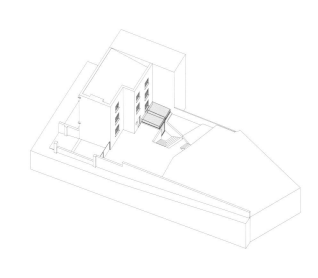

However, I don't think the final scheme was a compromise, given what we achieved. We decided to work with the existing light-well structure, which kept the budget down and left the diagram of the original house intact, something I think worked out nicely. To draw in more light we added a glass roof over the former light well to act as a lantern, and we expanded the basement – now the dining area – under the glassed-in space. We wanted to create the sense of sitting out under the canopy of the adjacent tree, while being comfortably inside. Creating the raised glass box over the space carries the reach of the room upwards and also prevents people on the paved terrace from walking onto the glass roof.

We also worked on the external stairs that lead up to the garden from the basement level. We carried out some excavation and pushed this stairway backwards, into a wider angle, so that more light could reach the lower floors and so that the view from the dining room moves up the slope of the stairs rather than hitting a solid vertical wall. The new stairs form a fan-shape that follows the geometry of the original garden, splaying at the corner of the terrace. This gives access to the main garden level along one side and leaves room for plants and ornaments on the other side. When you are in the dining space, the perspective is much wider than before, and you can look out onto a stepped garden of potted greenery.

We always knew that, due to its orientation, the glassed-in space would get very hot if we didn't contain the solar gain. Since the basement spaces of these brick houses are inherently cool, all you need to do is avoid adding extra heat (except in winter, when solar gain is a positive thing). So, at the back of the glass structure we installed a perforated aluminium sheet that forms a duct over a series of small fans that can be used to assist air extraction when necessary.

I've always enjoyed the way this scheme 'squeezes' the view through a tight opening rather than just fully exposing the back. This does tend to focus your view upwards through the roof and over the garden steps, and makes for a much more interesting sequence of spaces as you walk from inside to out.

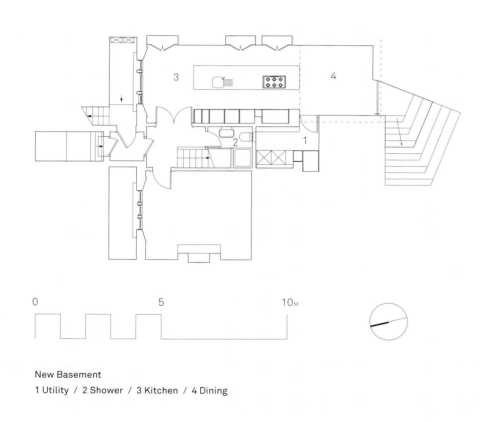

0   5   10 M

New Basement
1 Utility / 2 Shower / 3 Kitchen / 4 Dining

The geometry of the fanned steps corresponds with the angle of the original garden shape and creates a funnel-like path towards the house.

Completion date: January 2003
Location: Primrose Hill, London
Materials: Glass and Brazilian slate

A quest for purity_

Middlemiss Flat
Early Victorian terraced house

In some ways this is a classic English conservatory, a way of being outdoors even in bad weather. Obviously, it's also much more than that. For the Middlemiss Flat glass technology was pushed to a new level, both for the aesthetic quality and for the pursuit of innovation. However, the beginnings of the project were modest in terms of space. This was a large house in Primrose Hill, a villagey neighbourhood of early Victorian houses set beside the open green space of Regent's Park. The client occupied only a one-bedroom flat on the ground floor, but he had sole access to the south-facing garden, which he wanted to inhabit more fully. The garden had some mature planting, and there was little worry of being overlooked, so the idea was to create a space that projected out into the garden, like a conservatory. Beyond that, the aim for the client, and for us, was to create 'the ultimate glass box'.

The garden design was a crucial part of the process. Some of the more mature planting was kept, but we built a new, L-shaped paved area using beautiful large slabs of light-coloured slate. One leg of the paving was sunken and flooded to form a simple reflecting pool. As this is positioned directly south of the glass structure, the sunlight casts multiple rippled reflections onto the glass, which compound the many reflections from the faceting of the form.

The client for this project had a strong influence in the unadulterated form of the design. He pushed us from the start to make the detailing as pure and simple as possible. As a former buyer for a major UK design shop, he had acquired a collection of modern design prototypes and had a very well-trained eye. He was also used to scrutinising detail at a level appropriate for furniture, i.e., more finely tuned than is usually required for buildings. He had strong ideas of what he wanted, and his commitment, in the face of some compromises and practicalities (which we were careful to point out as the scheme developed), was something special.

The glass box is now both an extension of the interior room and a separate conservatory space. While you are in it, the garden surrounds you on three sides, with one side fully open to the living space. It can be separated from the living room by a pair of fully glazed sliding doors, which also allow for passive solar gain. Like a true conservatory, it is not meant to be fully habitable in very cold weather, but because of its orientation the space can be warmed by just a little sunshine in winter.

Making a pure glass box without any visible supports is a particular challenge for any designer or architect. That this scheme won awards for its innovation in glass technology is due in large part to the skill and imagination of our structural engineer, David Crooks of Fluid. The main difficulty was the desire to do away with vertical stiffening members that would normally be used in such a structure. These would usually be steel, or they could even be glass fins projecting into the space. But we felt that any vertical structure would detract from the sense of openness, as well as constraining how the space could be used. So David devised a foundation clamping detail, and Firmans, our excellent glass contractor, built a sample wall/roof/beam assembly. This was then rigorously tested. The overall proportions of the space were determined by the largest glass-toughening kiln in the UK at the time, 2440mm (8 feet).

One of the most important and less obvious details of the scheme is the ventilation system. I've always admired the way some old buildings use very simple but effective systems that do not rely on services engineers to design them. We knew that an almost completely sealed, south-facing, glass box was going to be hot in the summer. We tackled this by putting in a set of underground concrete pipes that run under the reflecting pool and end at a fan housing hidden in the greenery. The air is pushed through the ground, which is a fairly constant 12-14C at that depth, and enters the glass space through the joints in the paving slabs. There are also two high-level extractors at the back of the space, which create a cross-flow of air. The efficiency of the system shows that it is possible to build beautifully and sustainably.

The clamping detail and wall/roof/beam assembly were tested to destruction by loading it with sandbags until the wall panel buckled and exploded. The roof is a single sheet of glass, supported by the thinnest of glass beams. Glass walls were slotted into a solid slate base, leaving just a fine gap for rain water and fibre-optic lighting. Gaps in the floor slates also allow for air to be pumped in, while the high-level vents in the brick wall of the main house pull air out, keeping the space at external temperatures in the summer. Underfloor heating warms the space during the cooler months.

1   Ventilation gap
2   Slate slabs
3   Condensation channel
4   12 mm s/s brackets
5   Drainage channel
6   Fibre-optic lighting
7   Walls consist of 2 sheets of 12 mm toughened and heat-soaked glass laminated together with clear resin interlock
8   Pool

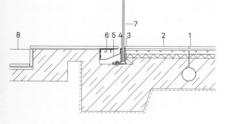

Two glass sliding doors are hidden in pockets in the walls (opposite) to separate the space in winter.

Fibre-optic lighting is used to provide light in areas that would be difficult to access for changing light bulbs. It also allows for completely different lighting moods: blues in the summer make the space feel cooler; yellows create a warmer atmosphere in winter.

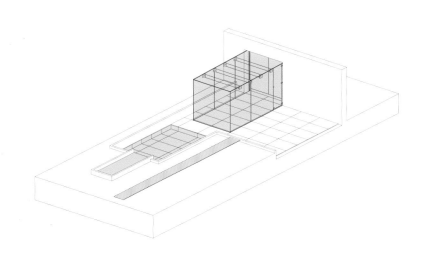

Completion date: February 2003
Location: Canonbury, London
Materials: White render, mill-finished aluminium and lino

Space for working and living_

Waldron House
Early Victorian terraced house

The Waldron House was a good-sized, mid-terrace house that had a verdant, west-facing garden. The problem, as in many of these houses, was with the lower-level spaces which, because of the raised garden level, received little or no natural light and were therefore very gloomy. There was also the problem of easy access to that outdoor space. The entrance to the house was on the upper ground floor (half a storey higher than the garden) and the kitchen was in the lower ground floor (half a storey below the garden). To reach the garden space you had to go down some narrow steps from the main floor. While the living spaces on the upper ground floor worked quite well, the lower-ground-floor kitchen was terribly dark. Though the goals here were familiar – better garden access and more light in the lower rooms – the approach had to fit the needs of these occupants.

We had a fairly easy task with the excavation, as about 75 per cent of the footprint of the new extension was already at that level. It is often the case that the gardens of these houses were filled using material excavated when the original house was built. So it is fairly loose, not solid rock. Even London clay, although very sticky, is easy to excavate, as it doesn't fall in as you dig down.

Using a single, double-glazed sheet of glass for the roof was an unusual but cost-effective solution. The common approach would have been to use an 'off-the-shelf' system that would have also been more complicated to install. This single sheet is perfectly robust, and it created a very simple and elegant way to bring abundant natural light into the kitchen.

The scheme was designed with a smaller door for day-to-day use and a larger door (above, at left) that can open up the space to the garden in warmer weather.

The couple were both creative people. The husband was a chef who wanted to be able to run his catering business from home. He needed preparation space that allowed him to cook for large events, so the importance of a well-functioning, spacious and well-lit kitchen was paramount. They also had a young daughter, so they wanted a family dining area, as well as play space and, of course, easy, safe access to the garden.

The obvious thing to do was to connect the kitchen directly to the garden. But before we went about it there were two elements of the original house that we all wanted to preserve. Firstly, there was the original door that led from the upper ground floor to the garden. It had a wonderful red, stained-glass window, and we all felt it would be a sin to lose that. Secondly, there was a full, mature shrub on the north boundary that provided greenery and privacy, which we couldn't move and really didn't want to kill. More fundamentally, we needed to address the different levels of access to the outdoor space.

For the new extension, we scooped out a lower section of garden. This allowed the kitchen to flow into an open garden space instead of butting up against the retaining wall and narrow stairs. We also extended this lower room, making its roof level with the upper ground floor. This resulted in three levels of outdoor space: a small patio area (on the roof of the new lower extension) just outside the original back door; the original garden level; and a lower patio in the excavated area beyond the kitchen. To avoid killing the mature shrub, we 'twisted' the two walls coming up from the lower garden. By this I mean that, though the walls are parallel in plan, they turn together as they continue outward, away from the planting.

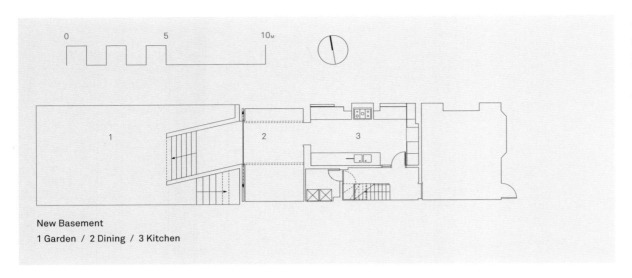

0   5   10M

New Basement
1 Garden / 2 Dining / 3 Kitchen

There was no real need for elaborate screening due to the surrounding planting and the position of the building. The concrete balustrade (below) provides shade from the sun, while the slots let in streams of light.

This was the first project for which we used reinforced concrete (for the balustrade and the roof deck outside the upper level) and our contractor made an excellent job of it. The balustrade to the upper deck is also acting as a beam: it's always nice when you can get something to perform more than one function.

As the balustrade for the upper stair is formed by one of these walls, it angles downwards as the lower stair rises, giving the illusion that the walls are opening out to the garden.

We wanted to get as much natural light as possible into the kitchen, which meant a partially glazed ceiling and large sliding glass door. We didn't have the budget to put any fancy structural glass on top. But we worked out that using a single piece of thick double glazing for the roof glass, with no complicated joints or preparation, was comparable to the fussier 'patent' glazing systems, which are made up of small pieces and require more time and labour to install. This big sheet of glass is structurally very sound – it can be walked on – and required almost no time to install. The aluminium fascia (what appears to be the frame for the roof of the extension) is also the gutter and allows rain water to run into the planter.

One of the things I like about this project is that, although it presented a set of common problems to do with trying to create modern living space in a nineteenth-century house, the result demonstrates the range of variation and innovation you can achieve, even with a relatively modest budget.

Completion date: January 2008
Location: Islington, London
Materials: Zinc and York stone

Adapting to a new phase in life_

Austin House
Early Victorian house

What do you do when you're coming up to retirement and the family home needs to change, but you love the area and don't want to leave? In the case of the Austin House, the clients decided to rethink their house in terms of their future needs and what would make it work better for them. This meant looking again at the kitchen and dining space, which were in the basement at the front of the house and were the darkest rooms in the building. They also reconsidered the back bedroom, whose small window had the primary view of the garden. When children grow up, often the kitchen/dining area evolves from a busy hub of activity to a place that is more about relaxing over quiet meals or morning coffee. In this instance we were able to make this room feel more pleasant and spacious by moving it to the rear of the house, where it opens onto the large, east-facing garden.

Above: one set of original French doors to the garden (at right) now give access to a small patio area outside the new 'flat'.

The new extension is made of timber walls and roof structure, all super-insulated and rendered, with the roof clad in zinc. The choice of materials makes the extension appear as though it has grown from the original house. Zinc is a good 'cross-over' material, being the visual equivalent of lead, which is the more traditional material.

There were, of course, other factors to consider in this project. The wife wanted to spend more time in the garden and re-orient the whole house to have better views in that direction. The couple also wanted to turn a section of the house into a semi-autonomous flat for their son, so that he could have a degree of independence while still living at home. In addressing these wishes we had to consider the fact that the street entrance is on the mid level of the house, raised above the height of the garden at the back, so it would be tricky to get light to flow all the way through. There was also the neighbours' extension, which runs along the portion of the garden closest to the house and creates quite a bit of shade.

Moving the kitchen and dining area from the front of the house allowed us to turn those rooms into a small separate apartment with a degree of privacy from the rest of the house. We then added an extension of about 4 metres at the back of the house and set the new space four steps lower than the kitchen, taking it down to the garden level. This creates a great sequence from the front door as you descend half a storey from the entrance to the kitchen and then another half a storey to the dining room at garden level. When you add a new structure to a house it's always important to make sure you don't then block the natural light from rooms deeper inside. Here we made the most of the change in the interior levels by placing a high-level window in the wall above the extension to let light straight into the raised kitchen area. I wanted to keep sunlight coming into the new space for as long as possible, so we also added a continuous section of glass set flush within the roof of the extension along the south boundary. This extends the enjoyment of the sun by a few hours and there is no problem with solar gain because of the house's eastern orientation.

As a large part of this project was about being able to enjoy the garden, we added fully opening doors at the rear. But we made the degree of openness flexible by using three sliding panels that can all be moved to the right and slotted behind the new block that houses the rain-water collector and storage space for hose pipes, etc. To enhance ventilation of the space, while being mindful of security issues, we worked with the door manufacturers to modify the sliding system and replace one panel with a sliding screen. This is particularly useful at night, allowing the doors to be locked securely while still admitting cooler air into the space. There is also a small extended roof canopy made of perforated steel. A continuing theme in our work is the modulation and patterning of sunlight. In this project, the screen and roof canopy, along with the creative placement of windows, contribute to this. I think this project is also about the way you can breathe new life into a house even after you've been in it for years.

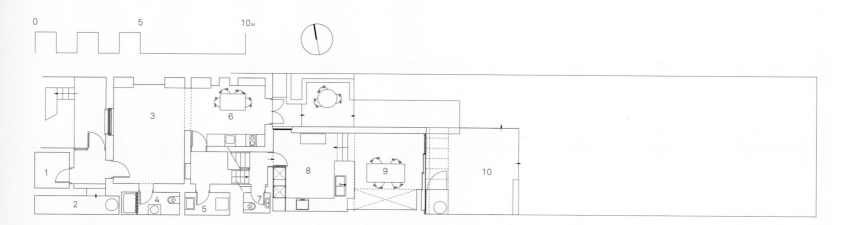

New Basement

1 Coal Hole / 2 Basement / 3 Son's bedroom / 4 Shower room / 5 Utility / 6 Son's kitchen / 7 WC / 8 Kitchen / 9 Dining / 10 Patio

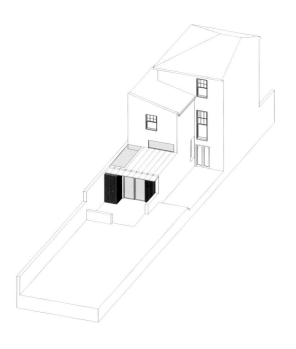

A small canopy of perforated steel extends beyond the roofline to provide a bit of shade. I think of it as being similar to wearing a sun hat – when the sun is strong you can still see but without so much glare. The steel has been galvanised so that it matches the zinc.

The scheme steps down from the entrance to the kitchen and to the dining room area, which is level with the garden.

Completion date: August 2009
Location: Camden, London
Materials: Slate and Cumbrian slate and phenolic plywood

Getting organised_

Cohen/Levin House
Victorian terraced house

Victorian houses are always a bit of a challenge, but the Cohen/Levin House was unusual. The main stair ran up from the front of the house instead of being at the back, as is most often the case. This made the front living room narrower, with the stair and hallway taking up a significant chunk of space. However, the arrangement also resulted in a back room that opened its full width onto the garden. The kitchen and dining area were on the lower ground floor and two bedrooms on the top floor.

The kitchen was made by 'Ben the builder', a most excellent carpenter. The units are clad in phenolic plywood, a material that the client found. It is normally used for shuttering concrete and has a smooth but hardwearing surface. The type we used has a dark finish that goes really well with the burnt-oak flooring.

The main challenge of this project was the fact that while the living spaces were of a decent size, the sleeping spaces were inadequate for a family with two young children. Also, the kitchen/dining spaces on the lower floor were very gloomy because, as you often find with Victorian houses, the garden was almost an entire level higher up. So the kitchen received very little natural light and looked onto a set of blank steps leading up to the garden. We needed to make better use of the space taken up by the stair and hall at the front of the house, to make the rear room relate more smoothly to the garden, and to create a good-size master bedroom suite.

To do this we proposed moving the kitchen and dining area from the basement to the middle (ground) floor, and connecting this directly to the garden. The lowest floor now houses a new master suite, which opens onto its own private courtyard garden. The upper floor still contains the children's bedrooms. The hallway that ran alongside (and cut space out of) the living room was removed. Now a small lobby area by the front door meets the stairs going up and provides a direct entry into the widened living space. This living area opens through to the rear room, now the dining room, but a sliding wall was inserted so that the two spaces can be separated when needed.

Rearranging the spaces, of course, didn't meet all of the needs of the family. In order to be able to accommodate the kitchen and dining area on the ground floor it was necessary to extend the house, which we did with a two-storey structure that contains the master bathroom on the lower level and the new kitchen on the middle floor. The two-storey extension aligns with the neighbour's existing boundary structure, but is angled slightly to

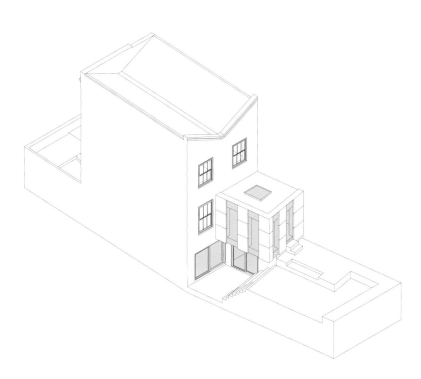

Due to the splay of the garden, the extension protrudes at an angle to the house, playing with sight-lines.

The glass panels have integrated ventilation at floor level and blinds at the top.

The glass sections of wall facing the neighbours are covered with a polarised film. This allows clear vision when looking straight on, but from an angle the glass appears to be etched. This is how we persuaded the planning authority that we would not be looking into the other houses.

The garden had been in a state of disrepair. The drainpipes were tidied away in the new scheme. Our only regret was losing the lovely sash window.

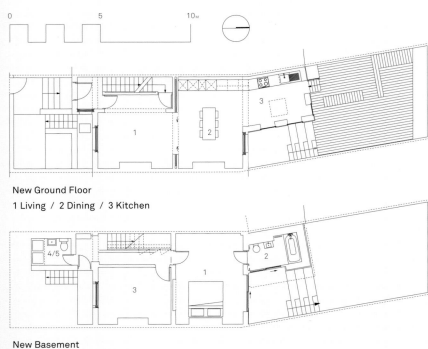

New Ground Floor
1 Living / 2 Dining / 3 Kitchen

New Basement
1 Master bedroom / 2 En-suite / 3 Study / 4 WC / 5 Laundry

The deep colour and texture of the Welsh riven slate, which we used to clad the solid sections, contrasts with the light airiness inside the space and reflects the fact that most London houses originally had slate roofs.

The master suite (right) has its own lower courtyard garden, which is accessible both from the bedroom and the en-suite bathroom.

widen the access from the lower courtyard. The kitchen now opens directly onto a timber deck and the garden beyond.

To make the two levels of outdoor space at the back and the uneven ground more accessible, we designed decking at different levels and a terrace of oversized steps, which can be used for sitting or for planters, coming up from the master bedroom. There is also a new deck at the upper level of the garden that provides a proper outdoor seating area. This might sound complicated on paper, but the end result is that the levels all lead easily from one to another, so that activity can flow in and out of the house with minimal barriers from room to room or from indoors to out.

Once the decision was made to extend, we had to think carefully about materials and the appearance next to the existing building, as well as the neighbours! We wanted to use glass because one of the problems we were trying to address was a lack of light in the kitchen and dining area. But we didn't want the family to feel too exposed, so we chose to alternate vertical panels of solid material with the glass. This way we could have that luxurious feeling of tall windows without having a completely transparent room. If we hadn't been allowed to use glass on the sides (which required some persuading of the planners), then the room would have felt dark and tunnel-like. However, using full-height glass would have compromised everyone's privacy. All in all, with the reorganisation of sleeping and living rooms, the open and enclosed spaces, I hope the home will work well for the family in the coming years.

How to green your old house_

When measuring energy use in buildings we consider roughly two categories: that used to build the structure, including the 'embodied energy' of materials; and the energy that a building consumes through its lifetime. For me, since I'm often working with houses that have already been built, the focus is very much on the latter, but with the added consideration of some energy-producing technologies.

In Britain and other countries like it, people are starting to realise that most of our housing stock will still be here for some time to come, and that previous generations have already invested energy in that building stock. So if we really want to reduce energy wastage, it makes sense to try to upgrade and adapt those existing structures whenever possible, rather than tearing them down and starting over.

Energy is principally lost from buildings in two ways: through the walls, roofs and floors via conduction; and through temperature changes from draught and deliberate ventilation from bathrooms and kitchens. Most people understand that loft insulation and double-glazing can reduce heat loss and hence reduce heating bills, but they don't always understand the variety of complementary solutions available. And there are different solutions for different types of structures. In modern cavity-wall structures it is fairly easy to infill the cavity with insulation, but on old solid walls (of brick or stone perhaps) the answer may not be so obvious. However, there are two key approaches: insulating on either the outside or the inside of the wall. For most structures, especially buildings in conservation areas with quite a lot of historic detail on the façade, it is not a sensible option to insulate on the outside. We are working on a solid brick 1950s building at the moment where over-cladding is a viable option, but for most historic building stock it doesn't make sense. Insulating on the inner wall is not without disadvantages, but these can be overcome with some careful consideration.

Firstly, remembering that there is a need for a breathable wall build-up, i.e., one that doesn't seal moisture inside, it is important to choose an appropriate insulation material. We prefer to use wood-fibre-based products that have a 'wicking' effect: that is, they can allow any interstitial condensation to be absorbed into the structure and then dry out as the wall warms in summer or from internal heating. This type of insulation comes in sheets, or batts, and is fixed to the existing plastered face of the wall. Then a fresh layer of lime plaster is applied to create a new, paintable surface.

However, well-insulated walls are of little use without good, draught-resistant windows. By far the largest proportion of energy lost through a structure is due to draughty windows. And the most common type of windows in historic houses are the multi-paned, double-hung sash windows. When it was invented, the sash window was a revolutionary device, elegantly proportioned, very spatially efficient and flexible in use. And it continued to evolve and be refined over hundreds of years. Over the last fifteen years or so this evolution has started up again. It has been a long road, but we are now producing highly energy-efficient, double-glazed, well-sealed timber sash windows that are still generously proportioned, elegant and easy to operate.

Opposite: Shepherdson House, completed 2009.

I don't agree with the conservation officers who insist that period sash windows should only be replaced with similar, single-glazed units. Although they had a good argument a few years ago, it no longer stands, as the technology has now caught up. The downside to replacing the old sashes with the new, improved versions is, of course, the loss of any period glass that is sometimes still present. These old panes often have a wonderful rippled distortion that only goes to emphasise the limited technology the original builders had to work with. In some circumstances, keeping those original elements of the house can outweigh the environmental concerns. In a 'listed building', windows need to be retained. In other cases, if the rest of the house has been made as energy-efficient as possible, you may still choose to opt for a few less-efficient but well-preserved historic windows. However, if energy efficiency is an issue, there are certainly solutions available that express the character of the period windows while achieving much better thermal performance.

In whatever way you address it, improving the overall thermal performance of your home ultimately relies on controlling air changes due to ventilation. This can be quite a simple matter of making sure that all air gaps are sealed, principally around doors and windows. If you don't have the budget to double-glaze your windows or insulate your walls, then the single most cost-effective thing you can do is to draught-seal your house. If you are not using the new sash windows, most older sash windows, as well as doors, can be retrofitted with some excellent brush-seal systems.

Yet, while minimising draughts is important, completely sealing your house up is not a great idea. Again, remembering our old building technology, it is important to understand that the breathability that is so much a part of how the old structure works relies on a constant air flow. The Victorians believed that draughts were to be encouraged, as they prevented the build-up of foul air, or miasma, which could spread disease (and they were right about that), and were essential for the open fires to work. My preferred strategy is to install a whole-house heat-recovery and ventilation system.

We installed our first system some years ago and it was an enormous box that took up the space of a small shower room. Nowadays, you can get a mechanism that is only slightly bigger than a toaster and is very cost effective. In essence, they work by taking the warm, foul air from bathrooms, which would normally be thrown out along with all of its valuable heat energy, and channel it through a heat exchanger. There, the heat is transferred to the fresh air coming into the building, which is then distributed to all the living and sleeping areas.

About five years ago I decided to use my own house as a guinea pig for trying out solar panels. There are two key types of panel available – solar thermal hot water systems, or photovoltaic systems. (The 'hot water' in the title refers to the fact that it generates only hot water – the panel has a glycol liquid in its veins; whereas PV panels actually store energy that can be used for electricity.) My personal experience with this system has been very positive: every year we get from four to nine months of hot water without having to turn the gas boiler on.

I think the only thing that really needs improving is the control systems, perhaps with some kind of sensor to allow the system to turn on and off when appropriate. I'm sure this will soon be available, but as most of this technology is fairly new, clients need to have a bit of a pioneering spirit in using them.

Whatever the technological advances, the most effective green strategies start with using less energy to achieve the same levels of comfort. Once you've spent some of your budget on these, most of which will pay for themselves in a very short time, then you should look at whether it makes sense to generate some of your own energy. Using good strategies for energy efficiency, it is possible to live in an original Victorian townhouse and have zero carbon emissions. It is just a matter of what you are prepared to sacrifice (and invest in) to save the planet! What we are trying to do in our work is to see if we can find a way to help our clients enjoy modern standards of comfort without it costing the earth.

Opposite: They may be difficult to source but modern double-glazed sash windows that adhere to conservation standards of style and proportion are available.

Completion date: January 2006
Location: St John's Wood, London
Materials: Italian purple granite, mill-finished aluminium
and St Aubin limestone

Cooking and art_

Roman House
Mid-Victorian house

Set in Maida Vale, a well-heeled, leafy area on the fringes of London suburbia, the Roman House is a mid-Victorian that was fittingly grand and well preserved. Owned by a couple with a substantial art collection, the house needed to have a secure, controlled environment for the display of artworks, including some very large pieces. Equally important was the wife's desire for the house to have a stronger relationship with the outdoor space and for a kitchen that made you feel as if you were cooking in the garden. The garden was large and east facing, but it wasn't easy to reach or enjoy.

The garden had been accessed via a utilitarian metal stair leading from a garden roof terrace that was attached to the back of the house at the level of the first-floor main living room. This terrace and stair cast a lot of shade onto the kitchen and dining space on the lower level. The first move was to bring the kitchen into the garden, as the clients had asked, and make it open directly to the outdoors. But instead of creating a room that looked and felt like an extension of the house, here we decided on a pavilion-like structure that would feel more linked to the outdoors. To emphasise this idea the roof sits on one single central column and the ceiling tapers up at the edges. The treatment gives a visual 'lightness' to what is actually a very heavy roof, being clad in stone so that it presents an elegant, textured surface outside the main living room on the first floor. The kitchen ceiling is also fluted with integrated lighting, as again we wanted to create the impression of something delicate and light, such as a piece of folded paper, rather than a weighty construction.

Inside the room we created a serious culinary centre, and the workspace became a tribute to a wonderful material. The main worktop is a large L shape made from a beautiful purple granite with a flamed surface that gives it a deep, textured appearance. The worktop follows along the wall, turning at the corner in enormous sheets and then continuing to the outside wall, making one large, seamless surface that flows from inside to out. The glass fits cleanly into that surface, and the corner has an opening casement to get quick cross-ventilation when cooking. Full-height units were mounted on the side and back wall.

As the orientation is to the east, we didn't need to worry here about too much solar gain. But, as in other east-facing schemes, we did want to admit some southern light to extend the enjoyment of daylight for those few precious extra hours. So the roof is separated from the wall by a clerestory window that runs along the full depth of the extension. This lets in the low winter sunlight when the foliage has died down.

The original kitchen was at the front of the house and this space became a formal dining area and a gallery for the art to be on display safely away from direct sunlight. The new kitchen now has a more informal dining space for day-to-day use.

This project demonstrates a response to a very clear design brief with the aims of making space for art and for a kitchen that was highly functional and connected easily to the garden.

The original first-floor window opened onto a terrace that was accessed from the garden via a metal stair (above, at left). The window to the right was added later, but we decided to copy it to maintain the symmetry of the rear façade.

New Ground Floor

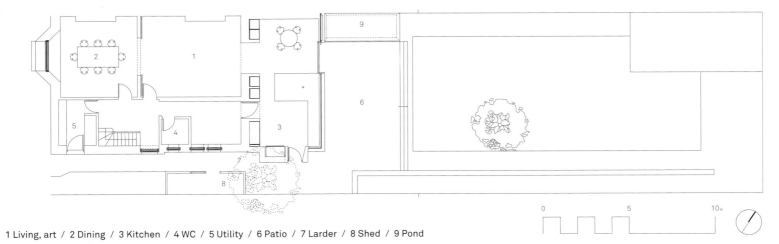

1 Living, art / 2 Dining / 3 Kitchen / 4 WC / 5 Utility / 6 Patio / 7 Larder / 8 Shed / 9 Pond

0   5   10ᴍ

We used a glazing system, which was newly on the market, that encased the frame within the double-glazed units, making the metal nearly invisible. This allows the glass to go right up to the edge of the unit, providing a wonderful reflective quality along the whole surface of the door.

The ceiling has been 'folded' like a piece of origami to make it feel lighter. The lighting has been positioned to emphasise the folds.

One experiment we tried here was to mirror the inner surround of the roof-light (right). This 'reveal' had to be splayed in order to avoid clashing with the external window sill of the existing façade above. The mirrored surround now acts as a periscope to give a view of the sky instead of looking on to the underside of the window sill. It is another way that we made the roof plane feel paper thin, rather than seeming like a thick, solid mass. Another effect of this mirror is that it reflects the higher, direct sun, sending it back into the darker area of the kitchen.

The worktop and external wall are clad in this beautiful purple granite that was actually part of a kitchen manufacturer's range. We had to persuade them to give us some extra so that we could clad the exterior, as they had bought the entire quarry. I believe Gordon Ramsay has cooked in this kitchen, and if he had any complaints about it, I haven't heard them.

Completion date: December 2010
Location: Hampstead, London
Materials: Powder-coated aluminium and hardwood decking

A project of ups and downs_

Turner House
Victorian semi-detached house

Situated just off the ancient London parkland of Hampstead Heath is a small enclave of Victorian houses, a few streets that project like a bubble into the corner of the heath land. The whole area is on a steep slope, and all of the houses have difficult relationships with their gardens. On one side of the terrace the gardens are well below the houses, and on the opposite side the houses are well below the gardens. With the Turner House we had the second situation. On my first visit I was surprised when, after passing through the grand Victorian entrance, I walked into what was effectively a basement space at the back of the house. There was no connection to the garden either from the basement or the upper living room. This was a big house, and there was plenty of space to work with, but all of it was dark and poorly organised.

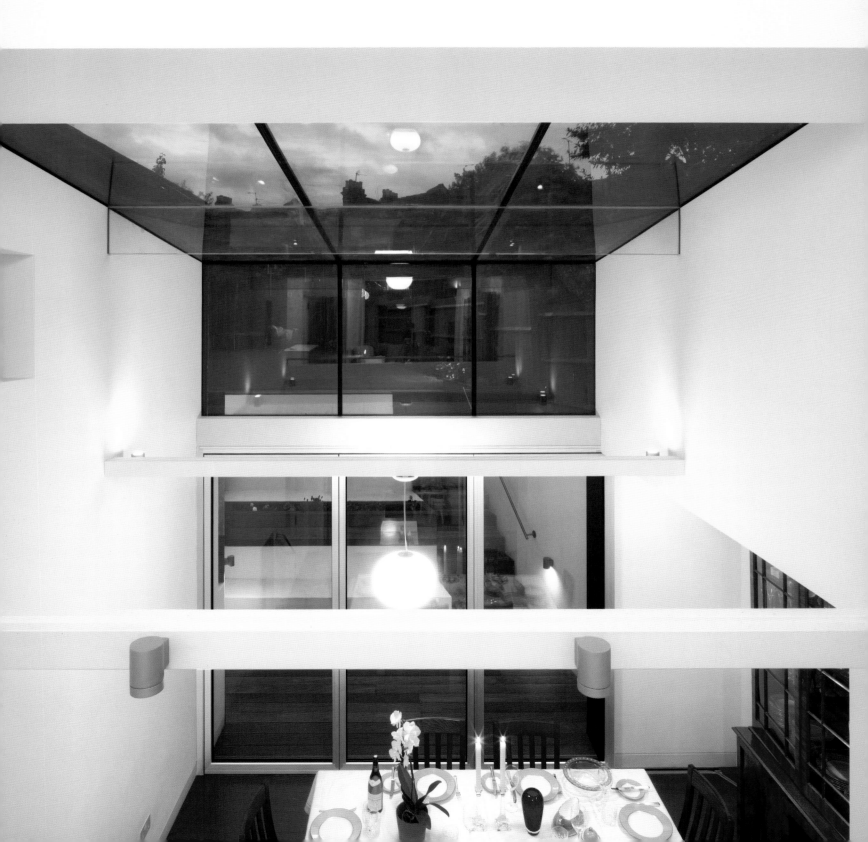

The clients were a couple with a young family, and they were in a hurry to move in. After coming up with a whole-concept design and the resolution of the 'grand plan', we decided to split the project into two phases, so that we could get on site as soon as possible. The upper floors were included in phase one of the build. We negotiated the price with some trusted builders – Ben and Andy – and within two months of starting the project, they were on site, fitting the bathrooms and putting in a temporary kitchen upstairs. While this was going on, we submitted the planning application and worked up the scheme in detail for the lower floors. Fortunately, client and builder got on well and the phase-two works went to Ben and Andy as well, so they were able to move almost seamlessly from the first to the second part of the build.

There was a reasonable budget for the scheme, but there are always limits, so it was decided to focus on a higher specification for the shell of the extension, and keep the fit-out costs on the interiors down to a minimum. So, on the inside, for example, we created a very simple initial kitchen that should get the family through the first ten years or so and can then be easily upgraded. The important thing is that we designed the spaces to be as flexible/comfortable/efficient as possible.

This scheme is mostly about the cross section, about making connections between rooms from front to back and the outdoors even though, by necessity, some of those connections have to travel over different levels. At some point in the house's history a previous owner had made an effort to get some natural light down into the basement space, but being well below ground level it wasn't possible even to see the garden from there at all. The next level up was also living space, but this too was separated from the garden: a utility room and the roof of the kitchen below interfered with the flow outside.

We followed our preferred strategy of connecting the house and the garden, but in this case the scheme connects on two floors rather than on one. This was the result of taking away a section of the floor between the ground and first floor at the back, and thus creating a large double-height space. This opens onto the garden at the lowest level, but also provides lots of light and a full view of the stepped-up green space through the double-height glazed rear wall and roof. In addition, we connected to the garden at the upper level through a hall which contains a 'utility wall' with a lot of storage.

In this way, we brought some of the house up to the garden, and some of the garden down to the house. Despite the steep gradient, we also wanted to make the garden rise more gradually away from the house. We achieved this by cutting down and stepping the ground, creating a scheme of wide stairs and stepped planters.

The interior space, too, is stepped up from the kitchen so that the dining area is on the same level as the garden seating area. The sight-lines were carefully planned to make sure that there were good views even from the lower kitchen space. Upstairs, large internal doors allow the front living room to be well and truly separated and to isolate television noise from the rest of the house. The lower front living area is used as a play space and will become the more informal reception room when the kids are older. All in all, it's a family space.

I think the best thing about this project is that the client was brave enough to give up some floor area to achieve a better quality of space. The split section and double-height rooms give an unusually generous feel to what is really a narrow townhouse.

The roof was split into three panels to avoid the cost of craning a single large section of glass into place. This method also works well with the window lines of the original house. The roof along the boundary is set down from the glazed extension, which means that the main addition isn't visible from the road. It also reduces the impact on the neighbours' views, and provides a convenient platform to access the roof for cleaning the glass, a very important consideration for any glass extension.

Section
1   Living
2   Kitchen
3   Dining
4   Storage
5   Garden
6   Mezzanine

New Ground Floor
1   Lounge
2   Entrance hall
3   Kitchen
4   Dining
5   Utility
6   WC
7   Cloakroom
8   Plantroom

0   5   10 m

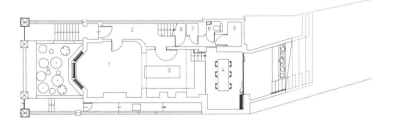

One detail we have tried for the first time here is the lighting frame (see p. 95). With large glass ceilings it is often a challenge to find an appropriate position for some sort of ceiling light. Here we have suspended a light from a pair of skinny timbers that run across the upper portion of the space (and are used to hide the wiring as well).

Although the kitchen is the lowest level of the house, by opening it up to the upper level with stairs, clear sight-lines and the glazed double-height structure, we made it an interlocking space. Widely visible and accessible, it is now the focal point of the house, and allows all the living spaces to have a relationship with each other.

The door system is a single-track slider that allows all the doors to be stacked away to one side. This arrangement has the advantage over the more commonly used 'sliding-folding' systems in that you can have bigger panels but the doors don't need a furniture-free zone to allow room for opening and closing.

The garden steps, like the planters, are covered in high-quality hardwood decking and can be used for seats. A level area was created just beyond the back door that provides enough room for sitting outside. The planters were carefully designed to 'break down' the scale of the surrounding walls and hence get away from the sense of being in a deep space surrounded by high, blank walls.

The method of grading the garden with different levels eliminates the problem of having a single balustrade or retaining wall cutting across your view out the back.

Completion date: May 2008
Location: Islington, London
Materials: Galvanised steel, black glass and stainless steel

From a pub to a studio to a house upside down_

Taylor House
Victorian pub conversion

London is full of Victorian conversions, and this project involved a particularly intriguing reincarnation. The building had housed a great pub, but it was bought in the early 1990s by a private developer who split it into two flats – one occupying the top two floors and the other having the ground floor and basement. Our clients had the lower flat, which had a fantastic open space at ground level with just four cast-iron columns in the centre: this would have been the bar area. The lower floor, which had been used mainly for storage of food and drink was, not surprisingly, a dark and difficult space. The brief was to turn what had been laid out as a studio flat into a more sensible four-bedroom house. We did this basically by turning the house, in terms of traditional arrangements, upside down.

The axonometric and images show the multiple routes through and around the garden. This arrangement avoids any dead ends and creates a sense of a continuous flow of space with access to various points and views.

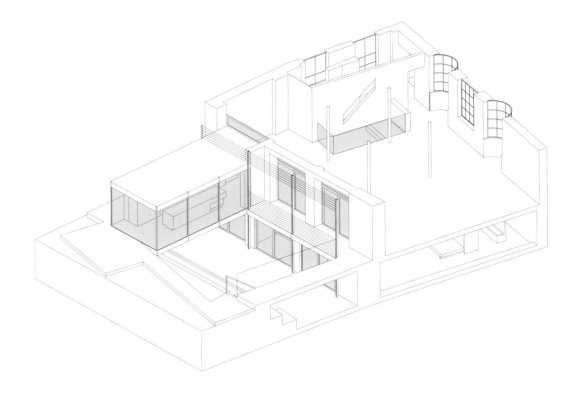

The clients were a creative young couple who were both very interested and knowledgeable in design and very exacting in their tastes. They have strong Japanese connections, and this influenced their taste and elements of the design. Another more prosaic influence was the fact that there were people living directly above. We knew this would present a challenge in terms of pipe-work and services, as well as privacy. Although our clients have exclusive use of the garden, the upper-floor flat has a projecting balcony that overlooks it.

There wasn't much of the original space that was worth keeping except the three outer walls that face the street and neighbours. I thought of the project as building a new house underneath another (the top flat). To do this we excavated part of the garden so that the basement level can open onto a flat, usable outdoor space, and we cut a double-height space out of the front of the living space. Both of these strategies were about unifying the two floors as one house and blasting as much light as possible to the lower level, which was now considered an important, functioning part of the house, rather than just secondary quarters or a store room.

However, the lower floor was still going to be somewhat darker, so it was a better idea to invert the standard model of having bedrooms above the living space and put the them downstairs. This way, those main living spaces could look directly onto the garden and receive lots of natural light through a glazed façade. The entire back wall was removed, and with the excavations this meant we could create a two-storey elevation of glass. A balcony runs along the higher level, and it projects to the same line as the neighbours' upper-floor balcony, keeping the view from above to a minimum.

The garden is treated as another room of the house. All the internal spaces look onto it, and you can access the outdoor area from different rooms. The planting is designed for a predominantly shaded space, hence the strong emphasis on green plants, but it bursts into colour in the late spring.

Previous pages, at left: it takes a trained eye to spot it, but the glass-to-glass corner on the kitchen hides the structural column, which means that the roof has no visible support along the whole of the main façade. This really enhances the sense of openness when you're in the kitchen. As all of the glass is fixed here, we put in an electrical floor vent beneath the kitchen island; it allows cooler air from the under-croft space to flow up into the kitchen. My favourite detail was an idea of the client's: he suggested putting an outdoor shower below the kitchen. This required a careful study of sight-lines and we established a position that means that only your feet would be on view to a nosey neighbour.

Left: the kitchen is the most dramatic form and thus received extra attention. To give the walls a more 'taut' quality, the glass continues beyond the floor and ceiling boundaries. The glass was back-sprayed black where it covers the structure behind it, providing a wonderfully reflective surface. This was an idea that we came back to in other projects.

Rather than being closed off into separate rooms, the activity of the family, as well as the natural light and air, can now easily circulate through and around the open-plan kitchen/dining and living area that surrounds the stairwell. We also added a 'Juliet' balcony so that the family can eat breakfast there with the feeling of floating above the greenery of the garden.

The 4-metre-high light box in this tall space helps link the two storeys and blasts light into an area that is away from natural light.

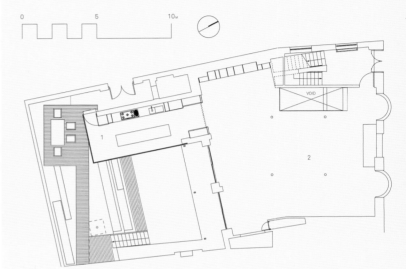

New Ground Floor
1   Kitchen
2   Living

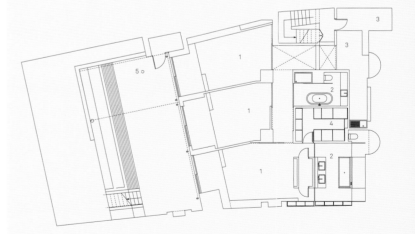

New Basement
1   Bedroom
2   Bathroom
3   Plant/utility
4   Wardrobe
5   Outdoor shower

The garden balcony has a delicate balustrade, which doesn't block the view from indoors, and leads to a light steel bridge on the east wall that connects to the raised level of the garden.

The form of the bridge is matched at the other end of the balcony by the parallel structure of the kitchen, a dramatic addition that jumps across the newly excavated garden space to the larger garden beyond. I wanted it to feel as though you were floating in the garden as you cooked, and the floor-to-ceiling glass allows for that. The bridge sitting across the garden space has a correlating glass balustrade. You can access the kitchen from the side, as well as from the open living space, and we have recently added an external eating area at this corner for al fresco dining in warm weather.

A constant theme of my work is to get a flow of continuous movement from space to space without any 'dead ends'. This scheme is one of the best examples of that effect as there are at least ten different circuits of the house you can make from living to bedroom to garden to kitchen and back through the living space again. The lower floor shows the Japanese influence and has large sliding walls/screens that allow a change from fully open plan to total privacy. Though the clients initially insisted that the house not be designed for children, sure enough one came along just as work was completing. And while some of the finishes are not totally childproof, we did try in the basic layout to give the house the flexibility to work as a family home, and it has adapted well.

Above: in the family bathroom we made use of the concrete soffit and lots of mirrors to expand the sense of space.

Right: in the master suite, a solid teak bath and basins are set against the same brown Zodiaq® (reconstituted stone product) that was used in the kitchen.

Completion date: February 2011
Location: Teddington, London
Materials: Zinc and walnut

Righting old wrongs_

Dick/Ellery House
Late Victorian terraced house

Located just outside a small rail station in south London, the Dick/Ellery House is part of a little stepped terrace. When we first looked at it, we realised that it was going to need some repair work, but it wasn't until we were on site that we fully appreciated the problems hidden within this innocent-looking structure. Most Victorian houses were built specutively, i.e., a builder would erect a group of five or six houses, hoping to sell them on. The quality of the original build varies enormously, even across London, and interestingly it can have very little to do with the appraised value of the house. I have seen large, expensive houses in Kensington that were more poorly built than a modest terrace in Hackney. This one, though it presented a tidy front to the street, had not been built well. It had also undergone a number of so-called repairs, which had only added to its problems.

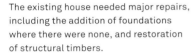

The existing house needed major repairs, including the addition of foundations where there were none, and restoration of structural timbers.

Opposite: the single circular steel column holds up the whole corner. It is set back from the glazing so that the doors can rotate around the corner. The kitchen counter runs out into the garden and becomes the enclosure for the rain-water collection tank. The interior is protected from afternoon sun by a projecting zinc canopy that clearly defines the new and old structures.

We have known these clients, Frank and Maria, for some time, as we had done some initial concept-design work for them on a previous house in north London. Unfortunately, just as we were progressing with that scheme, the planning authority introduced a new local planning constraint that effectively killed the project. As some consolation, I offered Frank and Maria a discount on any future project they wanted to do, and three or four years later they got back in touch to discuss a new home. In the meantime, their children had flown the nest, so now they were looking for a house that would be primarily for the two of them.

This is a house we have added nothing to in terms of extending the structure. In the main, what we have done is repair and take away. We removed the whole ground floor, including the external walls to the rear. We removed the stairs, most of the interior fittings and sections of the roof. These were clients who had the vision to understand that what they needed was not more space, but better space. They also had the foresight to have the garden designed and built at the same time as the work was being done to the house. This was particularly important as the new house is now integrally related to the garden.

Internally the new stairs became the focal point, weaving up through the main spaces. A large roof-light provides a great source of natural light and ventilation above this stairwell. We also used a glass partition to let the light from the top of the stairs flow into the spaces below. The top floor now contains a fantastic master suite and a smaller guest suite – perfect for a couple who can now pamper themselves.

The stairs became the centre of the house, a light, airy core. A roof-light provides lots of natural light and ventilation, while the glass wall on the ground floor lets sunlight flow into the lower rooms.

Opposite, above: the four large aluminium sliding and stacking doors – on a single-track slider – allow you to remove the corner completely.

The garden was built at the same time as the work was being done on the house. So the integration with the outdoors became almost seamless, with planters and level decking providing a continuous flow of forms and materials.

The kitchen is central to the ground floor, and the garden room is conceived to be used either for lounging, or as a larger, more formal dining space. The front living room is separated from the kitchen with a large sliding wall, which allows you to seal away the television sounds from the rest of the house.

To create the immediate connection with the garden, we used large sliding and stacking doors. We even removed the corner structure, so there is no barrier at all when the doors are opened. As the garden and the interiors were designed and built at the same time, we were able to incorporate the garden more fully. In a similar fashion, fixing the many problems of the old structure gave us scope for changing the interiors to something more suited to the needs of the clients.

I need to say something about the repair work, however, as it became a major contingency spend. Nearly every time we opened up a bit of existing structure, we had to rebuild most of it. The front bay window had been letting in water and all the timber lintels needed replacing. The raised timber floor at ground level was sagging, and it transpired that most of the joists were not sitting on any foundations. There were numerous other small things that needed putting right. But we were able to attend to all of these as well as making more useful, comfortable spaces, and the clients should now have a house that is in better shape than when it was originally built.

Above: the roof-light and glass balustrade allow natural light to permeate the stairwell and lower level.

Left: the sliding door allows the sitting room (and television noise) to be separated from the dining area.

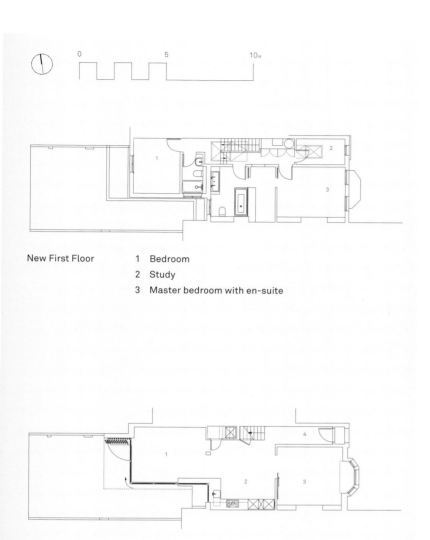

New First Floor

1 Bedroom
2 Study
3 Master bedroom with en-suite

New Ground Floor

1 Dining
2 Kitchen
3 Living
4 Hall

In the bath, the recess by the original chimney breast was used to conceal all of the pipework, and the mirror-backed glass shelving bounces natural light back into the interior.

Working with glass_

People often say to us, 'you're the guys who specialise in structural glass'. My response is, 'it's not the glass I'm interested in, it's the light and the view'. With hindsight it's easy to understand how we ended up doing so much with glass because of the buildings that we have been asked to work on. The typical Victorian house tends to prioritise the upper living rooms, which have the tallest ceilings and largest windows. However, most of our schemes are about transforming the lower floors into the main living spaces of the house. These were originally built as service spaces, and consequently have low ceilings, minimal windows, and little relationship with the garden.

Using glass is an obvious means of bringing light in and creating the view and the link with the garden – in other words, it brings the outside in. Our design exploration over the last decade has involved looking at how to increase the transparency of the building envelope, while simultaneously improving its technical performance. Although we're principally concerned with thermal performance, we've also been keen to investigate advances in structural design.

Glass began being used structurally in the early 1990s, a development that was heralded by Rick Mather's beautiful glass conservatory in Hampstead, north London. What set this building apart was the use of glass as the only structural element, i.e., there was no frame or support in steel, wood, or any other material. Even the jointing of the glass was transparent, being achieved with structural silicon rather than metal brackets. I remember seeing this project as a newly graduated architect and thinking, 'this is new'. It wasn't until I met the right structural engineer, David Crooks, who worked on Mather's original structure, nearly ten years later, that this kind of glass design became an option for my work.

Our first experiment was on Wadham House 1 (pp. 14-19). With this project we learned the basics of structural-glass construction – the lamination of three sheets of toughened glass to make a beam, and the span characteristics of a double-glazed sealed unit. Beams are laminated in sheets to build in redundancy, which protects against the failure of one of the glass support 'fins'. This design was developed with the understanding that in the manufacture of glass you can get 'nickel inclusions', flaws caused by the presence of nickel that are impossible to detect by sight, but which can cause the glass to explode spontaneously (as happened with sections of the glass canopy at London Waterloo station in the 1990s). Toughening is a technique that has been around for a while and has mainly been applied to glass used for doors. It involves re-heating the glass and allowing it to cool in a controlled manner. This treatment gives the glass approximately ten times the strength of normal plate glass, but it also makes it more prone to shattering (into millions of small cubes). Hence, toughened glass tends to be laminated together with other sheets, so that if one sheet shatters the other will most likely prevent the whole panel from falling apart. Laminating is done in a number of ways but in essence involves using a layer of 1mm-thick transparent glue to stick two sheets of glass together.

We began our own innovations with the Middlemiss Flat (pp. 58–63). Whereas Mather's conservatory used vertical glass fins in the wall plane to give it stability, we wanted to remove these to increase the transparency. David came up with the clamped foundation detail that

allowed the vertical glass sheets to be dropped into the ground, stabilising the glass, and so enabling us to do without the fins. In order to achieve the purity of the glass, we sacrificed a degree of thermal performance, which was not so critical on this scheme, since it is a conservatory and only meant to be used in warmer months. However, in future, we needed to find a better way of achieving the desired transparency, along with better thermal performance, for an extension that would be inhabited year round.

This aim initially led us to experiment with thermal shutters. We have used them in a number of ways, but the basic principle is to put an insulated shutter on the outside or the inside of a glass wall so as to create an extra layer – or skin – on the building, which can change the house's thermal performance either between day and night or through the seasons. One of the earlier schemes for which we developed this strategy is the Campbell House (pp 130–35), but probably the last will be Wadham House 2 (pp. 200–11), where the entire aesthetic language of the scheme is driven by the shutters. Shutters may no longer even be necessary since, recently, manufacturers have produced glazed units that are as efficient as a traditional cavity wall with 50mm insulation (the same as the most common external-wall construction that has been used across the country from the 1960s through to the 1990s). The product is a combination of two glazed panels that have a thin film suspended between them, with a protective air cavity on either side.

When looking at a glass structure's thermal performance another key consideration is orientation. Any structure that faces south and/or west will be prone to overheating in the summer months. Strangely, this is not something that the UK Building Regulations have anything to say about, so you can legitimately build a space that will become so hot you cannot live in it. The standard method of controlling heat in these situations is to put a film or coating on the glass. I don't like this solution, as it cuts out a lot of light, and in the winter months your glass is very dull. In other words, it's a glass treatment that defeats the point of having the glass in the first place. I prefer to use two different strategies – shading and venting. The degrees of each depend on the design, so if, for example, you're trying to get a 'pure' glass-box type of structure, you will want to reduce any frames or visible ventilation units, so you can introduce a hidden vent that can take the hot air out. There are multiple variations of shading and venting strategies in the projects in this book. But the important point is that glass is now made and treated in a range of methods and can be applied in a variety of ways to get the light and views that most people want to make their older houses feel more open and to establish that important connection to the outdoors.

Lastly, it is worth saying something about the choice between glass doors and a fixed-glass end wall. In the last ten years or so some sliding and folding systems for glass doors have become very popular. You will see these used in some projects in the book, but not many. As I mention with our work on Hall House (pp. 136 – 43), it is no accident that most photographs of houses using these systems are taken with the doors open, which usually looks great. However, when closed they can be far less attractive, as they often have thick frames that interrupt the view. It is worth remembering that although having doors that fully open up the back wall to the garden and fresh air is wonderful in warm weather, the doors will be closed for most of the year. So we have the conversation with nearly all of our clients about the balance between transparency and opening doors. In other words, the fewer doors you have (with the need for frames), the greater transparency is achievable. Pivoting systems and customised units are available, but will be quite expensive. For an openable system, we tend to favour sliding doors, as these can give you larger panes of glass and some of the frames currently on the market are quite minimal.

Opposite: Payne House, completed 2012.

Completion date: March 2009
Location: Muswell Hill, London
Materials: Zinc, concrete pavers and Corian®

A history of change_

Scott/Hanington House
Edwardian house

The story of this residence, like that of so many period houses in London, is one of change and adaptation. The Scott/Hanington House was built as one of four identical terraced houses that all formed part of a school at the turn of the century. The true order of use is not clear. It's possible that they were built as separate houses and then bought as a group to make the school. Luckily, they divided back down into individual units very easily, and the school left a legacy of nice period features, such as the beautiful parquet floors in the main living spaces. However, the spaces did not flow easily into one another, and the kitchen had been squeezed into the very small side extension at the back. The idea was to change again, this time into an up-to-date family home with a kitchen that could become much more than an afterthought.

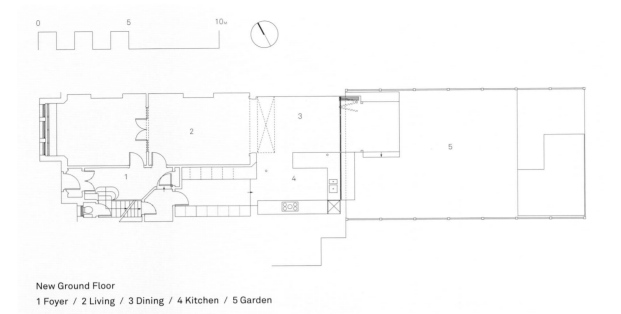

The three doors slide and fold back to open the dining area completely to the patio. These are the largest size that can be used in this system.

New Ground Floor
1 Foyer / 2 Living / 3 Dining / 4 Kitchen / 5 Garden

As if to emphasise the importance of the space for her family, the client came to the first presentation meeting with her three children and the grandparents. This was definitely to be a project that would be for the benefit of everyone, albeit focused around the kitchen. The original brief asked for a space that could be relaxed and sociable during the day, but something that would make a visual impact for parties and family gatherings when the entire ground-floor space could be opened up. The client was also a keen art collector (the house is filled with her own works and with pieces she collects by other artists), and she wanted plenty of blank wall space for displaying large paintings.

The old kitchen was a very long thin space going back to the entrance hall, and it was a challenge to know what to do with the darker section towards the centre of the plan. To begin with, we removed the tiny kitchen and filled in a new space across the whole width of the site. However, I felt that adding one big block would have been too massive a volume, out of scale with the rest of the house. So we stepped the form to create two different ceiling/roof heights – higher in the kitchen and slightly lower in the dining area. This approach had the advantage of placing the lower section of roof in front of, and level with, the existing main living spaces. This gave us the opportunity to add a roof-light that runs the whole width of the dining room at the point where the extension meets the old building, and in this way bring natural light into the new room and the core living space.

The position of the new kitchen was critical – it had to be a focal point of the house with views into all the other spaces, and I wanted to give it a strong relationship with the garden. The kitchen forms a J shape with the long leg reaching back into the darker section of the old house. That area is used for storage on one side, and has a long desk, where the kids can do their homework, on the opposite wall. At the other end is the main kitchen area with the sink and worktop facing the garden. An oversized, frameless window rises out of the worktop without interference from any indoor sill, allowing for an immediate connection with the garden. Outside, we created a sill made from a mesh box, which continues the worktop plane. This corresponds with a similar mesh box that we designed to hide the rain-water collection tank. The idea is that these mesh frames will be covered in growing ivy or clematis, so when you're cooking you will have a feeling of a worktop of flowers. I suspect that it will take some dedication to grow successfully. But this is one experiment in trying to allow the garden to take over the architecture.

The higher-ceiling kitchen structure stops at the garden wall and is framed with the zinc panels above and the sections of mesh sill below to distinguish it from the dining area, and to further break up the volume of a single block extension. While the kitchen allows for a great visual connection to the garden, the dining space was made to flow easily outdoors by way of a few key elements. Firstly, the large glass doors slide and fold back to open up to the patio. The flooring inside and out is exterior-grade concrete pavers, creating a continuous surface. And the roof overhang, also covered in mesh, makes a visual reach from the interior to the outdoors, as well as providing shade, external cover and some wonderful patterns of light. There are plenty of clean walls for hanging art now, and the whole family can use and move through the communal spaces, including the garden, with ease.

The roof overhang projects about 3 metres and is a skinny steel frame clad on the top and bottom with a steel mesh, like the two outdoor boxes. As the sun shines through the mesh, the shadows overlap and create fantastic patterns.

The stepped cross-section was emphasised on the back elevation by turning the zinc roof-cladding down the wall in front of the section of taller ceiling in the kitchen (see p. 125).

The floor, inside and out, is made of concrete pavers. These are normal, exterior-grade slabs, but have been well sealed for use inside. They make a great, hardwearing floor for a very reasonable price. Underfloor heating was installed beneath the pavers.

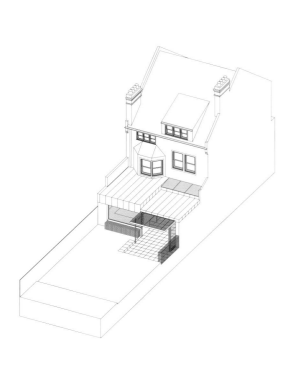

If you have the space, a dedicated desk for the computer is great in a family area (opposite, far left, and above). Here we combined it with lots of additional kitchen storage.

The gleaming white surfaces in the kitchen are made from Corian®. There are a range of colours to choose from, but I think it looks best in white.

Completion date: January 2004
Location: Muswell Hill, London
Materials: Powder-coated aluminium and maple veneer

Changing with the seasons_

Campbell House
Edwardian house

When it comes to rethinking a London house, there are a couple of things worth keeping in mind. One is that the housing stock is running out of space for roof additions, so sometimes the only option is to dig down. Another point to consider is that building regulation guidelines that dictate thermal efficiency are generally geared towards the coldest months of the year, and so are mainly concerned with keeping heat in. In the Campbell House, which is set on a sloping street, we took advantage of the natural grade of the site to carve out a new space below ground at the lower side of the house. We used glass to bring in light and form that crucial connection to the garden, but we also included thermal shutters to guard against heat loss in winter. Thus, we have a house that has successfully adapted to a growing family's needs and can change according to the weather.

Previous page: The outer walls are made from powder-coated aluminium panels that are hung on a timber frame. This frame is inset into a steel structure that sets up the cantilever. We used a top beam in the wall along the entire west elevation to get a rigid cantilever. We were expecting some bounce on the outer edge of the floor and the joint to the slot window at low level was designed to allow up and down movement in this area – in fact, we experienced very little movement.

The rain-water is fired from an aluminium downspout (see previous page) into a precast concrete hopper. The downspout adds a bit of fun when it rains, but we chose this solution to avoid having a rain-water pipe cut across the clerestory window, which might look like a column and ruin the floating effect.

A large family with teenaged children needed to expand their living space. They wanted a kitchen/dining room large enough for the older children and their friends to be able to congregate comfortably with the family. But they also wanted a separate room for the teenagers to hang out in on their own. The house was split level around a central stairwell. There was room to extend out the back, and an existing half-height basement space presented the opportunity to gain another room by digging down: instead of excavating a full storey, we needed only the depth of a further half storey. So we extended from the half of the house that is higher up the slope and dug further into the basement space below it.

The extension at ground-floor level is to the same footprint as the new basement room but cantilevers from the line of the original back wall. Thus the kitchen visually hovers above the ground, allowing a continuous line of glass around the perimeter of the lower room. The result is this quietly floating kitchen and dining area with a basement room below that receives natural light from an uninterrupted band of clerestory glass.

The cantilevered kitchen was a graceful design in its own right and adds a certain wow factor, but it was also a very useful solution for getting light into the lower floor. Though excavating to create needed living space is a good solution for these houses, too often the result is a dark, tomb-like interior. The trick is in getting enough natural light to keep the room feeling warm and healthy. We achieved this in two ways: firstly through the band of clerestory glazing along the three walls, and then by making use of a light well we created by adding a separate outdoor stair up to the garden. A large glass door at the stair entrance allows all the light from above the

These two images show the space in full summer mode (left), with the shutters stacked away and the side vent open for cross ventilation; and in its winter guise (right) which is more closed up. Of course, it can also be used in variations in between.

stair to flow into the basement. The result is a room that feels really warm and bright even without any artificial lighting.

Originally the project was conceived as three main family spaces – kitchen, dining room and terrace. We provided these, and, despite rooms being on different levels, we ensured that they interlock and open to each other for various arrangements from summer to winter. The kitchen has a large mobile island unit that can be moved into the dining space, while the dining space can move out onto the terrace, which has been finished with a long concrete bench.

One concept we experimented with here was that of living differently through the seasons, with flexibility of thermal performance as well as function. The extension is north-facing so we didn't have to worry about solar gain. But with the amount of glass used we were concerned not to let the new kitchen and dining space become too cold in the winter. The solution was to install a set of insulated shutters that can be placed over two sections of the glass. These sit flush with the wall when not in use, and slot neatly into the frames of the windows when in place. This project was about making the architecture adaptable, so that the family could change the use and the thermal performance of the house with the seasons. It's a simple idea, similar to the way we change clothing for different times of year. Fortunately, the building regulation requirements weren't too rigid, and in this instance we were able to make a more flexible scheme work.

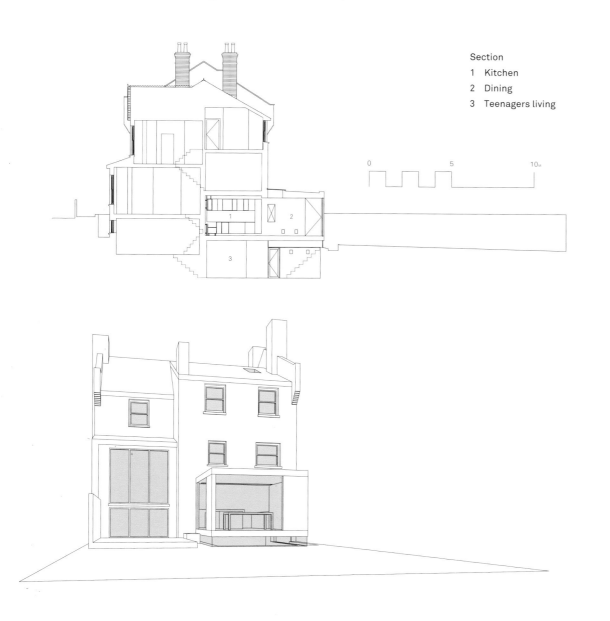

Section
1 Kitchen
2 Dining
3 Teenagers living

The garden stair to the lower space (opposite) is mainly for the teenage children, and allows for a continuous loop of circulation: from kitchen to dining to terrace, down to the basement via the external stairs, into the central stairwell and back up to the kitchen. The band of clerestory windows and glass side door bring lots of natural light into the new basement room.

Completion date: January 2006
Location: Twickenham, London
Materials: Navara Blue limestone, mill-finished aluminium
and Zebranno veneer

Swapping awkward for elegant_

Hall House
Late-Victorian semi-detached house

Not many old houses come to us without having had alterations. Hall House is a large, late-Victorian semi-detached house in a neighbourhood of similar houses and was sitting on a fantastic wide plot with a large, east-facing garden. Unfortunately, it also had some poorly conceived extensions that were too dark and turned their back on the generous outdoor space. We wanted to replace those old extensions with something much more graceful and light. Our plan focused on maximising internal volumes while using high-quality materials throughout. The simple form of this new, wide structure was made to appear unusually delicate by honing down the perimeter details – where the glass walls and roof meet–to a slender strip of aluminium. Now the old structure and the new come together in a light, transparent space.

The house was owned by a couple with children who would soon be in their teens. They wanted a home that could function for an older family, with a hierarchy of living spaces and a focus on the kitchen. The first move was to demolish the 'Victorian-style' conservatory, which had been added in the 1980s, as well as a boxy brick kitchen extension. We then cut out all the structural walls on the ground floor to truly open the house to the new extension. We also opened up a path of circulation that connects our new spaces to the original living rooms, thus getting rid of 'dead ends'. The children particularly loved the fact that they could run around in a big circle from room to room.

Because of the fantastic width of the house at the garden elevation we decided to create a long, open, pavilion-like structure running right across nearly the whole plot. This, I felt, would provide the best array of spaces and light. Most building plots arranged along a street tend to be long and narrow. This is especially true of London's Victorian houses. And in these situations, you have to make a choice about which space will have the primary relationship with the garden – usually making a personal decision to have a garden-oriented kitchen, dining or living space. However, in this project we had the luxury of being able to set all three of these spaces across the width of the site, so that the garden view could be enjoyed by the family from all three areas.

The long end-wall of this pavilion was to be entirely of glass, as there were no issues of privacy or solar gain. This would contribute to the feeling of openness and provide total transparency. But there were several solutions to consider. The original suggestion was for a set of sliding and folding

The house had been given some ill-conceived rear extensions, which we did away with to create a single open space that had a seamless flow into the garden.

We tapered the walls and ceiling to minimise the profile of the structure, which is actually thickly built up and super-insulated. The frames of the five large sliding doors are recessed into the streamlined aluminium perimeter detail.

Although I am a great lover of open-plan space, we decided that it would make sense to give some degree of flexibility inside so that different family members could be doing different things at the same time without disturbing each other. So we added a floor-to-ceiling acrylic screen on a sliding track. This allows, for example, for the parents to have a conversation in the kitchen while the kids are in view in the next room, but acoustically separated.

doors of a type that were just starting to become commonplace when we were working on this project. But this would have required twelve sets of doors with accompanying mullions. For 90 per cent or more of the time that you are in the home the doors will be closed, and so it is the mullions that you will be looking at. With certain kinds of door systems, a room that looks fantastic when the doors are open may not look so good when the doors are closed. Having said that, there are times when these doors are the best solution. Either way, it is at least as important to consider the effect of any scheme with all the doors closed, as it is to appreciate the experience of being able to open them up.

For this project, we decided that five large sliding doors offered the best balance between openability and minimum disruption to the view. The doors are on three tracks that allow for three-fifths of the elevation to

be open at one time: so you can choose whether it is the kitchen and dining room or dining room and living room that are open together. The system has exceptionally thin mullions, which provide excellent transparency. The rest of the structure is super-insulated and quite thick. However, I wanted to avoid the appearance of a heavy roof and walls, which was why we created the tapering effect for the thin aluminium detail. Beyond this delicate framework, what was a series of small, disjointed rooms is now an open, continuous flow of space and light.

A good kitchen is an ergonomic space but it is also important to think about it as a social area. Here the island hides the clutter of pots and pans with a 'double-recessed' sink, i.e., an area of the worktop is set down from the main surface and the sink is dropped into this recess.

New Ground Floor

1 TV
2 WC
3 Study
4 Utility
5 Kitchen
6 Dining

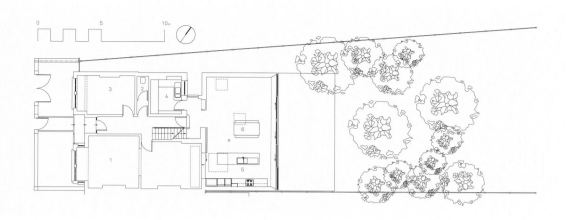

One of my favourite features of the house is in the first-floor master bathroom. We discovered on site that the whole floor of the master suite was sloping more than 50mm across its width. But rather than level this up we decided to use the slope to create the fall in the walk-in shower. This gives a completely seamless but effective floor design.

In a family with more than one child, it can be a good idea to have more than one basin.

Following pages: in this view it is easy to see that sliding doors with slender frames have a much more elegant profile than the more fashionable sliding-folding doors.

Completion date: January 2007
Location: Barnes, London
Materials: St Aubin oak and limestone

Room for meditation_

Jindal's Pavilion
Edwardian house

Jindal's Pavilion was another project that corresponded to changes in family life. The house is located in Barnes, a leafy enclave south of the Thames. This is an area of big houses sitting on large plots, and where some houses, like this one, still possess very spacious gardens. Our involvement with the main house was limited to sorting out an awkward corner of the kitchen. The focus here was on the garden space, which was home to a shed and some children's climbing frames. The children were growing up, and the client wanted to reclaim the garden and create a shelter for meditation that could also be used as an office/studio that was separated from the noise and bustle of family life.

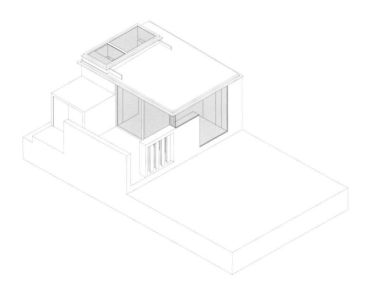

The structure measures 6 metres wide by 4 metres deep and just under 3 metres high.

The structure is a simple steel frame sitting on a piled concrete base (because the site is in a floodplain). The frame is infilled with timber and super-insulated and then clad in stone (and render on the non-visible faces).

The floor is paved in pale French limestone taken from the same quarry bed as the stone used for repairs on the British Museum.

The client was entering a new stage in his life: in addition to the fact that the children were now in their teens, he was starting to work from home. Getting rid of the shed and climbing frames, which were no longer needed, presented a great opportunity to add a new structure that would offer somewhere to work in peace. As a lifelong yoga enthusiast, he also wanted a calm, quiet sanctuary for meditation and exercise. The brief later evolved to include guest accommodation as well.

From the beginning, I wanted a very simple form that would become the focal point of the view down the garden from the house. The resulting structure is quite spare and evenly divided into two spaces – one inside and one outside. The idea was that the interior space looks out onto the enclosed external courtyard, and your view of suburbia is edited out, enhancing your focus while working or meditating.

At the time, I had been looking at the metal sculptures of the Basque artist Jorge Oteiza. I was fascinated by the way these works very lightly enclose a space and give it definition through folding material at the 'edges' without creating any actual physical boundaries. This concept of a lightly defined enclosure suited my idea for the pavilion, as I wanted it to be both separate and yet part of the garden. So the space is only partially enclosed by the walls, and movement, light and air are allowed to flow out from the corners.

The other principal idea behind the structure is flexibility, it adapts to a number of functions. The changes of use are achieved by the multi-functional timber wall (along the west side). The wall hides a number of furniture variations, including a fold-down bed and a fold-out desk, allowing the rooms to transform from bedroom to study to yoga space. The 'inside' half of the scheme can be closed off, for comfort or privacy, or entirely opened to the courtyard by two large sliding glass doors that tuck into a pocket next to the shower room at the south wall. Opposite the wall of

The storage wall, with fold-down bed
and fold-away desk, allows room to
change functions easily.

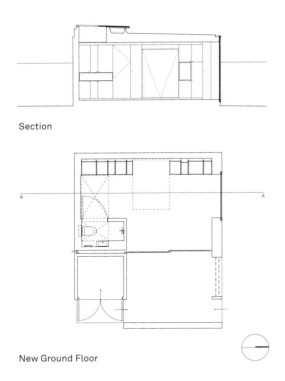

Section

New Ground Floor

built-in furnishings is a blank partition that defines the eastern side of the courtyard, blocking the view of the house next door. The north boundary is a combination of open and solid that screens the view towards the house.

Part of this north boundary is formed by the 'wonderwall', as it became known in the office. As the main façade of the new pavilion is north facing, I thought it important that it not appear in constant shadow when viewed from the house. I wanted it to catch your attention and encourage you to make the trip to the end of the garden. So we designed a screen wall made from vertical slats of glass, which are set in parallel lines but offset from each other to create more variation of light. The slats are etched on the side viewed from the house and have a 50 per cent mirror film on the inner, courtyard face. Looking at it from the house, the glass screen glows as the sun hits it at the back. On the other side, the mirror film reflects lines of light into the courtyard space, which was designed to remain empty of objects so that you can enjoy the changing shadows when meditating.

There are tight restrictions, which we had to adhere to, on the size and volume allowed for a garden shed. But the same restrictions do not apply to the external courtyard, so the whole structure (the covered and courtyard areas joined together) looks quite a bit bigger than the maximum allowable shed volume. Yet, because of its unenclosed design, it doesn't overwhelm the green space, and it answers all of the needs of a working father trying to find a place to retreat to without leaving the home environment. In a way, it seems to me that, as with the classic garden shed, this is the ultimate suburban male escape.

The glazing is set almost flush with the stone, and we've used a large, L-shaped double-glazed unit for the main back elevation to avoid breaking the glass into panels. This keeps the wall and roof visually separated.

Opposite: a shower room with a fully glazed enclosure sits on the south wall. All of the surfaces here are back-sprayed glass.

I always liked the idea that you could go on holiday at the end of your garden. Here, the bed folds down and the curtains pull out from a recess in the wall to create a private retreat.

Following pages: curtains and modernist design are often considered unhappy bedfellows, but I really like the contrast of the soft fabric and the hard edges of the scheme.

Completion date: July 2009
Location: Woodford Green, Essex
Materials: Red brick and mill-finished aluminium

Modern but mindful of the past_

Sandhu House
Interwar semi-detached house

The Sandhu House, a medium-sized, semi-detached house, was built to pre-war spatial standards, with some rather grand public rooms, and it had a lot of the original pseudo Arts and Crafts details still intact. The kitchen and pantry spaces were still extant but they were tucked away in the smallest ground-floor room and so quite cramped, which reflects the attitude to kitchen space at the time. The original house also had a great entrance hall, with its own fireplace, which opened through to a large living space (one of two) overlooking the garden. The aim was to have a much larger kitchen, of course, and better flow of spaces. Yet, while the clients were very keen to have a scheme that was modern, they wanted to ensure that whatever we added worked with the old building.

To allow the rear façade to maintain some of its integrity and preserve the period doors leading from the living room to the garden, the new kitchen/dining area was extruded in a linear fashion from its original position at the core of the house.

The initial intention was to have a glass box with frameless corners at the end of the kitchen section. But whenever you add a doorway you have to put a frame around the moving parts. Instead (to achieve more transparency), we continued the roof glazing so it folds over the side. This way the frame is not at the top corner junction and appears 'lighter'.

Opposite: the kitchen has an island with built-in breakfast area.

Previous pages: the new brick patio forms an almost seamless run of materials from the ground to the new wall to the old house.

The clients were a couple who had just started a family and had previously lived in a flat. This was their first house and new family home. Their brief was to create a large kitchen and dining area that would have a strong relationship with the garden. They were also in need of a separate family living space, apart from the more formal living room at the front of the house which has a large fire and grand ceiling details.

The original, small kitchen sat next to the second living space at the back of the house. This room had probably once been a formal dining room, but would now work as the more casual living area the clients wanted. The kitchen was on a slightly lower level from this living space, so we decided to extrude the lower room directly out into the garden, rather than adding on to the back living room. This allowed us to keep the fantastic timber-framed French doors, with their leaded-glass over-door panels (see previous page), leading from the living area to the garden.

The kitchen was then organised as a linear structure with a long central island that includes a breakfast area for the kids on one end. The space terminates with a glass cube that houses the dining space and allows long views from the kitchen area, through the dining space and into the garden beyond. The dining space also opens to the side and shares a new brick patio. This arrangement makes more sense of the original timber doors, as they open directly to this outdoor living space, which in turn provides a connection between the new dining area and the living room.

Internally the original pantry became the utility space, and we tucked a small WC on the ground floor (always a good idea when there are young children) under the stairs. A new opening and steps were put in to connect the kitchen with the living space, which is still slightly higher than the kitchen level and so naturally separated but not cut off. For this transition we designed a sliding wall that allows you to control the relationship between

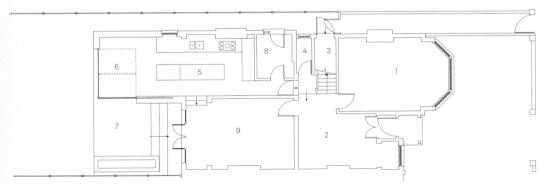

New Ground Floor

1 Formal living
2 Entrance hall
3 Store
4 WC
5 Kitchen
6 Dining
7 Terrace
8 Utility room
9 Casual living

the kitchen and living area: having a closed-off cooking environment or a circuit of movement around the ground floor.

Keeping in mind the clients' desire to respect the old house, we re-used the bricks that were taken out when we created the new, steel-framed opening to build the side wall. Hence, this new structure looks and feels as if it were part of the original building. Where we added new brickwork we made sure that it closely matched the red of the house. We also used brick to create the patio planter, a small but significant addition that helps to bring the garden right up to the house. The effect of the brick plinth has been lost somewhat by the subsequent addition of a timber deck built by a garden designer, but you can't control everything! For me, the most successful part of the scheme is how the new and old feel very comfortable together. I think this effect is principally a function of the brickwork, but also a result of the composition, i.e., the decisions not to cover the rear façade completely with a new, modern structure, and allowing elements like the timber-framed doors to maintain their integrity.

Instead of using ordinary lead flashing we chose aluminium for the frame around the brick part of the extension and enlarged it to clad the entire 'reveal' of the end wall structure. It makes a nice point of contact with the glazed structure and is a good reflector.

Half of the new wall, at left, uses bricks recovered from the house when we demolished part of the rear wall to make way for the extension. New bricks used on the corner and the patio were colour-matched to the original house to provide visual continuity.

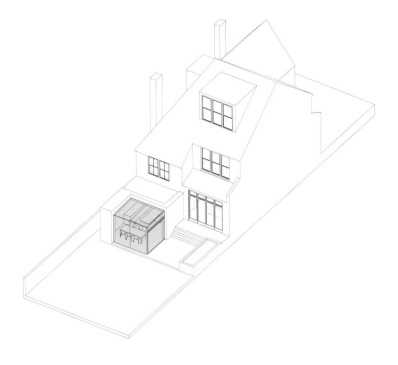

Completion date: September 1998
Location: Welwyn Garden City
Materials: Douglas fir timber

Bringing it all together_

Craig House
Interwar detached house

The Craig House, located in one of the original 'garden city' developments north of London, is actually made up of two separate houses joined together. Garden cities were part of a movement around the turn of the nineteenth century to create planned communities that included open green space with a balance of residential, industrial and agricultural use. The two houses here – simple brick workers' cottages – reflected the mix of Georgian and Arts and Crafts styles that were prominent in the area, Welwyn Garden City, at the time. The houses had been connected by a large hallway, but the organisation of spaces was a problem. An awkward collection of utility rooms and bathrooms took up an area that could offer prime living spaces with views out to the garden. The house needed some re-ordering and a much better relationship with the outdoors.

The scheme was built for my parents-in-law and is a commission that was instrumental in helping me to set up my practice. They wanted to rearrange the house so that they could better enjoy it in their retirement. The principal aims of the brief were to add a study space for Alwyn, a retired civil engineer, that would put him towards the centre of the house, and to improve the connection between the house and the garden, which had had a lot of love invested in it.

In adding on we created three primary new spaces: the conservatory, which opens from the living room; the breakfast room, which opens to the kitchen; and Alwyn's study, which sits at the centre of the new addition and can be accessed from these rooms and from the entrance hall. This puts Alwyn at the heart of the house and means that he is never too far from Rosemary, whether she is in the living room, conservatory, or the kitchen.

The new spaces are enclosed within a structure made almost entirely from timber and glass. Alwyn dusted off his engineering books and did the structural design for it himself. The foundation is simply two lengths of dwarf wall – engineering bricks built to a height of 20cm – which lift the whole structure off the ground. The timber frame rests on top of that, raised so that it appears to float just above ground level. It is a method that makes the extension appear lightweight, rather than as a heavy solid block. Being elevated in this way is also good for the durability of the timber, keeping it out of contact with damp earth and pooling water. The floating effect was further emphasised by setting the structural columns back from the glass line and actually cantilevering the outer edge of the floor.

The generous use of glass, of course, also contributes to the lightweight appearance of the extension. The rear wall is almost seamless glass, as is the wall along one side, and the flat roof. Wood slats run along one wall and across the ceiling to form trellising. This has become covered with greenery planted through a hole in the outside decking. The trellising and the growing vines help to modulate the sunlight through the glass without the need for other screens or shades. The slender profile of the trellis doesn't detract from the clarity of the glass and adds only a bit of solidity to the volume as a whole. The timber is Douglas fir and its red colour complements the red brick even as it has weathered over the years.

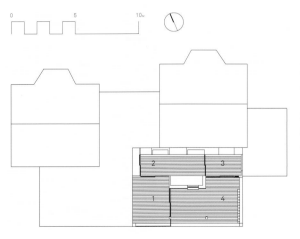

New Ground Floor
Extension
1 Conservatory
2 Study
3 Breakfast
4 External patio

Cultural shifts in house design_

I am often asked by journalists to describe the latest trends in house design. Having completed the number of residential projects that I have (there are probably another five built schemes for every one shown in this book), I can see several patterns developing. It is interesting to note that while some innovations are reversals of old ways of living, equally there are some trends that re-introduce old ideas.

The single biggest change that I think has driven an enormous quantity of our schemes is in the relationship between house and garden. I have always thought it slightly odd that the English, who have had such a long love affair with their gardens, so often live in houses that turn their backs on those outdoor spaces. I suppose this is a result of the fact that when Victorian houses were built, the garden was seen much more as a 'service' space or a yard. It might be used as a site for an outside toilet and a place to hang the washing, and its ground might be made up from builders' rubble (or any other rubble) left over from the house's construction. However, we do have a long tradition of building conservatories; adding one onto the side of your house is very much an English obsession. A lot of our work has been about making the main living rooms of the house have some of the qualities of a conservatory. In other words, we are trying to extend the enjoyment of sitting outside throughout the year when living in a climate that allows only a short summertime during which we can do it for real. Increasingly, our work involves making an unobstructed, physical link between the interior living space and the garden.

Closely connected to this trend is the desire to make the kitchen the focal point of the home. It is an irony that at a time when it is assumed that the art of home cooking (as opposed to watching it done on television) is on the decline, the kitchen has become the place where most of the family come together throughout the day. It has evolved from a purely functional space into the main family and entertainment space. Following on from this is the rise of the 'status' kitchen, which for some people says as much about them as their new car. More recently we've received requests from clients for a 'larder', an amenity that was common in my grandparents' time. In the past several decades, even the word was deemed old-fashioned. I think this is a great development – I still fondly remember the treasure trove that was my grandmother's well-stocked larder.

Another request that is becoming more common is for a 'super master bedroom suite'. This is an obvious choice for couples without children, but it is becoming a popular request for parents as well. Such a significant allocation of space and budget puts the rituals of sleeping, bathing and dressing up the chain of priorities, and I think the idea has been inspired at least partly by modern hotel design. A hotel suite is essentially a bedroom and bathroom, but hotel designers have been making this combination increasingly luxurious. People are coming home from these amazing hotel experiences and saying, 'lets have that in our house'. It is about the creation of a very private space that is just for that individual or couple, and it is where you spend money on no one but yourself.

A more market-driven trend that is sweeping through London is the basement craze. London has been constrained like no other city in the world (with the possible exception of Paris) in terms

of how high you are allowed to build. The forces of conservation in this country have essentially blocked the development of large parts of London beyond its basic Victorian framework. After the war, most of London went up a storey and many a mansard roof was built, but this was pretty much stopped with the introduction of 'conservation areas' in the 1970s. About ten years ago, people began to realise that the land values had become sufficiently high to make it worthwhile to enlarge a house the only way possible, and started digging. The practice began in the wealthier suburbs of Kensington and Chelsea, but has now started spreading out rapidly. Like all designs, there are good basements, and there are bad basements. The most important design challenge is to get daylight down to those lower spaces, and to make them seem as 'open' and less like subterranean rooms as possible. You can see the variety of ways this can be done through the projects in this book.

Some trends come and go and then return. The concept of the 'open-plan' interior has been around for nearly a hundred years now. But it was re-popularised in domestic architecture in the 1970s. However, just after 'open-plan' living was embraced by the major house builders (like those who designed the house I grew up in), there was a wave of a reaction against all things modern in the UK. The Modernist aesthetic all but disappeared, and Victorian architecture, with its traditional cellular spaces, became the main stylistic obsession. However, if you looked closely enough, you could see that many of these new 'Victorian' interiors still had a lot of open-plan characteristics. People still connected the rooms with large openings, and the dining spaces became part of the kitchen rather than being an entirely separate room. Our clients have varying attitudes to open plan, but I think the best approach is to create an adaptable open-plan space. Designed with moving walls and screens, it can include the best of both worlds: open when you want it, but enclosed spaces when you need some separation of people and activities. The projects for the Cohen/Levin House (pp. 76–83) and the Dick/Ellery House (pp. 112-19), among others, worked really well by separating television spaces from kitchen spaces through the use of a sliding wall.

Though we have worked on some high-end schemes, it is my firm belief that good design does not need a lot of money to build. Some of the projects in this book have been achieved with a very modest budget. All good design should be about getting the best value for money, regardless of whether you are on a larger or smaller budget. However, on the smaller budgets, a slightly different intellectual discipline is needed to get the maximum effect with minimal resources. I particularly enjoy the challenge of turning our creativity to not just the overall architecture, but to methods of procurement and construction. These are the keys to unlocking excellent value in a project. Construction methods have a huge effect on overall costs. For example, keeping the number of materials and trades to a minimum results in an economy of means. Procurement can increase costs, especially in the case of something like specialist glass work, which many contractors over-price because they are unfamiliar with the new technologies. We will often tender glasswork out separately and usually achieve a saving of around 25 per cent.

We have found that differences in social status do affect the schemes. It's true that most of our clients are fairly well off, and their wealth or status is often reflected in what they want in their houses. Interestingly, this follows the social hierarchy that existed in the (mostly Victorian) houses when they were built. For example, in a lot of the larger houses we still create rooms that once would have been for servants in the past, but these days are used for the nanny. In almost every scheme, however, the kitchen has moved out of the servants' domain and is very much part of the main living area.

Whether because the rapid increase in property values in London has made it difficult to move up to a larger house or because of the popularity of television programmes devoted to home building and improvement, more people with even fairly modest budgets are taking the decision to improve their lifestyle and sense of comfort by changing, adding onto or adapting the house they're in.

Opposite: Bird/Crews House, completed 2007.

Completion date: February 2000
Location: Wimbledon, London
Materials: Brick and oak

East meets west_

Ahmad House 1
Fifties end-of-terrace house

On a street of mostly interwar dwellings, this later house, owned by the Ahmad family, was built in the 1950s and is the odd one out. Sitting on the end of a terrace, it may have been constructed over a plot levelled by bombing during the war, or it may have been built on land that was once part of a garden belonging to one of the other adjacent houses. In materials, however, it blends in with the neighbourhood, being constructed from brick, namely Double Diamond bricks, the second most commonly used in London. These have a mottled, brownish-red appearance and are a familiar sight in most areas and suburbs of the city. In adding on to the house, we sought to preserve the very 'London' character of the construction while also bringing a bit of Eastern design to reflect the heritage of its long-term residents, who were our clients.

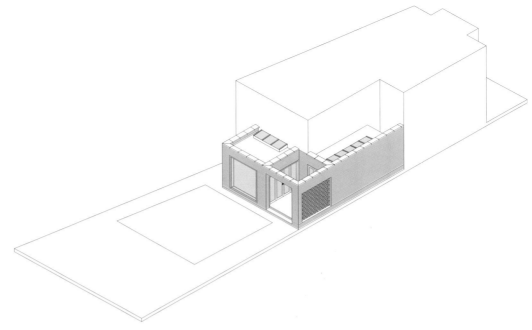

The builder found the original Double Diamond bricks, but we didn't realise that they would be metric instead of imperial sizing. Although this is not much on one brick it accumulates to make coursing very difficult. We managed to reduce the only potentially tricky junction down to about ten courses and the bricklayer did a great job of matching through.

The client, Naeem, had grown up in this house after his parents moved here from Pakistan in the 1960s. He now lived further in town (see pp. 42-47), but was spending a lot of time in the house again helping to look after his mother. He was concerned with making it a more comfortable house for his mother and for the large family gatherings that she enjoyed having here. The brief was to create a new kitchen and dining room that would be used principally by Mrs Ahmad, and to ensure that for family or social events the spaces at this side of the house could be easily designated to accommodate the women, while the front rooms would be used by the men.

The main task was to reorganise the spaces at the back of the house. As with a lot of end-of-terrace houses, the entrance was at the side, which meant that the hallway was condensed but the front living room was larger (not having an entrance hall cutting into it). The kitchen was still in its original, somewhat cramped, position in the small central room looking out onto the side of the house. The new extension is an L-shaped form that wraps around the original house, filling the side return (on the short side) and projecting out into the garden across the back of the house. The side return infill stops short of the original kitchen window, and here we only built as high as window-sill level. This resulted in a small roof that sits just in front of the kitchen window, and which is now planted as the kitchen herb garden. Below this flat roof is the space for the washing machine and dryer.

The addition was conceived as four distinct areas – kitchen, dining, sitting and external terrace – all interlocked, yet divisible for privacy. The original kitchen was enlarged and made to flow directly to a new dining area and then to the external terrace. To bring in some natural light we staggered the brick of the terrace wall by turning every other brick 90 degrees. This resulted in the nicely screened effect and textural intricacy that is resonant of traditional Indian methods of modulating sunlight. We enjoyed trying to create a fusion of English and Asian domestic architecture: the English conservatory (built so that we can keep warm while being 'outside') and the Indian veranda (where we can feel the cooling air while still technically 'in' the house). The perforated brick screen and the homogenous use of exposed brick on the internal walls and floor were definitely influenced by my travels to India, but these elements were achieved using local English materials.

Although the screening wasn't needed on this site for reducing solar gain, it is useful for creating privacy from the neighbours and for patterning the only direct sunlight that the patio receives (on summer evenings). With regard to the custom of having separate male and female areas for major social events, I think, in this case, the women got the better of the spaces.

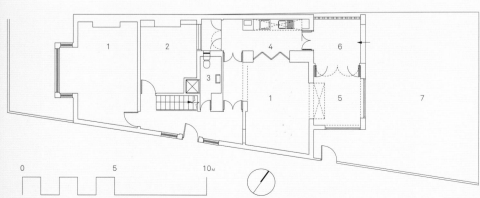

New Ground Floor
1 Living
2 Utility/bed
3 WC
4 Kitchen
5 Conservatory
6 Veranda
7 Garden

The two 'external' living areas are the link between the house and the garden. The brickwork was left raw internally so that it blurs the separation between inside and out. The two adjacent spaces (the patio and sitting room) can be opened to each other or separated, creating the effect of either a glassed-in conservatory or an open-air veranda.

Completion date: December 2009
Location: Farnham, Surrey
Materials: Stained soft wood and polished concrete

Updating modern ideas in the country_

Langermann House
Sixties bungalow

The Langermann House is in a pleasant location in the countryside outside of Farnham, about forty miles southwest of London. Though it was built in the 1960s, the house is very traditional in style. Set in the middle of a north-sloping site and surrounded by woodland, the house is a simple, duo-pitched structure with the upper floor set in the eaves of the roof. Previous owners had built multiple, uncoordinated additions, including a garage, on the south side of the building. The clients needed substantially more room, but rather than trying to marry a large modern extension directly to this modern version of a traditional form, we decided to create something fresh and new, while keeping some visible elements of the local architecture. So we focused on replacing the muddle of earlier additions with a structure that is separate but that is gracefully linked to the old house.

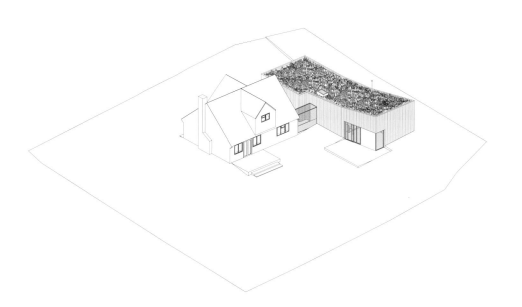

The clients are English and Scandinavian and needed a place both to live and to work. They had bought the house more for the potential of the plot than for the existing structure, but we decided it was possible to re-use some of the old successfully while adding the extra spaces that were needed. Since the approach is from the south, down a rough track, and the house is first seen at roof level, it was the roof that gave us the starting point for the design of the extension. We angled the roof of the new structure so that it was facing the approach, and covered it in sedum planting.

With the original house, the first thing to be done was to remove the collection of poor-quality earlier extensions and get it back to its original simple form. The new structure was then conceived as a completely separate architectural element on the site, and the original garage was absorbed into this new building. This makes the new structure look much larger than it is, but it was a way of unifying what had been a jumble into a single, more elegant, addition.

The separation of the buildings is a direct reflection of the organisation of spaces. The bedrooms and private spaces are in the old house, and the living areas and kitchen, where you might receive guests, are in the new building. These two forms are then joined with a simple, fully glazed linking corridor that almost gives you the sense of going through the garden as you make your way to the bedrooms.

The new form sits at a 90-degree angle, running east–west to the original house. This configuration keeps the whole house to the centre of the plot, surrounded by garden and then woodland. This position also gave us the chance to create a number of different aspects to enjoy. On the south side,

All the windows are openable and should
provide healthy air-flow, particularly the
high-level windows on the south façade,
which let direct sunlight into the space
for most of the day, but also provide
an escape route for the hot air rising
through the main space.

Inside is a smorgasbord of timber – used on the ceilings, framing and wall panels, and combined with an IKEA® kitchen (a brand of kitchen arrangements which I think are very underrated). The floor is a solid concrete base that has been polished and sealed. We were keen to have some thermal mass in what is otherwise a lightweight, super-insulated structure. Our hope is that the concrete will regulate the internal temperature in summer and winter.

opening from the kitchen, is a small, enclosed terrace for sitting out from morning to afternoon, when the sun is strongest here. The kitchen window can be used as a serving hatch from the work area. On the west corner, opening from the living space, is another terrace for sitting out in the evenings. These two outdoor spaces are quite different in feeling to one another, offering different views and greater or lesser degrees of enclosure.

The whole new building was based on a barn-like structure but, literally, with a twist. It is one simple volume made from a timber balloon frame, and clad in timber. The exterior refers to the local agricultural aesthetic in the area through the use of black vertical boarding. This cladding was cheap enough to allow us to continue using it on the garage and thus make it feel part of the new space. However, the new structure is a bit more complex in shape than the basic farm building. It slopes up from the garage, allowing for a tall living space indoors and offering a view outdoors, from the main approach, of its green roof. The form then twists slightly to hug the slope and allow more sun into the building and views out to the existing garden (rather than onto the back of the old house).

This project isn't so much a case of 'old' and 'new', since the original house was not exactly ancient. It was more about taking away years of ungainly extensions and presenting one low-profile volume that doesn't challenge the scale of the original house. It was also about finding a way to bring the house forward to meet the needs of a family using a more contemporary sensibility with regard to space, light and materials.

The main living space boasts a modern, highly efficient wood-burning stove, which should easily provide enough heat for the whole space. It is placed centrally to give optimum heat distribution to the spaces, which are organised around it.

The boarding acts as a rain-screen cladding and the ventilation is provided by a simple notch at high level, which also gives quite a classical termination of the wall plane.

Completion date: August 2006
Location: Farnham, Surrey
Materials: Hardwood decking and mill-finished aluminium

Limits and levels_

Cedarways
Seventies bungalow

Sometimes you have to look beyond the structure you are presented with. The original house, though unremarkable, was on a beautiful wooded site with great views in a southerly direction and not too far from the town of Farnham, in Surrey. It was a standard bungalow that was built in the 1970s and was starting to deteriorate. It had been built on a slope but the original design failed to make much use of the change in ground levels: the undercroft was used as a car park or storage. The plot is part of an estate, which has a restrictive covenant that prohibits residents from enclosing their gardens with any physical barriers, such as walls or fencing. This has the positive effect of making it feel as if the houses are set in open parkland. However, the downside is that residents can feel a bit like they are on show when they're in their own garden.

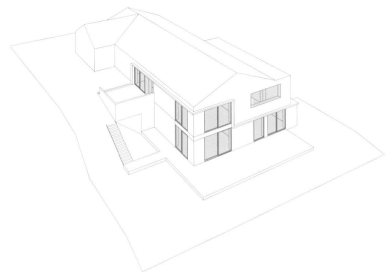

The clients, Helen and Alistair, were a young couple, self-proclaimed nomads, who loved to travel. However, they were at a point in their lives when, after having two children, they had decided to stay put for a while. They wanted to see if the house could connect to the garden, even though it was raised a storey above the slope, so that the children would have a safe place to play outside. They also wanted to create a guest suite, as well as an office space for Alistair when he was working from home. In their brief they said that their favourite place was the Barbara Hepworth garden in St Ives, Cornwall. I agree: it is a magical place, and knowing that it is something they admire helped me to get an idea for what was important to them in terms of space, light and materials.

Our main decisions were to move the entrance down to the lower level (where the car is parked) and to fill in the whole undercroft with the study and guest suite. We then cut a new stairwell into the centre of the house to connect the two floors, as previously a stair had run along the outside wall to an upper terrace. The central stair is now open to the living spaces so you get a real sense of the height of the two floors together.

The upper floor was opened out from small, separate rooms into one big space. The lower level now leads out onto its own terrace, which follows along the perimeter of the ground floor and helps to complete a circuit of paths around the house. The study is near the front door so that visitors on business do not have to go through the private rooms of the house. A large, sliding wall divides the lower floor so that the guest suite with its sofa bed can be opened to become a large play area, while the shower room is tucked into the back of the space against the hillside where there is no natural light.

Though we wanted to concentrate the budget on space rather than finishes, the outside of the building needed something to lift it and connect the old to the new. We had very little budget for this task so we decided to draw a line around the building: below that line we built new but above it we did minimal work. The line became a physical marker when we made the new aluminium gutter around the structure. Below it we added new doors and windows.

We opened up a corner window for the dining space (right) and added a Juliet balcony so that the family can eat breakfast there with the feeling of being in the tree canopy.

Rather than being closed off into separate rooms, the activity of the family, as well as the natural light and air, can now easily circulate through and around the open-plan kitchen/dining and living area that surrounds the stairwell.

Even with the building work complete, this house doesn't offer itself as a huge design statement, but it's probably my favourite example of how to achieve maximum effect with minimum cost and disruption. We decided to put less of the budget towards finishes and more towards getting the most space possible with the best layout. This is always an important part of the briefing process in terms of trying to understand where a client's priorities lie. The choices we made here are difficult to comprehend fully in the photographs, though the scheme is one of the richest, spatially, that we've done. One very sensible budget strategy, I feel, is to spend well on the structure and to use less for the interiors, which have a shorter lifespan and can be more easily upgraded later on.

In an unusual but satisfying continuation of the scheme, I was asked back four years on. The original clients had to move house, and the new owners wanted to look at following through with some plans we had developed but were never able to complete with the original budget. It would be very satisfying to complete some of the original ideas we had about the overall space.

The outside space also benefits from new timber decking, which has since weathered down to a silvery hue. The kitchen opens out onto a private terrace that we added at the back of the house. This area, combined with a bit of simple landscaping, helped to create a play area. There is no physical barrier, so we didn't contravene any of the estate rules, but there is a safe defined space that keeps the children from straying into the road.

Before

Completion date: October 2010
Location: Barnet, Hertfordshire
Materials: Polished stainless steel and ceramic floor tiles

Floating over greener pastures_

Black House
Eighties cul-de-sac house

On my first visit to the Black House I felt as though I were approaching the last house in north London before countryside proper takes over. I went to the end of the tube line, then cycled out on my Brompton until the houses ran out. At the front door it still seemed a bit like London, but when I went through to the back garden it was like being in deepest rural England. Raised up from the surrounding fields by about 2 metres, the house has a fantastically open aspect at the back, with a view over an expanse of green hills in one direction and the march of houses going towards the city in the other. The goal was to achieve more living space and make the most of the bucolic aspect.

Previously, about ten years before, the house had been altered by an architect whose work I respect very much. That project had opened up the ground floor and created one flowing space, which was divided by a series of furniture 'pods'. I think there had been plans to extend, but the budget wasn't there for the construction at the time. Instead, a number of sliding doors were put into the back elevation, and costs were minimised by keeping the doors smaller and thus not requiring any steel supports.

The clients were a creative couple who had older children. They had had quite a bit of experience doing up property and had their own builder. This is something that normally rings alarm bells for me, since if the client has too close a relationship with the builder it is easy for the architect to end up as the fall guy when problems occur. However, I'm glad to say that this was not the case here. Eugene, the builder, did an excellent job and respected what we were trying to achieve.

The rear rooms look onto a proper field, which is inhabited by only a farmer and his cows. The impression from this perspective is of being in the country rather than a suburb.

By adding wings, one wider than the other, instead of a single block, we created a lot of interior space but avoided the impression of a heavy mass added onto the back of the house. The space between the wings makes a lovely, enclosed patio area that can be used for dining or just sitting outdoors, and it is totally private.

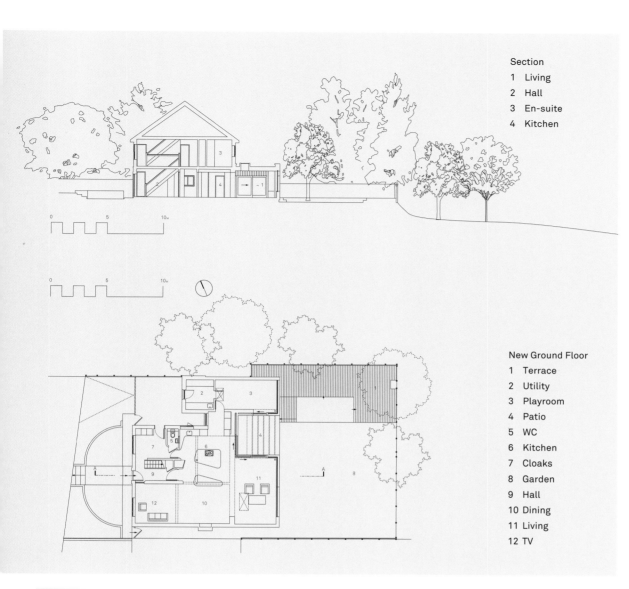

Section
1 Living
2 Hall
3 En-suite
4 Kitchen

The interiors converted to an open-plan layout in the first renovation and we continued this idea, making the spaces layered but not cut off from one another. The large windows at the back bring in a lot of light, but the addition of the skylight makes the room feel even brighter. The client's choice of furniture really sets off the space.

New Ground Floor
1 Terrace
2 Utility
3 Playroom
4 Patio
5 WC
6 Kitchen
7 Cloaks
8 Garden
9 Hall
10 Dining
11 Living
12 TV

The plan was not to undo the earlier fit-out; we didn't want to spend any budget redoing things that were already in place and that were functional. So only minor alterations were made to the existing interior. The new scheme involved adding on at the back. We created two wings – one extending the family living space, and the other providing a separate living area for the kids, along with some much-needed utility space. We left a gap between the wings that became an enclosed patio area leading out from the kitchen. This allows the kitchen to maintain a strong relationship with outside and means that it does not get lost at the back of a deep-plan volume. The new patio is accessed from all three sides – the family wing, the kids' living space and the (now recessed) kitchen. Set between the two extended wings, it is open to the wonderful views while being protected on either side from wind and from the prying eyes of neighbours.

Though three separate parts, the two wings and patio were conceived as one long horizontal composition, a single piece rather than two extensions and a void. The windows are playfully stepped up and down so that the solids and voids create an asymmetric rhythm rather than a strictly regimented volume.

Whereas the main house is brick, for the extension white render is the predominant material. Normally rendered walls such as these would be topped with a heavy flashing, which helps to seal the roof joints but breaks down the crisp sculptural quality of the wall plane. Here we worked with the builder to evolve a detail that could weatherproof the top of the render without using flashing. This single material gives the walls a lovely abstract quality and makes a coherent block in which only the window openings break up the volume. The thick patio floor, laid in porcelain tiles, keeps to the same solid form, again helping the three parts of the extension to act as a unified whole.

The windows are made from high-performance, frameless glazing, which minimised intrusion on the pure planes. We then continued with the idea of treating the render as a thin abstract plane and used mirrored stainless steel for the reveals and sills. This gives the walls a strange lack of depth, making them appear less heavy, while also bouncing light into the space.

The overall impression is of a lightweight structure, rather than a heavy block extension. We stepped the building down at the back, so it would be largely hidden from view at the front, and nobody but the farmer in his field would see it in relationship with the landscape. I think it must be quite something to see the structure lightly floating 2 metres above the cows.

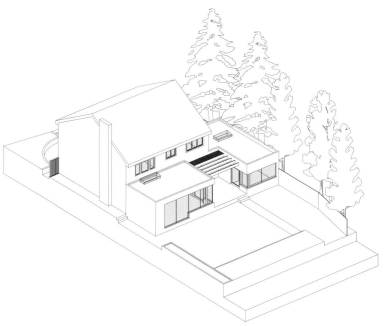

Polished stainless-steel window reveals reflect the light but also help to dematerialise the wall.

Completion date: November 2008
Location: Bromley, London
Materials: Zinc, walnut and white porcelain flooring

Improving on imitation_

Martin House
Nineties mock Tudor house

The Martin House was a very unusual one for us to work on, and I was intrigued by the challenge. Built in the 1990s to a developer's standard model, it was finished to a surprisingly high level of specification. However, from a basic design point of view, the two-storey, mock-Tudor structure was not very inspiring. It sits on the corner plot of a housing estate in South London with a line of shrubbery screening it from the close proximity of the properties next door. The clients, Neil and Mandy, had been living in the house for a while and had two boys reaching their teens, so they needed some variation in living arrangements, not to mention a bit more space. Though they were not unhappy with the style of the original house, I think they possibly had become converts to modernism, as we added some large, light rooms that are less imitative and designed to better complement their family lifestyle.

The main pitch of the zinc roof on each block of the extension is set back from the parapet. This means we could have a horizontal capping along the end wall, which gives a much cleaner line.

The dining area opens onto the new, enclosed terrace along the south side and onto another 'open' deck area to the west, giving it a dual aspect outdoors as well as views through the rooms inside.

The original house was basically L shaped, with a small, dark kitchen set along the short side, away from the garden. Our scheme created four new spaces: an enlarged, open-plan kitchen; a games room for the kids; a dining room that opens to the garden; and a new outdoor 'living room' (terrace). To do this we added a long, thin structure that fills the site along the south boundary. This rectangular volume is broken in the middle by the enclosed terrace, so along the south elevation there are three distinct areas: the dining area, the terrace and the games/TV room, with the kitchen providing access to all three. We left the kitchen in its original position. But we opened up walls so that it became much lighter and now has sight-lines through to the front of the house and also to the new spaces, and through these glazed rooms to the garden.

The other rooms are like satellites, so different family members can use each space separately, but they all feed back to Mandy's kitchen. We played with the views across these spaces, and I particularly like the view from the TV room across the private terrace through to the dining room and out to the garden. This is a very rich layering of spaces, which means that, although the whole interior feels open, each area is clearly defined for its own use. The modern, open aspect of the interior is really emphasised when the southern sun comes through the hedges along the boundary and sends amazing shadows into the rooms, which are reflected in the different panels of glazing.

For the new structure, we chose an overall form that hugs the side of the existing building, but we pitched the roofs of the two added rooms to follow the lines, or 'lock' into the old structure. Though these roofs follow the line of the old in their basic shape, they are covered in a newer material, zinc, which is more in keeping with their modern character. However, the external render on the new extension connects with the rest of the house. In addition to harmonising with the form of the original house, the raised rooflines created tall, airy interior spaces, well above the standard 2.4-metre height used in the original building.

This began as an unlikely project for us, looking at a late twentieth-century imitation of a style that is hundreds of years old. We feel strongly that it is possible to create light, open spaces that are suitable to a contemporary lifestyle regardless of the qualities of the original building.

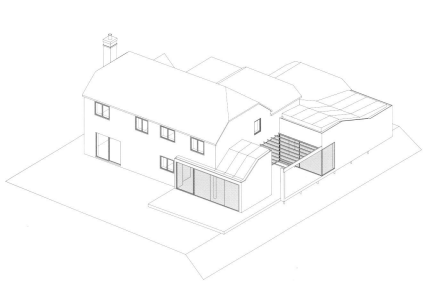

The kitchen is finished in beautifully clean white surfaces and white, terrazzo-style floor tiles. Walnut veneer was used on the block that houses storage and oven units, giving a warm centre to the design.

On the other floors (p. 197 and below right) we used parquet, which connects to the walnut veneer used on the service core at the centre of the house.

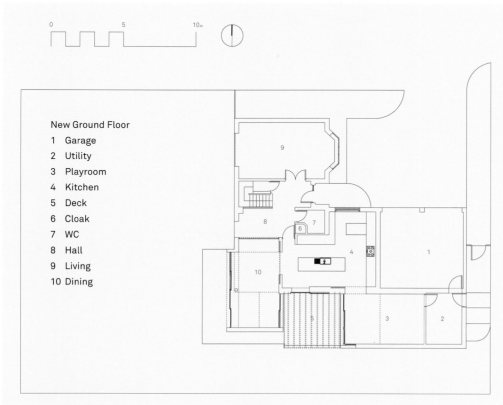

New Ground Floor
1 Garage
2 Utility
3 Playroom
4 Kitchen
5 Deck
6 Cloak
7 WC
8 Hall
9 Living
10 Dining

Completion date: July 2010
Location: Compton Green Field, Bristol
Materials: Polished honeycomb aluminium,
Fundermax® boarding and polished concrete

Bright ideas for green living_

Wadham House 2
21st-century zero carbon house

The house we call 'Green Orchard' is situated just north of Bristol and sits at the end of a small country lane. From here it seems as though you could be miles from anywhere. In reality, the plot is just behind a large industrial and retail estate and not far removed from three different motorways. However, because of the topography, it is the wonderful wooded valley overlooking the Severn estuary, rather than the built landscape, that dominates the look and feel of the area. There is a small village nearby, but it is made up of no more than twenty houses strung out along a single lane. The lot is on the northwest-facing slope, and rises up from the lane by a good 5 metres. The land was purchased by my parents, the Wadhams, at auction, and included an existing house that stood in ruins at the back of the site. So the project seemed ripe with opportunity.

This is the second scheme that I've built for my parents, and it proved to be as challenging as the first project we did together ten years earlier (see pp. 12–17), especially since, rather than adding on to something, we were building a completely new structure. The house we envisioned was going to be a place for them to retire to, the house of their dreams. Therefore, the object for me was to make this house special for them but also easy to live in and care for.

In a move that was either very brave or slightly foolhardy, they purchased the plot without planning permission. And because the original building had not been lived in for a long time, we had to start from scratch and persuade the planning department that the site should still be viewed as having a residential-use class. For this we employed the services of a good planning consultant. This is something I would recommend to anyone, as no matter how good your design is, if the site is not designated for construction of a house, you're not going to get anywhere. Fortunately, we were successful, but the process did put some limitations on the design.

The main constraint was due to the fact that the site is in 'green belt' land (which is normally protected from development), so we were not able to build a new house that had a volume more than 40 per cent bigger than the original house. This was a major headache, as the original 'house' had been little more than a garden shed. We finally hit on the solution of putting half of the house into the ground, and the planners were happy with that. This did blow the budget, however, because digging a basement is always an expensive task. As a result, we had comparatively little left over to fit out the interiors. But we all agreed that building the space had priority, and we

The kitchen is located at the heart of the house, with views to the living, breakfast and dining spaces. At the same time, it has enough enclosure so that the chef can make plenty of mess while cooking.

In resolving the challenges of maximising the view and the thermal efficiency of the house, we came up with the distinctive rhythm of glass, shutter, glass, shutter all around the building.

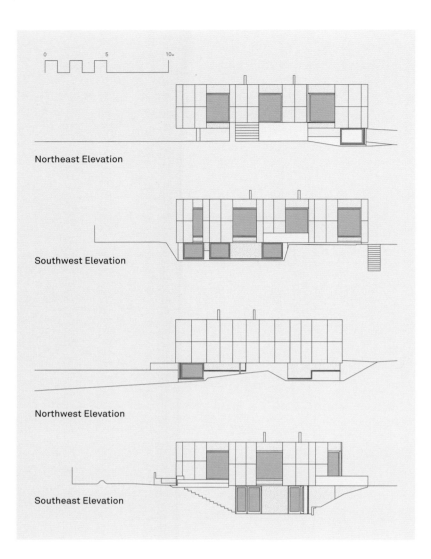

Northeast Elevation

Southwest Elevation

Northwest Elevation

Southeast Elevation

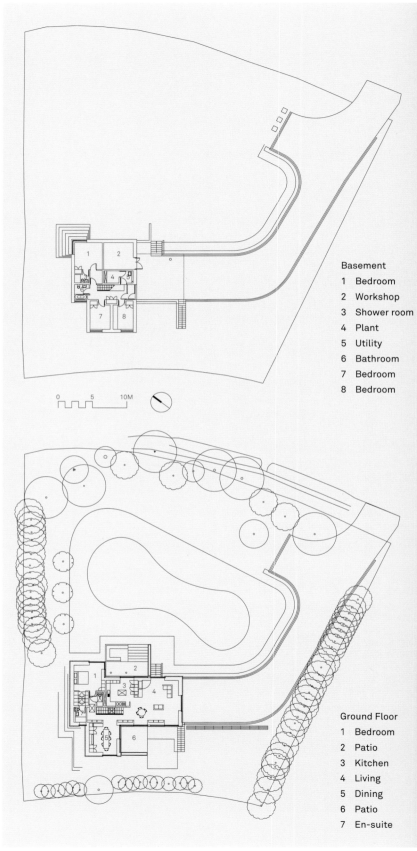

Basement
1 Bedroom
2 Workshop
3 Shower room
4 Plant
5 Utility
6 Bathroom
7 Bedroom
8 Bedroom

Ground Floor
1 Bedroom
2 Patio
3 Kitchen
4 Living
5 Dining
6 Patio
7 En-suite

could use some creative ingenuity to get the most out of the smaller budget for the inside.

My first visits to the site left me with a strong sense that there were good aspects in most directions. There were only the two neighbours who needed to be considered, but they were both quite some distance away. There were long views out towards the north to the Severn bridges, yet there was also the sun coming onto the back of the site. We started the plan by deciding that the house would look in all directions.

As the lower floor was to be pushed down into the ground we knew that the best light and views would be from the upper level. So naturally this floor would contain all of the living space. The master suite is located on this floor as well, so most of the time the house is used as a single level. The lower floor contains the guest accommodation, service equipment and a workshop for my step-father, who was a professional carpenter.

The primary aesthetic aim of the house was a desire to see in all directions, but my parents also wanted to be as green as possible. To see how far we could get towards zero carbon emissions, we began with the

The system of shutters not only allows variations in light but degrees between a wholly open and tightly closed up volume. This ensures that the house is sensitive to weather conditions and uses its thermal efficiency to best advantage.

simplest of passive energy strategies – super-insulation. We decided to take this further and design the skin of the building to have an adjustable thermal performance. So while the solid walls have high-quality insulation, the large sliding glass openings have degrees of thermal protection. They can be opened or closed to cross-ventilation, but they are also equipped with large, motorised insulating shutters that close across them. The idea is that at night or when no one is at home, the whole exterior of the building can be shut down so that all the heat is kept inside. It's also possible to close one whole elevation with shutters if, for example, the sun is uncomfortably strong.

With the views opening up all around the house, the garden became a very important part of the project, so the house and garden were designed very much together. Working from interior to the outside, the kitchen is the focus of the whole site, opening out onto a morning terrace to the northeast, and onto an evening terrace on the southwest.

If you are building a basement it tends to make most sense to do it in concrete. As we were doing this, we decided to continue using concrete to

Basement

1 Kitchen / 2 Bedroom / 3 Hall / 4 Utility / 5 Workshop

The concrete on the walls (opposite) was formed using 'sterling board', sheets made from compressed strands of softwood that are placed inside the timber formwork before the concrete is poured. It is quite absorbent, and we had to test a few samples to get the preparation right. We put a sealer on the board to stop the concrete sticking to it, but the concrete was still able to take on the wood-strand pattern of the board. It gives the walls a subtle but unusual texture.

Downstairs are three bedrooms (one has an en-suite bathroom) and a family-sized bathroom. There is also a separate utility room, and a dedicated plant room. Outside is Fred's workroom (he was a carpenter and still enjoys working on small projects).

form the slab of the upper level. Above that, the top of the house is constructed completely of timber (studwork covered in plywood, and filled with insulation). This gives a great combination of high insulation from the timber system along with good thermal mass from the concrete. These strategies provide a very stable interior temperature throughout the year, avoiding some of the problems of modern, low-energy, lightweight designs that have wild variations of temperature.

On the floors in most of the basement rooms we left the concrete exposed, and on the walls we used 'sterling board' shuttering (panels made from compressed strands of softwood) to form the concrete as it dries. The layered strands of wood leave an impression in the concrete, giving the surface a strong texture and a more organic quality. On the floors, the concrete slabs are simply ground down to expose the aggregate and polished to a smooth, reflective finish.

Because of the insulation levels and our ability to make the house airtight, we decided not to have a boiler. All the heat for the rooms and for hot water in winter would come from a system attached to the wood-burning stove. (In summer, water is heated using solar panels.) In practice, the system generates far more heat than is actually needed but, as we knew, the heat can be very

concentrated, so we used a heat-recovery ventilation system and a small set of traditional radiators to distribute the heat around the house.

The most notable features on the exterior of the house are the mirrored panels. These are made of honeycombed aluminium. Initially polished to a bright finish, they will weather down to the point where they give just a partial reflection, allowing the building to pick up the greens of the surrounding landscape.

Building new has different challenges to building onto something that already exists. When you have an existing building, you have something to react to or against. This can be a much tighter constraint, but in many ways requires more skill to get it right. Building new requires a different mentality: the question is not so much, 'how do I solve this very tight problem?' but 'how do I decide whether it should be this way and not that?' A lot of new-builds can also have tight constraints but, despite the size and budget limitations, Green Orchard had few, so it was particularly fun to work on. The two key drivers were: are we getting the most out of the landscape and can we make architecture that has an aesthetic that comes directly from a zero-carbon challenge? We hope we have answered both of those demands in a satisfying way.

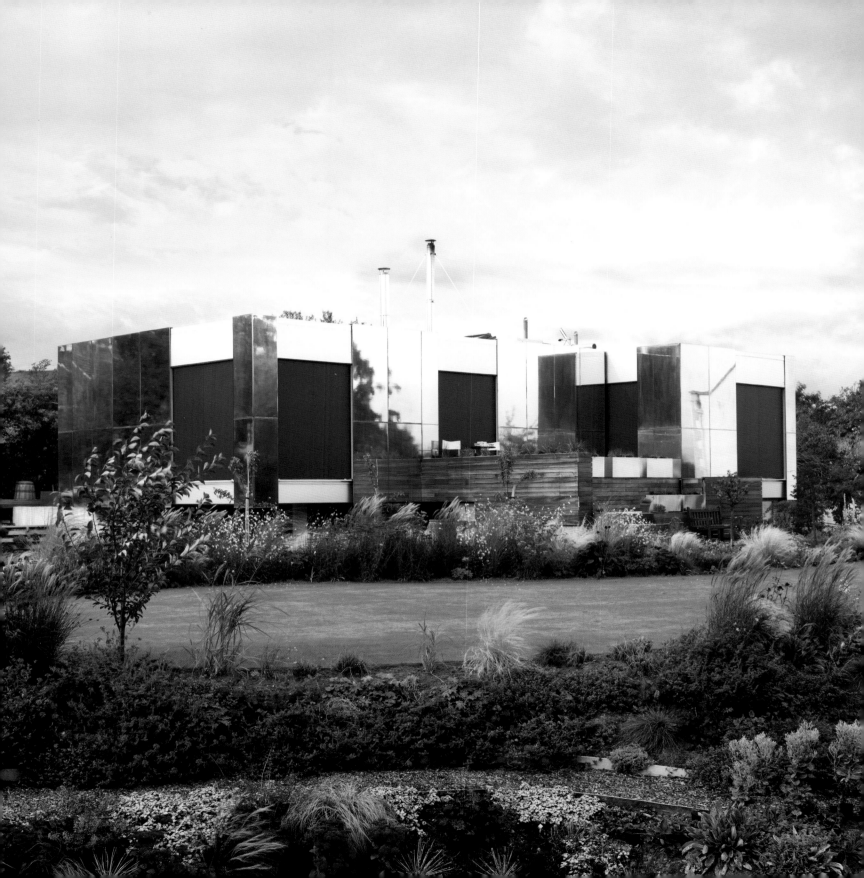

Paul Archer selected biography_

1967–
Born in London, England. Brought up near Bristol

1985–91
University of Liverpool, BA (Hons) and BArch (Hons)
Year out with Architecton, Bristol, working on historic buildings
Travels through Europe, visiting works by Le Corbusier, Mies van der Rohe and Carlo Scarpa

1991–94
Works for Tom Mellor and Partners, near Preston, England
Job architect for the Pathology Lab, Royal Lancaster Infirmary
Registered Architect, RIBA northwest region
Runs unit at Liverpool University with Gladys Martinez
2nd Prize, Holy Island Competition with Gladys Martinez

1995–1997
Travels to Nepal and India
Works for Tonkin Design, Hong Kong, designing many bars and clubs in Beijing, Singapore and Bali
Visiting tutor at the Chinese University of Hong Kong

1998–1999
Returns to London to set up Tonkin Architects UK
Runs unit at Greenwich University with Paul Pindelski
Finalist for Building Design Young Architect of the Year

1999–
Sets up Paul Archer Design in London

1999–2004
Visiting tutor at Cardiff University School of Architecture

2002
Nile cruise visiting ancient Eygptian tombs and temples

2005
Selected for Architects' Journal '40 under 40'
Travels to USA, looking at the architecture of New York

2007
Wins Architects' Journal 'Small Project of the Year' award for Collins House

2008
Travels to Finland, visiting buildings by Alvar Aalto and Reima Pietila

2009
Wins New London Architecture 'Most Sustainable' and 'Best Use of Glass' awards

2010
Sets up Paul Archer Homes, a small development company converting London townhouses
Winner of 'Excellence in Architecture', H&R Awards

2011
Travels down US west coast, visiting Sea Ranch and Great American Lodges
Belmont Road finalist in Brick Awards

2012
Grand Designs magazine lists Paul Archer Design among 'Top 10 Architects' for residential design
Shortlisted for Building Design Architect of the Year, Small Projects
Grafton Cresent, new-build house in Camden, London, filmed for Channel 4 Grand Designs television series

Paul Archer Design staff

Our Studio:

Gareth Allison
Joseph Anthony
Hiran Bandaranayake,
Matthew Barnes *
Graeme Bothwell *
Tim Browne
Emily Burnett *
Cameron Burt *
Eduardo Chopo Zaragoza
Jim Colman *
Fiona Craig *
Jenni Dang
Ultan Donagher
Richard Draper *
Richard Gill *
James Griffiths
Lisa Harrison *
Annette Hasspacher
Jade Huang
Aoife Kelly *
Rima Khatun
Ayhan Koya *
Jack Larking

Katie Livermore
Melanie Lochore
Siobhan Maguire *
Cherry McAlister *
Steve McConaghy
Frank Mueller
Susanna Mussotter
Abigail Nisbet
Emil Neumann *
Elizabeth Partington *
Volha Prus *
Mark Ratke
Eike Sindlinger
Jakub Skalimowski *
Robert Sterry *
Linda Stewart *
Lindsay Strachan
Hannah Stringer
Jon Tarbatt
Lucy Tietjens
Chloe Van Der Kindere
James Watkins

* Current

Index

Acknowledgements

About the authors

Thank you to all of my clients for wanting something special, and for having the patience often required to achieve that. Thank you to all of the builders and consultants who have helped us to make ideas into reality. Thank you to my staff for all of the hard work and creativity over the years. Special thanks to David Crooks, without whom many a glass structure wouldn't have stood up. Thanks also to my parents for being the best of clients, and for coming back to do it all over again. Thank you to Robert Sterry, Richard Gill and Emil Nuemann, my associates, for making the office function. Lastly, thank you to Linda Stewart and Lisa Harrison in my office, to Phyllis Richardson and to Peter Dawson at Grade for making this book happen.

Paul Archer studied architecture at Liverpool University, graduating in 1991. In 1993 he moved to Hong Kong and worked for Tonkin Design on many residential, office and restaurant projects, before returning to the UK in 1996 to become a founding director of Tonkin Architects. He has taught at Liverpool University, The Chinese University of Hong Kong, Greenwich University, North London University and Cardiff University. He set up Paul Archer Design in 1999, focusing on high-quality residential work. He was included in the Architects' Journal '40 under 40' list in 2005. In 2007 he won the Architects' Journal 'Small Project of the Year Award' for the Collins House (pp. 52-57). In 2012 he was shortlisted for the Building Design 'Architect of the Year Award'. His projects have been featured on the television programme Grand Designs, in books such as HousePlus (Thames & Hudson, 2005), and in The Guardian Weekend, the Architects' Journal, Grand Designs and other popular and professional journals.

Phyllis Richardson is the author of several books on contemporary architecture and design, including the XS series (XS, XS Green, XS Extreme), HousePlus, New Sacred Architecture and Nano House, and the creator of Archetcetera (www.archetcetera.com).

Photo Credits

Front Cover: **Marcus Peel**
Back Cover: **Will Pryce**

Paul Archer: pp. 2-3, p. 14 above left, p. 17, p. 28 right, p. 36 below right, p.55 above left, p.60 above left, pp.65–9, p. 72 above right, p. 81, p. 90 right, p. 114 above left, p. 138 below right, p. 159, p. 181 right, p. 185 above right, p. 188 below, p. 213 lower three images; **Will Pryce:** pp. 7–8, p. 19, pp. 21–5, p. 27, p. 28 left, pp. 29–33, p. 30, pp. 32–3, pp.43–7, p.50, pp. 53–4, p. 55 below left and right, pp. 56–7, pp. 77–80, 82–3, p. 89, p. 90 left, pp. 91–3, pp. 95–101, pp. 108-11, p. 122, pp. 137–43, pp. 145–51, pp. 153–7, p. 164, pp. 171–7, pp. 179–80, pp. 182–4, 185 left and below, p. 187, p. 188 , pp. 189–93, pp. 195–9, pp. 201–10; **Nick Guttridge:** pp. 10–11, p. 71, p. 72 left, pp. 74–5, p. 113, p. 114 above right, pp. 115–19, pp. 125–9; **Jonathan Moore:** p. 13, p. 14 above right, pp. 15–16, **Marcus Peel:** p. 35, p. 36 left and , pp. 37–41; **Linda Stewart:** p. 49; **Paul Smoothy:** p. 59, p. 60 right, pp. 61–3; **Ben Blossom:** p. 85; **Helen Fickling:** pp. 103–7; **Antonov Roman:** p. 121; **Richard Waite:** pp. 131–5; pp. 160–1, pp. 167–9; **Getty Images:** p. 163; **Timothy Soar:** p. 213 above.

Beatle Crazy!

Beatle Crazy!

memories and memorabilia

RICHARD BUSKIN

Published by Salamander Books Limited
LONDON

A Salamander Book

Published by Salamander Books Ltd.,
129-137 York Way,
London N7 9LG
United Kingdom

9 8 7 6 5 4 3 2 1

© Salamander Books Ltd.

ISBN 0 86101 773 0

CREDITS
Editor: Will Steeds
Designer: John Heritage
Consultants: Jeff Augsburger (US), Paul Wane (UK)
Filmset: SX Composing Ltd., Rayleigh
Memorabilia photography: Gregory A. Linder Photography, Normal, IL; Michael Dyer Studios, London (© Salamander Books Ltd.)
Colour reproduction: P&W Graphics Pte. Ltd., Singapore

Printed in Spain

ACKNOWLEDGEMENTS
The Publishers wish to thank Jeff Augsburger and Paul Wane for allowing Salamander Books Ltd. to photograph items from their extensive collections of Beatles memorabilia, and for their help and advice throughout the project.

Thanks also to Kenji Maeda of the Tokyo Beatles Fan Club and to Hiroto Yui for allowing us to reprint Mr. Yui's report on The Beatles' July 1, 1966, concert in Tokyo.

Page 2: Beatlemania takes hold in Britain, late 1963. Next stop, the World.

Page 4: The newspaper feature that coined a new term: Britain's *Daily Mirror* of Sunday, November 2, 1963 dreamed up the word that has entered the English language.

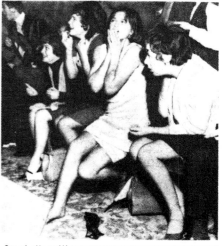

DAILY MIRROR, Saturday, November 2, 1963 PAGE 3

BEATLEMANIA!

It's happening everywhere.. even in sedate Cheltenham

Out of this world! These are the symptoms of Beatlemania.

The with-it bug bites so hard ..

EVERYONE, everywhere is catching it. IT is called **Beatlemania.**

Earlier this week it swept Sweden.

Last night, it hit sedate Cheltenham—traditional home of retired brigadiers, colonels . . . and the Ladies' College.

And if you haven't got it yet, these fantastic pictures show just what Beatlemania can do.

Cheltenham loved it.

The four pop-singing Beatles took the stage of a cinema for two concerts —the start of a five-week British tour.

Screamed

And 1,800 Beatlemaniacs squealed and screamed . . . right through the opening number.

Beatles leader John Lennon, 23, bawled for quiet. It just brought more squeals.

As Lennon and his fellow-Beatles, Paul McCartney, Ringo Starr and George Harrison, struggled manfully on, girls left their seats and rushed to the stage.

Two fans fell into the orchestra pit. The second show reception was even more ecstatic.

Hundreds stood on their seats, waving coats and umbrellas.

Programmes were thrown on to the stage—with telephone numbers written on them in lipstick. . . .

OUT OF THIS WORLD! The strong arm of the law holds back a fan with a bad attack of Beatlemania.

Pictures by Mirror Cameramen Bill Ellmann and Maurice Tibbles.

contents

the beatles

Great Britain in late 1963 and early 1964 . . . The Reverend Ronald Gibbons of the Trinity Methodist Church in Basildon, Essex, publicly asks The Beatles to record *Oh Come All Ye Faithful, Yeah, Yeah, Yeah* for his Christmas congregation; 'Beatle wigs' go on sale at 30 shillings each, as do 'Beatle chewing gum', 'Ringo Roll' and guitar-shaped 'Beatle cakes'; George Harrison receives 52 sacks containing some 15,000 cards on his 21st birthday, together with four large mail hampers packed with gifts (including a full-size door in which to place his '21st keys'); and Leeds University Law Society elects Ringo Starr as its Vice-President.

The United States in 1964 . . . 24,000 rolls of Beatle wallpaper are flown in from Britain in order to try to meet demand; an official at the British Embassy in Washington angers Ringo by snipping off a lock of his famous hair; in *Billboard* magazine's 'Hot 100' singles listing for April 4, The Beatles are placed at numbers 1, 2, 3, 4, 5,

▶ *I'll Get You – To the amusement of the kids and the consternation of his colleagues a bobby hits the stage, tussling with a fan who appears to have escaped by slipping out of her clothes. Still, The Beatles play on, for this most un-British kind of behaviour was fairly typical in the latter part of 1963, as was the young, mixed-sex audience packed into the auditorium of the Pavilion Gardens Ballroom, Buxton, on October 19.*

'I hope to have enough money to go into a business of my own by the time we do flop. It may be next week, it may be two or three years, but I think we'll be in the business . . . for at least another four years.'
George Harrison, 1963.

31, 41, 46, 58, 65, 68 and 79; and, when Ringo goes into hospital to have his tonsils removed, hourly radio bulletins report on his step-by-step progress.

'Beatlemania'. In the *Oxford Dictionary of Current English*, the suffix 'mania' is defined as both 'enthusiasm or admiration' and, in its more extreme sense, as a 'special type of mental disorder'. Clearly, judging by some of the crazy behaviour that people indulged in during that brief but unforgettable era, both terms could aptly be applied, for Beatlemania knew almost no bounds and no limits in terms of age, race, creed or colour. Indeed, for a few years the world had The Beatles under its skin, and the hold that the band asserted over the public consciousness during that time – finding its way into almost every facet of everyday life – has yet to be matched in popular culture.

'Dearest Paul, George, Ringo & John,' wrote a besotted, forward-thinking American girl in 1964. 'Please tell me where you will be every day for the next ten years. I want to plan my schedule.' She need not have worried, for the Beatlemania phenomenon would only last from 1963 until 1966. Indeed, after the group performed its final live concert – at San Francisco's Candlestick Park on August 29, 1966 – the fan worship continued, but the fever was undeniably over.

As to the word itself, 'Beatlemania' was coined by the British newspaper the *Daily Mirror* in its edition of Saturday, November 2, 1963. That morning, it reported on the mayhem that had taken place both before and during The Beatles' concert at the Odeon Cinema in Cheltenham, Gloucestershire, the previous day. Then, in the edition of Tuesday, November 5, the word popped up again – this time in the headlines. The night before, The Beatles had appeared in the Royal Command Performance, held at London's Prince of Wales Theatre, and with just the right mixture of good humour and great music they had managed not only to win over the stuffy audience but also – in the words of the *Daily Express* – to 'Rock the Royals'.

On November 10, the entire nation witnessed all the fun first-hand when the show was broadcast on the ITV network. Yet this was not the first time that the British people had encountered Beatlemania – that had occurred several weeks earlier, on October 13, when a bill-topping appearance on the TV show *Sunday Night at the London Palladium* had brought the phenomenon into Britain's living rooms.

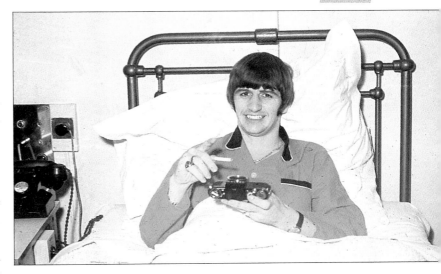

▲ *Ringo smiles for the press cameras – meanwhile using his own as an ashtray – prior to the operation to remove his tonsils at London's University College Hospital on December 2, 1964. Fortunately, the operation would not affect his singing voice.*

the beatles

Following that appearance, on the morning of October 31, hundreds of screaming teenagers had gathered on the roof of the Queen's Building at London's Heathrow Airport to greet the band on its return from a tour of Sweden. As luck would have it, the American TV presenter Ed Sullivan happened to witness the scene as he travelled through the airport, and it would be the Fab Four's appearances on his Sunday evening CBS network show which, in February, 1964, would set off Beatlemania in the US.

By the end of 1964 it seemed as if the whole world had succumbed to the Beatlemania epidemic. Yet, while no one could be quite sure as to when it would end, there were already arguments about when – and where – it had started. In the band's home town of Liverpool, for instance, local kids could place it as far back – and as precisely – as the night of December 27, 1960, when The Beatles performed at the Litherland Town Hall, shortly after returning from their first club stint in Hamburg. More than 500 hours spent on stage in Germany had shaped the group into a force to be reckoned with on the thriving Liverpool scene, and as a result the teenagers at the Litherland gig were among the first to work themselves up into a frenzy over John, Paul, George and Pete (Pete Best, the drummer who eventually would be replaced by Ringo Starr).

▶ Ed Sullivan conducts a short interview with The Beatles on April 17, 1964, in the walled garden of Les Ambassadeurs, the London club which served as the location for the discotheque and casino sequences in A Hard Day's Night. The interview was broadcast on May 24.

'I first ran into The Beatles in October, 1963 at London Airport. There was an enormous crowd of kids gathered round. . . I didn't even know who The Beatles were, I'd never heard of them. But that night I booked Ringo Starr, Paul McCartney, George Harrison and John Lennon for three shows, for $10,000.'
Ed Sullivan, 1974.

the beatles

The Beatles on stage at the Circus-Krone-Bau in Munich, Germany, June 24, 1966. The Fab Four's tour of (the-then) West Germany also took in Essen and Hamburg which, just prior to the end of their live career, seemed fitting, as they had last played there as relative unknowns in 1962.

During late 1963, the British press had a field day reporting on teenage hysteria throughout the land. In this instance, some of the fans who 'went wild in a fantastic stampede' camped out overnight to make sure of getting their concert tickets. Hopefully the male contingent were wearing the 'warm winceyette pyjama separates' advertised beneath the Beatles story.

After that, The Beatles would go from strength to strength on the local scene, yet the degree of fan worship which they were to enjoy between 1961 and mid-1963 would still be no greater – and not nearly as widespread – as that lavished on many of the other pop idols of the day. The adulation accorded to British singer Cliff Richard, for example, was of a very different order, while Elvis Presley was on another planet in terms of fan-worship. But the development of Beatlemania was so sudden and so powerful that there could be no mistaking that here was something unique.

This leads on to the main question as to why so much attention was suddenly devoted to a group which, just months before, had enjoyed nothing more than a small – if loyal – following among a few teenagers in a handful of provincial dance venues? What was it that prompted fans around the world to fight for tickets to watch an act which, on its first venture south of Liverpool in December, 1961, had managed to attract a grand total of just 18 people to a Saturday night concert at the Palais Ballroom in Aldershot?

Was it due to the band's remarkable talent? Undoubtedly. To their hard work and gritty determination? Certainly. To the careful grooming and plan-

the beatles

ning of manager Brian Epstein? Undeniably. But still, why? What made The Beatles *so* different that even unique talents such as Elvis Presley or Frank Sinatra never quite enjoyed the level of adoration that the Fab Four received? Essentially, it was a case of being the right people in the right place at the right time; they catered (perhaps unwittingly) to needs and desires that were prevalent then.

In the 1950s, Britain was still recovering from World War II. The fight against fascism had cost the nation dear, and rationing, drab fashions and a general austerity were still the order of the day. In this context, the advent of rock 'n' roll in the latter half of the decade acted like a tonic on the country's bored youth, for the music seemed to offer them a new way of life, and the release that they had been looking and waiting for.

Fifties America led the way in music, the British following with cover versions of US hits, not to mention a host of British 'Elvises'. However, by the early 1960s, those who had at first copied were now beginning to adapt, innovate and perform the material in their own unique style. Consequently, when the 'British Invasion' took place in 1964, the Americans heard the music that they had originated being exported back to them in an altogether different form.

For the British, after years of American domination of both the film and music scenes, it made a welcome change to have a home-grown craze that the world was shouting about: four ordinary boys-next-door with a devil-may-care attitude towards all of the fame and fortune, yet living out a fantasy on behalf of everyone

▲ 'Cuddly', 'lovable', 'cheeky', 'happy' and 'wholesome' were adjectives frequently applied to the Fab Four during 1963 and 1964, and ones which they would later do their best to distance themselves from. Early on, however, they were content to drive female concertgoers wild by shrieking while shaking those 'moptop' hairstyles.

'The "Mersey Sound" is the voice of 80,000 crumbling houses and 30,000 people on the dole.'
The Daily Worker, 1963.

► *Brian Epstein turns to face one camera while his protégés are captured by a few hundred more lenses on their return to a fan-infested London Airport on February 22, 1964. The US had been conquered, the rest of the world was about to capitulate too, and it was Brian's belief and devotion which had made all of this possible.*

else. Such prosperity was undreamed-of territory for most British people in the early 60s, and the novelty of this situation was reflected in a skit which The Beatles performed with comedians Mike and Bernie Winters on the TV variety show *Big Night Out*, taped on February 23, 1964. The group arrive at the studios (presumably from the US) and enter through a door marked 'Customs'. The Winters, dressed as customs officers, ask to search inside The Beatles' suitcases and, when they open them up, what do they find? Why, wads and wads of cash! Yes, the 'Swinging 60s' were truly under way, and the British were not just along for the ride but, assisted by an ever-willing media, were actually leading the procession.

In early 1960s America, on the other hand, the prosperity and optimism that had characterised the previous decade seemed to be under threat: for two deaths contributed to, and somehow made tangible, a sense of unease. The first 'death' was the virtual demise of the first wave of rock 'n' roll. Little Richard had opted for the church instead of the 'devil's music', Chuck Berry was in prison for statutory rape, Jerry Lee Lewis was out of favour after marrying his 13-year-old cousin, and the army had transformed Elvis into a latter-day version of Perry Como. In their place, American kids had to make do with a bland diet of high-school smoothies: Tab Hunter, Bobby Vinton, Frankie Avalon, Shelly Fabares, Fabian, Connie Stevens, Troy Shondell and, of course, that king of the genre, Pat Boone, to name but a few. Compared to the earlier rockers these singers were timid, sterile and, the worst of all, approved-of by most parents.

By 1963 there were definite signs of an up-turn in American music (with ingeniously crafted pop gems being issued courtesy of legendary producer, Phil Spector, and by those surfing hot rod specialists, The Beach Boys), but then the assassination of the 34th President, John Fitzgerald Kennedy, on November 22, 1963 stopped the entire nation (and, indeed, much of the world) in its tracks.

Following Kennedy's death it was as if the people of the US were in a collective depression, and whereas in the 50s American rock-and-rollers had invigorated the drab British scene, this time it was The Beatles who seemed to offer a ray of light to the Americans. John, Paul, George and Ringo touched down at New York City's Kennedy Airport on February 7, 1964 – 11 weeks to the day after the murder of President Kennedy – and their timing could not have been better.

Nor, for that matter, could their talent for quick quips and witty repartee. Facing the full force of the American media machine in an unrehearsed airport press conference, all four Beatles immediately rose to the challenge and, in the process, managed instantly to win the hearts of the US press and public alike:

Q: Are you embarrassed by the Beatlemania and near-lunacy that you create?
John: No, it's great. We like lunatics, it's healthy!
Q: How do you account for your phenomenal success?
John: If we knew, we would form another group and be managers.
Q: Have you heard of the 'Stamp Out The Beatles' campaign being organized by a group of Detroit students, and exactly what do you intend to do about it?
Paul: First of all we would bring out a 'Stamp Out Detroit' campaign.
Q: What do you think of Beethoven?
Ringo: Great, especially his poems. I keep cracking that gag every day.
Q: Was your family in show business?
John: Well, me dad used to say me mother was a great performer.

▲ A Hard Day's Night *opened in the US on August 11, 1964, a month after its British debut and eight days prior to the commencement of the band's first full concert tour of America. Budgeted at a mere £180,000 ($505,000) and shot in eight weeks, the film earned back $1.3 million (£464,000) during its first week in the US, where screenings in 500 cinemas across the country were accompanied by as much screaming as at concerts.*

Q: Exactly when do you feel you will retire?
George: When we get fed up with it. We're still enjoying it now, and we enjoyed it before we made any money.

Soon, all four Beatles would have clearly delineated personalities in the eyes of media and public alike: John, the cynic with the razor-sharp wit; Paul, the cute one; George, the quiet one; and Ringo, the sad-eyed clown. The Beatles were a breath of fresh air and for Americans, used to so much home-grown talent, there was the added attraction of being presented with a showbiz phenomenon from outside the US. Take all these factors – the music, the personalities, the novelty value – stir well and sprinkle in that American penchant (fed by eagle-eyed entrepreneurs) for carrying a craze to its logical (or illogical) extremes and, before you can say 'instant recipe', you have Beatlemania on your hands.

So it was that the craze took hold on both sides of the Atlantic and, soon after, much of the rest of the world appeared to follow suit. For example, when the Beatles arrived in Adelaide, Australia, on June 12, 1964, an estimated 300,000 people gathered outside their hotel in the hope that the Fab Four would make a 'royal' appearance on the balcony; and, during a four-day stay in Japan in June, 1966, a total of 35,000 security men had to be employed.

Today, it is virtually impossible to convey a true sense of what Beatlemania was like to someone who was not alive at the time. Contemporary newspapers, TV programmes and films can relay the facts – but they only tell half the story.

▲ By the time that The Beatles performed their final concert, at San Francisco's Candlestick Park on August 29, 1966, security measures meant that they were surrounded by wire fencing and policemen rather than by their adoring fans. Positioned at second base, the band performed a standard 33-minute show before exiting in an armoured truck.

live and kicking

'I remember being totally numb. We were sitting way, way up and I needed binoculars just to see the four Beatles. Even then, you had to be aware of where each of them was standing to know who was who. Because of all the screaming I could only hear one song, *Can't Buy Me Love*. I couldn't hear anything else, not even their talking in between songs, but it didn't matter. It was enough to know that they were just there, within the same mile as where I was sitting. That's all I cared about. I didn't care if they didn't sing.'

Kathy Doty was a 15-year-old schoolgirl when, for the first and only time, she 'saw' The Beatles performing live in concert. The date was August 15, 1965, and the venue was Shea Stadium, home of the New York Mets baseball team. Having made the two-hour trip with her sister from their home in Weston, Connecticut, she was one of the 55,600 shrieking, hysterical fans who had paid a total of $304,000 for the privilege of seeing their idols in the flesh. The attendance figure that night created a new ▶

Programmes from historic shows such as the two at New York City's Carnegie Hall are scarcer, and have a higher value, than those which were sold at regular tour concerts.

▲ *The high and low ends of the concert ticket market: an unused ticket, bearing a photo of The Beatles, can be worth up to 15 times the value of a small stub simply printed with the group's name. Indeed, during the group's final US tour there were more unused tickets than ever before.*

▲▶ *In similar demand in their day – but of somewhat less historical value now – were 'fun' items such as this American beach hat and Japanese pennant. Fans could either stare at the latter on their walls or, should they care to, run them up flagpoles when The Beatles came to town.*

world record for a pop concert, as did The Beatles' share of the takings – $160,000 (then just in excess of £57,000) – but all Kathy could do was to stand dumbstruck, with her mouth wide open, and then start to shake:

'I just could not believe it [she now recalls]. My life could never have gotten any better than it was at that moment! Around me there were the tears and the screams and people jumping up and down, and all the while I felt like my head was going to explode. To this day it is still the most overwhelming feeling that I have ever had. I was off in another world and I could have died just from the pure excitement of that moment.'

Kathy's recollections of the legendary Shea Stadium concert sum up what it was like to attend most of the band's shows during the Beatlemania years, especially in Britain and the US. Events rather than concerts, they consisted of barely controlled mayhem, with tens of thousands of teenage girls screaming their lungs out, creating a massive noise which smothered the sound of the music. From the fans' point of view, however, it was sufficient just to be present for, as Kathy said, the performance itself really was not all that important.

As for John, Paul, George and Ringo, they usually performed their set of 12 songs in less than 30 minutes – and then it was straight on to the next city and the next show. Today, it is usual for major rock artists to tour only every few years, but up until the mid-60s live concerts were the lifeblood of a successful act, and frequent tours were viewed as a vital way of sustaining and capitalizing on a band's success.

The Beatles performed about 1400 gigs between 1957 and 1966, including a substantial number in earlier guises as The Quarrymen, The Beatals, The Silver Beats, The Silver Beetles and The Silver Beatles. The majority of these appearances, however, took place before the Fab Four found fame in 1963 and, during this period, they often played at two, and sometimes three, dif-

◄ It Won't Be Long – On August 3, 1963 The Beatles earned £300 ($840) for their final gig at the Cavern Club. Two years later their take was a princely $160,000 (£57,000) for performing in front of a record-breaking 55,600 fans at New York City's Shea Stadium (below), and 12 months to the day after that event a 32,164 audience in Washington DC was standard. Such is the stuff that dreams are made of.

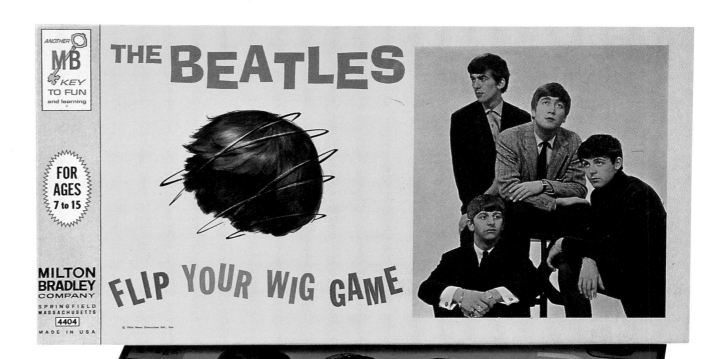

▶ *Oh, the agony of it all! Two young girls sob their hearts out for their heroes during one of the shows on The Beatles' autumn tour of Britain in late 1963. No doubt afterwards they told everyone that they had had a great time! This was the band's fourth British tour in nine months.*

◀ *The 'Flip Your Wig' game is perhaps one of the most famous of all Beatles-related artefacts, if for no other reason than its ludicrous title. The idea of the game was to accumulate the Beatle Cards and Wig Cards. The first player to complete matching sets – Paul's wig with Paul's guitar, and so on – won the game. Sounds exciting, yet for some reason it just did not catch on! Still, the garter (bottom right, this page) was a popular item, though never worn by group members!*

ferent venues every day (they also spent some 800 or so hours on stage in Hamburg). Once they became famous, The Beatles' number of live appearances diminished, much of their time being taken up by recording and filming commitments.

'The music was dead before we even went on the theatre tour of Britain [John Lennon told *Rolling Stone*'s Jann Wenner in 1970]. We had to reduce an hour or two hours' playing – which we were glad about in one way – to 20 minutes and go on and repeat the same 20 minutes every night . . . That's why we never improved as musicians. We killed ourselves then to make it, and that was the end of it. George and I are more inclined to say that. We always missed the club dates because that's when we were playing music.'

John's comments reveal how much The Beatles enjoyed the live performances that they gave before the outbreak of Beatlemania. For it was in the small clubs and dance halls around Liverpool and Hamburg that they were able to establish a proper rapport with their fans, responding to requests, cracking jokes that could be heard and monitoring reactions on faces that were close enough to be seen. 'What we generated was fantastic, where we played straight rock, and there was nobody to touch us in Britain,' Lennon told Jann Wenner. 'As soon as we made it, we made it, but the edges were knocked off.'

Certainly, in a much-reduced, embryonic form, Beatlemania was alive and kicking in Liverpool as far back as 1961 and 1962, when queues would stretch the length of Mathew Street prior to one of the group's 277 performances at the Cavern Club. Located in what was then the warehouse district of the city, The Beatles played there not only in the evenings but also at lunchtimes, when teenagers from nearby shops and offices would cram into the tiny, musty basement to catch their idols on stage.

Jim Mawer was a member of The Kubiks, a warm-up band which sometimes shared

◄ *When designing logos, a task that clearly troubled merchandisers was deciding how to spell that famous refrain from* She Loves You. *'Yeah, Yeah, Yeah,' would have been correct, yet time and again they managed to come up with 'Yea, Yea, Yea,' 'Yeh, Yeh, Yeh,' or, as on a poster for the news short,* The Beatles Come To Town, *'Ya...! Ya...! Ya...!'*

◄ *An example of how much things changed for The Beatles, and their fans, during a matter of months. Here, crammed into Birkenhead's Majestic Ballroom on April 10, 1963, the kids are so close they can almost touch their idols. Soon, however, it would be a feat just to see them, let alone hear the music – especially in the US, where the group often performed at large outdoor venues.*

the same bill as The Beatles at the Cavern, and in a 1982 interview with this author he described the club's atmosphere:

'The whole place smelled of some kind of disinfectant, sweat would be dripping off the walls and many of the kids would be stomping [he recalled]. The Beatles used to mingle and chat with everyone else. They played hard rocking numbers in those days, and Paul would sometimes take the microphone off its stand for a number like [Ray Charles'] *What'd I Say* so that he could put it down amongst the kids for them to join in the singing. He and John did a lot of the singing, but Stu Sutcliffe, who was then the group's bassist, would also go up front after giving his bass to Paul. He used to do one particular number, *Love Me Tender*, in his dark glasses, and the girls would go crazy. Then he and Paul would change back again.'

Another 'Cavernite' was Keef Hartley, later to be a drummer with Ringo Starr's former group, Rory Storm and the Hurricanes, before finding success with John Mayall's Bluesbreakers and his own Keef Hartley Band. In an interview that I conducted with him more than two decades later, he recalled how the unrehearsed, often irreverent on-stage banter between John and Paul was decisive in sealing the band's local popularity: 'I'm sure that a lot of the people who went regularly to the Cavern were almost more entertained by that than by the live music,' he asserted.

Still, it was certainly the music that focused national attention on the group in 1963, when *Please Please Me, From Me To You, She Loves You* and *I Want To Hold Your Hand* all made it to the number one slot in the singles charts, thereby kick-starting Beatlemania on a massive scale. Quite *why* the mayhem began to take place during the band's concerts around Britain was, as has been discussed, due to several different factors, but it is altogether easier to trace *when* it began.

Capitalizing on the smash-hit single of the same name, The Beatles' first album, *Please*

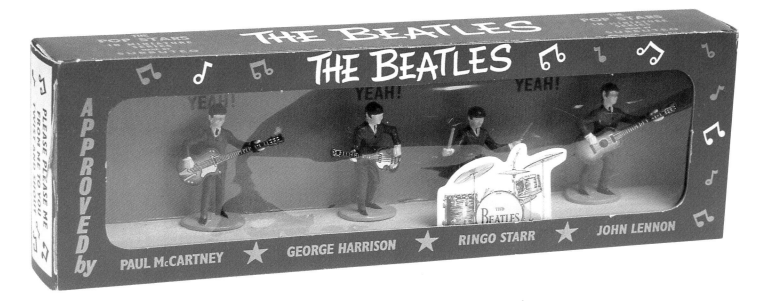

▲ The models of George and Paul appear to have traded places, and the guitars seem to be just a touch on the large side. The figurines were manufactured by Subbuteo who, in Britain, are usually associated with model soccer games.

▶ A twin-headed 'Beat Bongo', manufactured in the US by Mastro. The bongo set would now fetch up to $900 (£600) if in its original, boxed condition.

Please Me, was released on March 22, 1963 and by early April there were already clear signs of what was in store. The *Kilburn Times* of Friday, April 12 reported that there were 'piercing screams from the female element in the audience' throughout The Beatles' second London concert at Kilburn's Gaumont State Ballroom on April 9. The following week the *Middleton Guardian* carried similar reports of wild behaviour at The Beatles' concert at the local Co-operative Hall on April 11.

After this, fuelled by ever-increasing press coverage, Beatlemania really took off. Marilyn Greenfield was a typical 13-year-old, caught up in all of the frenzy, when she first saw the group perform at the *New Musical Express* Annual Poll-Winners' All-Star Concert at the Empire Pool, Wembley, London, on April 21, 1963. The Beatles performed four songs immediately before headliners Cliff Richard and the Shadows closed the show, and Marilyn recalls how she had a fit of the screams along with all of the other girls: 'I just got carried away with it all and really wanted to scream', she says. 'I loved them so much – they were so wonderful, so fantastic – that I just had to! The excitement when they came on . . . I wanted to faint! Afterwards, my throat would be killing me and I'd feel totally exhausted.'

André Rogers, who sat next to Marilyn during *Another Beatles Christmas Show* at London's Hammersmith Odeon on January 5, 1965 confirms that 'She was sobbing her heart out most of the time! Many of the girls were, while the guys, I think, were pretty embarrassed by it all.'

John Eustace, on the other hand, reacted differently to the screaming and crying when he saw The Beatles' concert at the Odeon Cinema, Lewisham, on December 8, 1963: 'I can remember thinking, ''Why don't these silly cows just shut up and let us hear the music?'' Aside from all the girls there were also quite a few guys and some older women too. Even then you kind of knew that this was history being made, and I don't think that would be the case with any of the five-minute wonders who we've had since.'

Rudolph Valentino, Frank Sinatra, Johnny Ray, Elvis Presley . . . it seemed as if the screams of the fans were getting louder with each succeeding generation, reaching a crescendo in the 60s. Indeed, screaming seemed to have become a way of life for female teenage concert-goers (and airport-goers), and so it is hardly surprising that The Beatles, who were at the very top of the tree, experienced an atmosphere bordering on sheer lunacy.

Meanwhile, following the band's final Cavern gig on August 3, 1963, the size and prestige of the concerts also appeared to grow and grow: from the first properly organized foreign tour – and first example of Beatlemania abroad – in Sweden at the end of October; to the subsequent frenzied Autumn tour of Britain, punctuated by the Royal Command performance on November 4; and then all the way in 1964, playing international venues ranging from the Olympia Theatre in Paris and the Stadium in Sydney to Carnegie Hall in New York and Los Angeles' Hollywood Bowl.

Yet, by the time of the landmark Shea Stadium concert in New York City the following year, The Beatles were already resentful of the fact that their musical performances were largely irrelevant to the hordes of fans who flocked to see their shows: 'I reckon we could send out four waxwork dummies of ourselves and that would satisfy the crowds,' John Lennon said in 1966. 'Beatles concerts are nothing to do with music any more. They're just bloody tribal rites.'

Faced with trying to play in circumstances such as these without the benefit of today's high-tech sound systems (the band's equipment amounted to no more than their set of small on-stage Vox amplifiers), the four musicians would sometimes give up the struggle and simply mime. After all, who would know the difference? And, when it was obvious that even their between-songs patter was inaudible to large sections of the

► Marlene Dietrich, the Queen Mother, Pinky and Perky: all were upstaged by The Beatles when they performed their most important concert to date, prompting Britain's Daily Mirror to utilise its newly coined phrase as a headline for the second time in no less than three days.

▼ By the end of 1963 J, P, G and R were resigned to spending their lives in a succession of hotel rooms, dressing rooms and cars. Still, despite John's and Paul's expressions, it must have been a little more fun to be travelling through the British drizzle in the back of a limo rather than in a beaten-up old van.

24

▶ *There was a complete line of official Beatles jewellery, some of it even supposedly designed by the managing director of their own merchandising company. For all the good taste of the items, however, it is doubtful whether any of the group would have actually chosen to wear such 'high-class' pieces.*

▼ *Which brass pin infringes copyright and which one does not? Easy, really, as the one on the left could be any old beetle, albeit one with a few strategically placed musical notes on its back, whereas the one on the right is carrying a photo of the lads themselves. The fact that it also has shorter legs does not affect the price.*

◀ *The detailing is of a superior quality on these figurines. The individual stances and slightly differing 'moptops', the correct guitars (right down to Paul's Hofner bass and George's Gretsch), the collarless jackets and Cuban-heeled boots – all are accurate. The only problem is the colour co-ordination – blue jackets and green trousers? Ugh!*

25

◀ *When, just prior to their first US trip, the Beatles played a three-week engagement at the prestigious Olympia Theatre in Paris, they were faced with audiences who were more interested in* local *chanteuse Sylvie Vartan and Texas-born singer Trini Lopez. After the first night, the newspaper* France-Soir *showed remarkable foresight by branding the group as has-beens, while the famous Parisian department store, Les Galaries Lafayette, cancelled plans to fill one of its main windows with Beatles-related merchandise. Still, after that initial gig the Fab Four were past caring, having just learned that* I Want to Hold Your Hand *had leapt 43 places to number one in the US* Cashbox *singles chart.*

audience, Lennon would often mock this farcical situation by throwing his arms up in the air, looking skywards and mouthing some gibberish in the manner of a power-crazed dictator addressing his adoring masses. As a result, however, the screams would grow even louder.

With The Beatles' standard of live musicianship fading fast, Japanese TV cameras captured a couple of the group's concerts at the Nippon Budokan Hall in Tokyo on June 30 and July 1, 1966. Although as Beatles-mad as audiences in Britain or the US, the Japanese fans were far more reserved, and waited for each song to end before enthusiastically voicing their approval. Ironically, this served to ensure that the tired, flat renditions were only too audible, and for once the band would have been well-advised to invite the audience to scream *more* during the songs.

This, however, was just one of many indignities inflicted on The Beatles during their tours. Others included being paraded before Australian fans in an open-top truck during a torrential rainstorm at Sydney's Mascot International Airport in June, 1964; being trapped inside an aeroplane for 45 minutes when 5000 frenzied fans broke through the police lines and airport barricades in Houston, Texas, in August, 1965; and being subjected to an exploding firecracker thrown on the stage during an August, 1966 concert in Memphis, Tennessee, after having received an anonymous telephone call earlier that day threatening the assassination of one or more members of the group . . . not exactly The Beatles' idea of fun.

Then, on top of incidents such as these, there was the sheer tedium of touring: of moving from one high-security hotel bedroom to another, and then of travelling to and from the venues in a variety of limousines and even armoured trucks (necessary to prevent The Beatles from being ripped to shreds by manic teenagers). The words of Paul's fictitious grandfather in *A Hard Day's Night* summarised the situation perfectly: ''I thought I

◀ *The brass, guitar-playing, 'moptop' featured on this brooch bears a closer resemblance to the Hunchback of Notre Dame than to any of The Beatles.*

▲ *A carved wooden corkstopper of, believe it or not, George's head. Made in (the-then) West Germany, it is difficult to tell this one apart from its three colleagues.*

◀ *The cloth-covered 'Official Mascot Doll', complete with 'authentic' cardboard guitar.*

live and kicking

▶ *During the 1965 US tour, the two shows at the Sam Houston Coliseum on August 19 were marred by some of the worst fan riots that The Beatles had yet encountered.*

▼ *Feeling the strain backstage at Shea. Behind a weary Ringo are road manager Neil Aspinall and John.*

was supposed to be getting a change of scenery and so far I've been in a train and a room, and a car and a room, and a room and a room.''

Eventually, having taken the money and run more than enough times for their own liking, The Beatles decided to call it quits as far as the concerts were concerned, and this decision effectively killed off Beatlemania. By the time of their final concert, performed at Candlestick Park in front of 25,000 people on a chilly San Francisco night in August, 1966, it could be said that in effect The Beatles were not one, but two different bands: one was the 'studio' Beatles, who were by now recording songs as varied as the neo-classical *Eleanor Rigby* and the psychedelic, quasi-religious *Tomorrow Never Knows*; the other was the 'concert' Beatles, who never bothered trying to perform this type of ground-breaking material on stage, but who instead continued to churn out the 'moptop' numbers which they had outgrown, yet which the squealing fans still expected to hear. Considering how concerts help to sell records and records help to sell concert tickets, it now seems almost inconceivable that The Beatles did not perform even one of the 14 tracks on their ground-breaking *Revolver* album at any point during the last tour. Even with the basic concert equipment available at the time it would have been possible to reproduce at least some of the songs, but The Beatles were just not interested. Indeed, so blasé was their attitude, they did not even bother to rehearse together prior to this final tour.

A change was in the air. George, always the most reluctant participant in the craziness surrounding The Beatles, murmured, 'Well, that's it, I'm not a Beatle anymore,' as the band's aeroplane left San Francisco after that final concert. By this time even the ever-enthusiastic Paul was inclined to agree, but this would never be the opinion of the thousands of loyal, adoring fans for whom John, Paul, George and Ringo would always be the 'Fab Four'.

▼ *On tour, The Beatles rivalled the Royal Family as publicists for Britain. Note the Union Jack on this Japanese ticket.*

THE ✳ BEATLES
ビートルズ

22389

7月2日《土》 6:30開演 // 日本武道館
主催一読売新聞社・中部日本放送
協賛一ライオン歯磨・ライオン油脂　後援一日本航空・東芝音楽工業

扉　員　階　E 列　13

南階スタンド

SOUVENIR PROGRAM

THE BEATLES

MANILA, PHILIPPINES
RIZAL MEMORIAL
FOOTBALL STADIUM
JULY 4, 1966

▲ *Paul's and Ringo's expressions sum up how they and their colleagues were to feel after their less-than-happy visit to the Philippines.*

◀ *Despite Japanese audiences' good behaviour, angry demonstrations took place outside Tokyo's Nippon Budokan Hall when The Beatles performed in this sacred martial arts venue.*

29

the beatlemaniacs

'Some of them even threw jelly babies in bags and they hurt like hailstones, but they could have ripped me apart and I couldn't have cared less.' So commented a breathless but enthusiastic Ringo Starr following The Beatles' first performance before a US concert audience, at the Washington Coliseum on Tuesday, February 11, 1964.

Recently arrived in the land of their rock 'n' roll dreams, John, Paul, George and Ringo were on a definite high: not only had their first appearance on *The Ed Sullivan Show* been an extraordinary success, but they had also received a welcome from the whole country which they could not have imagined in their wildest dreams.

The unthinkable had happened: four working-class guys from Liverpool who, a mere two years earlier, had been playing at the local Casbah Coffee Club, had now managed to conquer the nation which had produced the likes of Elvis Presley, Little Richard, Chuck Berry, Gene Vincent and Jerry Lee Lewis. The ▶

Although The Beatles paid less attention to their fans as the years went by, they continued to provide Official Fan Club members with a specially recorded (and increasingly bizarre) message each Christmas.

OFFICIAL MEMBERSHIP CARD

BEATLES FAN CLUB

Name.....................................

Address.................................

Trudy Medcalf   *Dawn Hister*

PRESIDENT   VICE-PRESIDENT
ONTARIO'S OFFICIAL BEATLES FAN CLUB
Compliments of CHUM-1050

◄► *A selection of fan club membership cards. Beatles fan clubs sprang up all over the world, many of them informal; some of the club Presidents evidently utilised the cards for a little self-promotion.*

▼► *Imagine seeing this through your car's rear window! Some fans seemed to be prepared to go to extraordinary lengths to glimpse their idols.*

world was at their feet, and for a brief, unbelievably exciting period the screaming girls, media overkill and general mayhem only served to confirm this fact.

In the August 1964 issue of *The Beatles Book*, Johnny Dean, the Editor, announced that the magazine could now boast well in excess of one million readers every month – and in September, pen-pal requests had to be held back for a couple of months in order to cope with the deluge. That same month, the Official Beatles Fan Club revealed that it had 58,000 members in Britain alone, and a special telephone number (COVent Garden 2332) had to be set up to deal with up to 100 enquiries every hour from Beatle People. Indeed, local area fan club branches sprang up not just throughout Britain, but in countries all over the world, including nations as diverse as Ceylon (now Sri Lanka), Mauritius, Nigeria, Jamaica and Mozambique. The total worldwide membership was to soar to seven figures during the coming months.

No wonder that Ringo could not have cared less about the jelly babies at that first US concert. Within a very short space of time, however, the euphoria began to wear off for the band and, as early as June, 1964, newspaper reports began to appear in which The Beatles' annoyance with the 'jelly baby barrage' – it was particularly bad during their shows in Sydney – was the main theme. At a time when universally complimentary coverage portrayed all four as smiling, happy-go-lucky boys-next-door, Paul was quoted as saying, 'I keep asking them not to chuck those damned things, but they don't seem to have the sense to realise we hate being the target for sweets coming like bullets from all directions.'

And the reason for all this nonsense? A flight of fancy in a publicity profile of the group back in 1963, in which it was stated that those fun-loving 'boys' had a particular liking for jelly babies. Once the piece had appeared it was a matter of 'no sooner mentioned than done' for the (over-) eager-to-please Beatlemaniacs. If it was jelly babies

32

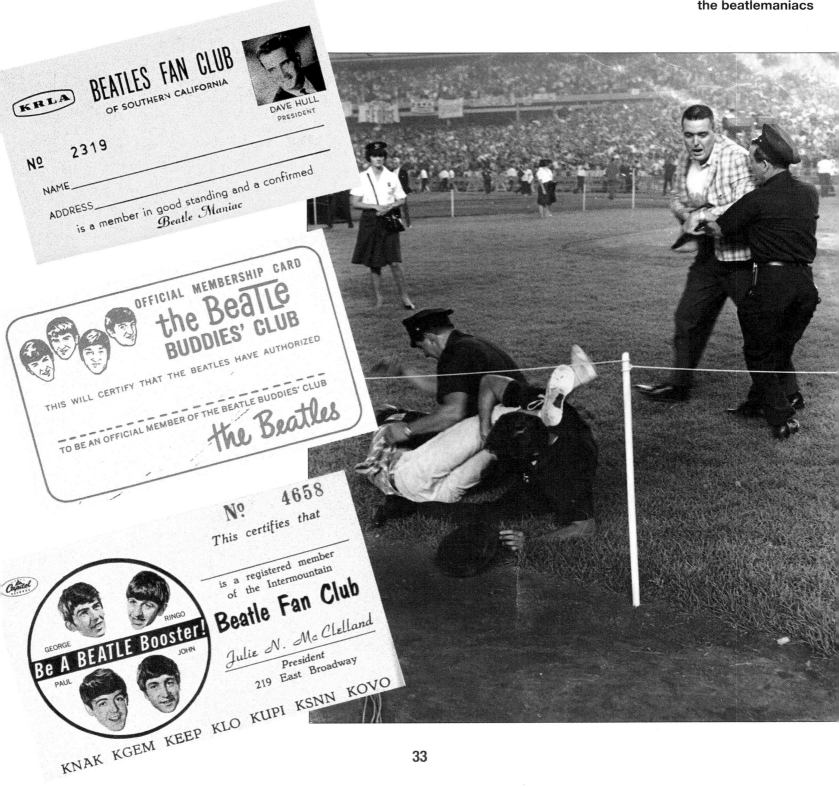

To ensure that Beatle People kept their minds on their education as well as on their Liverpudlian heroes, there were numerous helpful items for them to use in conjunction with their school work. Leading the way in such a responsible (and profitable) manner were Select-O-Pack, who produced assignment books, folders, pencil cases and school report covers, most of them adorned with the same Fab pic. As for the pencil case; then it cost just 49¢, now it is worth as much as $300 (£200).

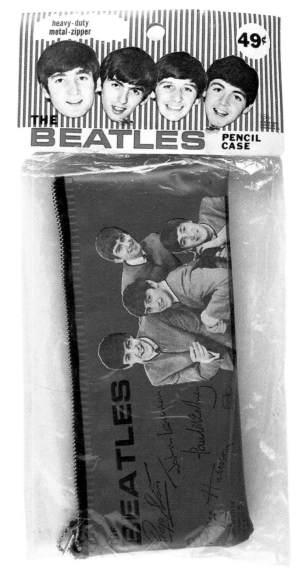

that the Fab Four liked, then it was jelly babies that they would immediately get — thousands of them, sailing through the air to the accompaniment of sobs and screams and strewn all over the stage during concerts. Even teddy bears would be thrown — some specially gift-wrapped for the occasion. In the light of such exuberant generosity it was fortunate that the publicity hacks had not made up a story about The Beatles being keen collectors of exotic knives!

During those mad days some of the fans seemed to be prepared to risk life and limb to get to meet (and even – perhaps – to touch!) their heroes. This was especially true in the Beatle-crazy US of 1964. As the group left the stage of the Seattle Coliseum on August 21, a girl fell from an overhead beam and landed at Ringo's feet; at the Public Auditorium in Cleveland on September 15 more than 200 Beatlemaniacs charged the stage and held up the show, before being captured in a large net by mounted police; at a hotel in Dallas on September 18, a chambermaid was kidnapped and threatened with a knife in an attempt to get her to reveal the location of The Beatles' suite; and in the same hotel a number of other girls had to be rescued from the air-conditioning shaft.

At this time there were also numerous cases of American teenagers going missing from home – most of whom were eventually tracked down in London, where they had travelled in the hope of meeting their idols. One 13-year-old from Newton, Massachusetts spent $400 of her savings on the 3000-mile journey, which ended successfully when she met The Beatles in their dressing room at the Astoria Cinema, Finsbury Park, on November 1, 1964. The girl's mother had to fly over to Britain to collect her but, according to a local Boston newspaper, she did not seem to be at all angry about the escapade, reportedly stating, 'They're such nice boys. I've become a Beatle fan myself.'

Other fans, meanwhile, were more restrained in their ambitions. Marilyn Green-

◄ So careless were some merchandise manufacturers they even failed to spell the band's name correctly (see top left). Still, when The Beatles gazed out of their bedroom windows at Miami's Deauville Hotel in February, 1964, they could see that at least the girls on the beach had made no such mistake (below).

35

field, for instance, felt as if she had won the national lottery when a London school friend gave her what was supposedly a lock of Paul McCartney's hair, which had been placed safely on some cotton wool inside a small box. 'Paul was my favourite, and my friend promised me that her uncle had cut his hair in a barber's shop,' recalls Marilyn. 'Obviously the biggest load of dross ever, but I walked around with this neatly wrapped lump of hair inside my bag for years! That way I could feel just a little closer to him.'

In Japan, meanwhile, 16-year-old Hiroto Yui used his school bag to smuggle a couple of cameras into Tokyo's Nippon Budokan Hall, when he and a friend attended The Beatles' evening show there on July 1, 1966: 'There were police guards posted all around the venue, and there were even about 40 of them directly behind where we were sitting [he recalls]. The whole idea of trying to take photos, therefore, seemed pretty daunting, but while the opening acts were on stage, one of the guards patted me on the shoulder and said, "My son is crazy about The Beatles. Are they so great?" I said, "Yeah, of course. They are brilliant!" We began to chat and I then told him that my friend and I had cameras with telephoto lenses but no film inside, and asked if we could use them as telescopes to see the group better. Incredibly, he agreed, and today I have the photos to prove it!'

In a strictly ordered society this was fairly risqué behaviour, but of an altogether more manic nature were the vigils and car chases (that is, rampaging kids chasing The Beatles' car on foot), which took place on the other side of the Pacific. When, for instance, the Fab Four first visited the US in February, 1964, thousands of hysterical fans held a vigil outside New York City's prestigious Plaza Hotel. Among them was 14-year-old Lorraine Rendino, who now asserts that even if she failed to see the moptops it was enough for her 'just to be breathing the same air.' Lorraine recalls:

'Every time a car drove out the rumors would fly – "There they are!" or "Yeah, that was Paul!" – and everyone would start chasing after it...Then, two minutes later, another car would come out from another exit and it would be, "No, that's them!"'

Running after the cars failed to pay off, however, and, despite repeated calls to the hotel switchboard, Lorraine never managed to speak to The Beatles on the phone either: 'We never made it past the lobby and so we spent many hours outside, standing five deep all around the building and just screaming at the windows. You see, some of the guests would open their windows, wave a little bit, then slam them shut and this would set us all off! At the same time, we'd study the newspaper pictures taken of The Beatles in New York to try and find clues as to where they may be visiting. We were like amateur detectives!'

Whereas Lorraine did eventually get to see The Beatles in concert (both at Carnegie Hall on February 12, 1964 and at Forest Hills Stadium on August 29 of the same year), the only glimpse that 16-year-old Mark Lapidos was afforded was through one of the car windows which Lorraine and her friends had missed. This event took place in a Miami alleyway on February 21, 1964, as The Beatles were leaving the Deauville Hotel to embark on their journey back to London. Lapidos remembers:

'I was knocking on the window and [The Beatles] were waving back to me. While the police were holding all of the kids back on the other side of the street, I'd made my way past the parents, and so as the car turned out onto Collins Avenue I ran after it for about 50 yards, waving at them as they waved back. Just me! There were no other people on the street. It was absolutely amazing...a real thrill.'

Five years later – on Friday, June 13, 1969 – Mark was standing with a friend outside the Apple building at 3, Savile Row in London, talking to John Lennon who was the sole Beatle in residence that day. Lennon had been refused a visa to enter the US due to his

April '66

▲ Bulletins, books and records were sent free to all paid-up members of the two main fan clubs: the Official Beatles Fan Club in Britain and Beatles (USA) Limited.

▼ This flight bag is one of numerous counterfeit items which are now falsely passed off as original 1960s merchandise. Many have even been printed with 'official' logos.

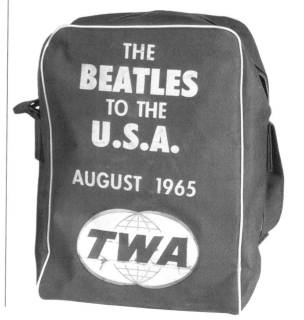

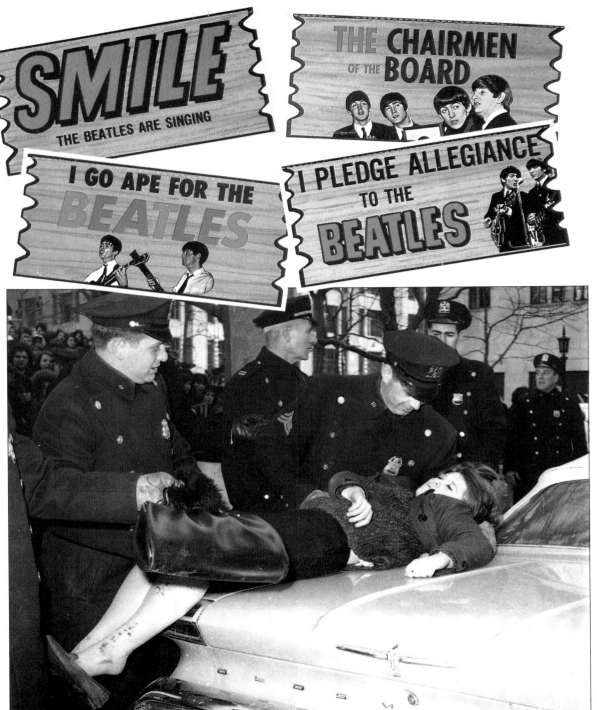

◀ *The Beatles Plaks series comprised 55 cards, and they were only marketed for a short time in certain US cities. Nowhere near as popular as other trading card series, the Plaks featured some fairly tenuous slogans – after all, it was Frank Sinatra who was known as the 'Chairman of the Board'!*

◀ *What a state to get yourself into – lying comatose on top of a car, being pawed at by New York City cops. A fun session of Beatle-spotting outside the Plaza Hotel evidently got out of hand here, overwhelming this poor girl in February, 1964.*

37

▼ *Considering how The Beatles earned their livings, toy instruments were probably among the most appropriate forms of merchandise. This 'New Beat Drum'* featured Ringo's face, his autograph, and a stick-wielding hand. It was popular with British teenagers in the mid-60s, even if not with their long-suffering parents.

► *In the wake of The Beatles' success a plethora of toy guitars flooded the market, in much the same way as instruments bearing the name and image of Elvis Presley had* done during the mid-50s. Rock music was still a young art form, and as such it inspired small children to mimic the idols whose performances they saw on TV.

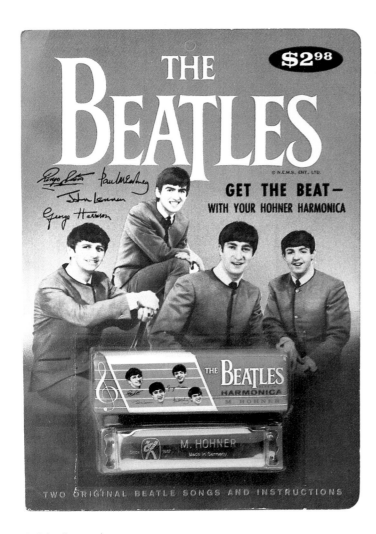

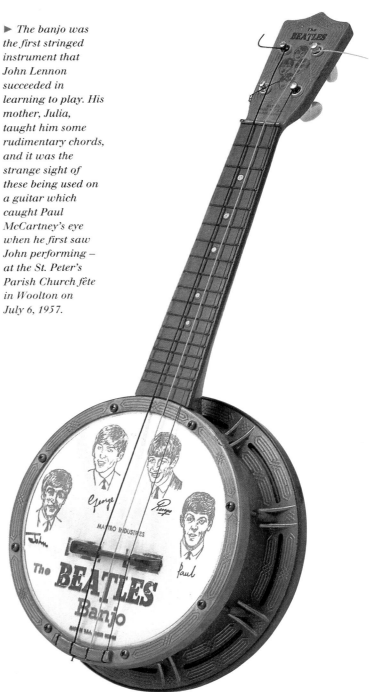

► *The banjo was the first stringed instrument that John Lennon succeeded in learning to play. His mother, Julia, taught him some rudimentary chords, and it was the strange sight of these being used on a guitar which caught Paul McCartney's eye when he first saw John performing – at the St. Peter's Parish Church fête in Woolton on July 6, 1957.*

▲ *John Lennon's harmonica-playing was a trademark of The Beatles' earlier recordings. Lennon acknowledged that he had been inspired by the mouth organ solo on Bruce Channel's 1962 British hit, Hey Baby.*

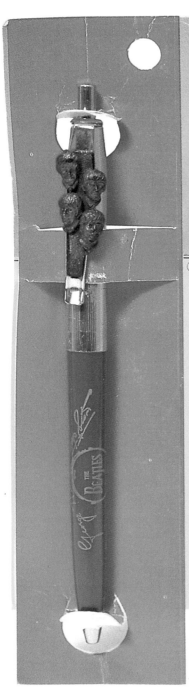

© NEMS ENTERPRISES LTD., 1964   CUT ON DOTTED LINE, FOR

Ludwig

THE **BEATLES**

OFFICIAL
Ballpoint Pen

- **FINE QUALITY**
- **RETRACTABLE**

TAKES STANDARD REFILLS - AVAILABLE ANYWHERE!

Manufactured under official license for the manufacture and distribution of Beatle Pens in the U.S. and Canada. Manufactured and printed in USA, by PRESS-INitial Corp., Providence, R.I.

◀ *It was hard to miss the point that this was the official Beatles pen. The barrel displays the autographs of the four and the group's bass drum, while those four famous heads adorn the clip.*

Blow up!...a FAB BEATLE **Balloon**

THE **BEATLES** ©

UNITED INDUSTRIES, INC. SOUTHINGTON, CONN.

▲ *A photo of the group, some 'hip' copy – and yet another item with which to woo the fans rolls off the production lines. The 'Beatles' logo with the long 'T' remains, incidentally, a copyrighted insignia.*

40

drug conviction the previous year, but Lapidos had thought of a solution. He happily offered John his own passport, complete with a photo of himself sporting long, centre-parted hair, moustache and granny glasses! Okay, so it was not exactly a mirror image, but hey, still worth a try! Lennon looked at the photo, thanked him for the thought, and politely rejected the offer.

During the late 60s, fans, sightseers and the plain curious were a constant presence outside either Paul's house in Cavendish Avenue, in the London suburb of St. John's Wood (McCartney was the most amiably accessible of the four), the nearby EMI Studios in Abbey Road or the Apple offices. A core of particularly hardened Beatlemaniacs would hang around these places hour upon hour, day after day, come rain or shine, for months and even years. Names such as Margo Stevens, Carole Bedford, Big Sue, Little Sue, Gayleen, Willie and Knickers all became familiar to The Beatles as these fans seemed to turn up wherever the group went.

When one of their number discovered that Paul was in the habit of leaving his back-door key under a particular flowerpot, some fans would let themselves into his house while he was out in order to peek around and grab a few mementoes; socks, ties, underpants, anything they could get hold of. Others, who held non-stop vigils outside 3, Savile Row, were dubbed the 'Apple Scruffs'. George was later to write a song about them.

Indeed, although Beatlemania was mainly a phenomenon of the earlier years, the popularity of the band remained such that, even later on, the chance that they might appear together could bring a city to a standstill. Sample, for instance, the world première of the feature-length cartoon, *Yellow Submarine*, which was held at the London Pavilion cinema in Piccadilly Circus on Wednesday, July 17, 1968. This was the last time that all four Beatles jointly attended a first-night opening – none of them would even turn up for *Let It Be* – and, with the central London traffic being halted by the massive crowd of

▲ *David Stark (far left) lurks behind George Harrison in the lobby after the* Yellow Submarine *première.*

▼ *Aside from The Beatles, another Liverpudlian gift to the world was Scotts Bakery's delicious 'Ringo Roll' bread.*

Autographed Portraits of THE BEATLES

John
George
Paul
Ringo

WAGON MASTER WESTERN **BEANS** BEATLES OFFER
YOUR CHOICE 25¢ EACH
AND 2 LABELS FRO...

◄ *Even Wagon Master Baked Beans got in on the act. Marketing hand-drawn portraits of The Beatles in this way did not infringe any copyrights, so long as they were not obviously based on specific photographs of group members.*

▼ *A bamboo plate, complete with lanterns, dragons and a translation of The Beatles' name for that 'authentic' Chinese effect. In the central scene, taken from the set of A Hard Day's Night, model Pattie Boyd (far left) grooms her future husband.*

四頭披
THE BEATLES

people trying to catch a glimpse of the group, not to mention the massed ranks of photographers and police (the latter doing their best to maintain some order), it was like 1964 and 1965 all over again.....and even in 1968 some people were clearly still prepared to go to almost any lengths – or heights, for that matter – to meet their idols.

On that July day, David Stark, a 15-year-old London schoolboy and full-time Beatle-spotter, was one of several teenagers who had managed to get on the roof of the London Pavilion to watch the crowds gathering in the streets below. Yet when David and a friend then attempted actually to gatecrash the première, entering the theatre's upper tier and bluffing their way past an usher and the manager, their efforts were rewarded far beyond their wildest expectations.

By coincidence, The Beatles' own places had already been reserved in the section of the theatre they had talked their way into, and once the four had taken their seats David and friend spotted two empty places immediately behind Paul McCartney, and next to Keith Richard of The Rolling Stones. The intended occupants, Mick Jagger and Marianne Faithfull, were still in the US, and so Keith had no objection to the two boys sitting there once the lights had dimmed. Stark recalls his feelings at the time:

'It really was quite unbelievable. There we were, watching The Beatles' new film with all of them sitting right in front of us! Afterwards, while The Beatles were waiting in the foyer for their cars to arrive I also got the chance to say a few words to John and George. Apart from that, the most vivid memory I have of that night is the incredible sight of thousands and thousands of people crammed outside the cinema, all chanting the chorus to *Yellow Submarine*.'

This in fact would be the last real occurrence of large-scale Beatlemania prior to the group's demise, although John, Paul, George and Ringo were to make one further public appearance, on the roof of the Apple building on January 30, 1969. On that cold,

▲ Can you truly imagine decorating your kitchen or bathroom from top to bottom with these Beatles wall tiles? To break up the monotony the makers also provided a fifth tile, portraying the group performing together.

◀ The Beatles get down to business in their central London fan club office in 1963. Sorting through the mail with them are Joint National Secretaries Bettina Rose and Mary Cockram. To protect her privacy, Mary used the pseudonym Anne Collingham on all fan club correspondence.

◄ *Ideal for use both at home and on the road: a biscuit tin, bearing the usual array of images; and a thermos flask, with an illustration of the group members sporting their 1965 military-style uniforms. The thermos was also sold in a set that included a lunchbox and brunch bag.*

blustery winter's day they gave an im-promptu 42-minute performance which would prove to be one of the saving graces of the *Let It Be* film and which, more im-mediately, brought London's midday traffic to yet another stop in the streets below.

As the sounds of *Get Back, I've Got A Feeling, Dig A Pony, The One After 909* and *Don't Let Me Down* wafted down from the roof of the Apple building, people of all ages got out of their cars, stopped walking, or rushed from the nearby shops and offices to hear – and, they hoped, to see – more of what was going on. Some even went so far as to make their way up to the roof itself by climbing staircases on the outside of the building. One elderly Londoner who stopped to watch the scene surely spoke for many people – young and old – when he com-mented:

'I think The Beatles are classic. You can't beat 'em. They're all out on their own, they've got a style of their own, and, well, in my opinion, I think they're a lovely crowd. They've got good quality, they can sing well, and . . . well, what else can I say but that they're all good people.'

A young woman agreed, pointing out that 'It brightens up the office hours, anyway,' and with crowds clogging the central London streets it took complaints from local shopowners and the intervention of the police to bring matters – and, as it turned out, The Beatles' live career – to a halt.

When Paul's statement that he, John, George and Ringo would not be working to-gether again was released in April, 1970, it immediately made newspaper and TV head-lines around the world. 'They started when they were younger and we were younger, and all through these years we've just de-veloped with them and grown up with them and they, like, belong to us,' a heartbroken girl told a TV news reporter as she and other fans gathered outside the Apple building on the day of the announcement. 'There will never be another Beatles. Never.' A fitting epitaph from a true Beatlemaniac.

◀ A British-made desk calendar displaying an important, if only partially correct, date: on Feb 7, 1964, The Beatles arrived in the US for the first time. That day, however, was a Friday, not a Sunday.

▼ 13, Emperor's Gate, Kensington, London, was where John, wife and child lived as 'the Hadleys' from November, 1963 until July, 1964. Fans used to hang around outside the house for hours.

the front page

'Yeah! Yeah! Yeah! You have to be a real sour square not to love the nutty, noisy, happy, handsome Beatles.' *Daily Mirror*, November 5, 1963.

An easy reference to that most well-known of contemporary catchphrases, some semi-mocking 'hip talk' and an assortment of fun adjectives describing the Fab Four: these were the ingredients for many a newspaper column during 1963 and 1964. The Beatles' star was on the rise and it was still fashionable to build them up, rather than to attempt to knock them off the pedestal which the media had placed them on in the first place. That would come later.

During the early stages of Beatlemania it was almost as if John, Paul, George and Ringo could do no wrong. Of course, there were the odd aberrations, such as John beating up Cavern DJ, Bob Wooler, at Paul's 21st birthday party and in the process gaining The Beatles their first national press headline – 'Beatle in brawl' – on the back page of the June 21, 1963 edition of the ▶

Reading stories of teen angst and trying to decide on 'the greatest controversy of all times' was one way for kids to busy themselves back in the 60s. By the way, it was Elvis who wore the crown . . . Royal Crown hairspray, that is!

47

Daily Mirror; or, the following year, the 'controversial' Beatle's refusal to make a formal speech at a Foyle's Literary Luncheon held in his honour, prompting the *Mirror* to send up yet another popular song with 'I Wanna Hold My Tongue!'; or a sour-faced George Harrison throwing his drink at an over-persistent photographer during the group's visit to the Whisky-A-Go-Go nightclub on Hollywood's Sunset Strip in August, 1964 (the diligent cameraman managed to capture the incident on film and, as a result, it received widespread coverage in the US press).

For the most part, however, it was good news all the way, and another rich source of stories were the fans themselves – tales about girls screaming, girls fainting, girls getting crushed, and so on, were favourites. In late 1963 this subject filled hundreds of column-inches in the British popular press, and the international press then eagerly took up the theme wherever The Beatles toured over the next three years. *The Seattle Daily Times* of August 22, 1964 was one of numerous publications to go as far as calling in an 'expert' on the matter – in this case a Dr. Bernard Saibel, who was pictured at a concert 'surrounded by scenes of frenzy', where he observed the teenagers becoming 'frantic, hostile, uncontrolled, screaming, unrecognizable beings'. Blaming adults for 'allowing the children a mad, erotic world of their own,' he went on to describe how 'normally recognizable girls behaved as if possessed by some demonic urge, defying in emotional ecstasy the restraints which authorities try to place on them.' An impressive analysis, and one which concluded, of course, with the advice that The Beatles' concerts should be stopped, 'if only for the good of the youngsters'.

Another equally interesting diagnosis was that made in August of the following year with regard to the condition which apparently afflicted two 'teenage blondes', who had perched themselves on a 22nd-floor ledge of New York City's Americana Hotel, and who refused to leave until Paul

◄ *Paul and Ringo during the taping of The Beatles' second appearance on the British TV show* Thank Your Lucky Stars, *February 17, 1963. Unfortunately, stills such as this are all that survive of the group's British TV performances from October 1962 through to August 1963, when such material was at last considered important enough not to scrap.*

◄ *While The Beatles and British comic Ernie Wise donned straw boaters and striped jackets for a rendition of 'Moonlight Bay' on British TV's* The Morecambe And Wise Show *on December 2, 1963, Wise's partner, Eric Morecambe, opted for a 'hip' Beatle wig and collarless jacket.*

◄ *The hairpiece worn by Eric Morecambe (see top) would have been made in Britain by the Bell Toy Company; the packaging carried the slogan 'Be With It, Wear a Beatles Wig'. At left is the 'lifelike' US version, made by Lowell Toy Manufacturing; it was produced in such large quantities that examples are now worth a fifth of the value of the British wig.*

▲ *Oh, yes, can't you just see Mum, Dad and the kids all fighting over who should go next, dragging magnetic filings to create hairstyles for those bald Beatles! There again, this was Britain in 1963 . . .*

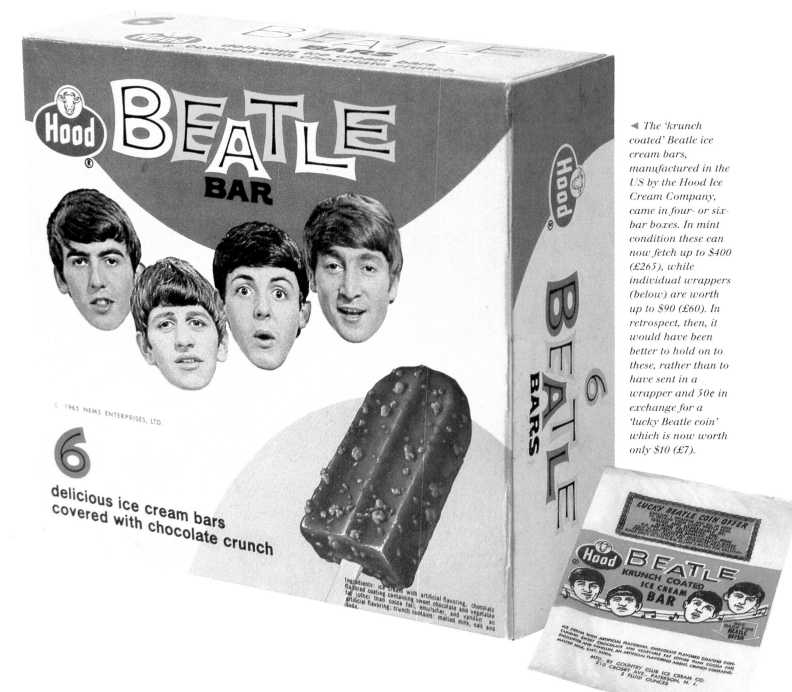

◄ The 'krunch coated' Beatle ice cream bars, manufactured in the US by the Hood Ice Cream Company, came in four- or six-bar boxes. In mint condition these can now fetch up to $400 (£265), while individual wrappers (below) are worth up to $90 (£60). In retrospect, then, it would have been better to hold on to these, rather than to have sent in a wrapper and 50¢ in exchange for a 'lucky Beatle coin' which is now worth only $10 (£7).

McCartney came to the scene. (Police eventually grabbed them before he arrived.) According to the *New York Post*, doctors at nearby Roosevelt Hospital diagnosed the case as 'acute situation reaction', while the paper itself simply dubbed the whole episode a matter of attempted 'Beatlecide'!

However, apart from the 'Beatles to split' rumours which began to find their way into the papers as early as the autumn of 1964, press and media coverage was almost exclusively positive and complimentary during those early years. Even the 'scandal' stories mentioned above were usually reported in an upbeat manner, and if an article concerning some less-than-friendly Beatle behaviour did make it into print, it was usually allowed to fade and die quite quickly.

Perhaps the reason for this was that The Beatles represented a welcome breath of fresh air in a world seemingly riven by wars, riots, assassinations and political scandal. Unsurprisingly, most people appeared to warm to them. Recognizing this, the popular press decided that it was in their own best interests not only to jump firmly on the Beatles bandwagon, but also to give it a hefty push to keep it rolling along. That way everyone would be happy – the artists, their fans and . . . oh, yes, the newspapers!

As a consequence of this, daily, evening, weekly and monthly journals in every city where The Beatles played during the years 1963 to 1966 – from London to Rome, New York to Sydney, Tokyo to Paris – gave extensive coverage to the pandemonium surrounding their shows, as well as relaying some of the inane things which had been gleaned from the preceding press conferences. ('The Beatles refuse to cut their "shaggy" hair', 'John likes to wake up at two in the afternoon', and so on.)

At the same time, they reported closely on the every move of each member of the group: on George's bout of influenza during the first US trip in February, 1964; on the making of the first movie, *A Hard Day's Night,* in March and April; on the occasion

▶ *In the Beatle-mad US of 1964 it was not uncommon for entire newspaper front pages to be dedicated to stories about the group and their fans. The tone of the articles was usually tongue-in-cheek and the content fairly trivial, but when the Fab Four hit town this was big news and, besides, the photos of mass hysteria filled space and made for eye-catching entertainment.*

▶ *A uniquely-shaped ticket to a US première of a uniquely popular film, and one that was soon recognized as 'the* Citizen Kane *of juke box musicals'.*

▲ *Wherever the Fab Four went there was the obligatory press conference. At first, The Beatles enjoyed firing off well-timed quips, but they soon tired of responding to the same mind-numbingly inane questions.*

◀ *In 1966, Bravo magazine sponsored the West German leg of The Beatles' final world tour. From June 24-26, the Bravo Blitztournee saw the group perform two shows each in Munich, Essen and Hamburg.*

▲ *'First in America' but by no means the last! Photo-based Beatles mags blitzed the US in 1964, and continue to do so whenever any kind of anniversary comes around.*

in March when all four collected their Variety Club of Great Britain awards from future Prime Minister, Harold Wilson; on Paul's buying a racehorse for his father's 62nd birthday present in July; on John's purchase of a six-bedroomed house that same month; on Ringo's operation to have his tonsils removed in December, and so on. It seemed that no event was too trivial to report.

Television and radio also played their part in stoking up the flames of Beatlemania. Both carried stories on all of the above events , while also taking advantage of the fact that they could, when necessary (or not, for that matter), give up-to-the-minute news-flashes regarding some incident or other involving the group. Always ready to carry matters to their (il)logical extremes, many US radio DJs, for instance, worked the nation's teenagers into a frenzy of anticipation by counting down the hours, and then the minutes, to The Beatles' landing on American soil on February 7, 1964. Kathy Iuliucci, then a 15-year-old schoolgirl from Connecticut, remembers the atmosphere that this created:

'I'd heard something about The Beatles and they didn't really interest me, but then I recall being in class and all of the kids suddenly starting to count down to when the plane was going to land at Kennedy [airport]. At that moment the teacher was probably more aware of The Beatles than I was, but with everyone counting down I thought, ''There might be something to this!'' That was the first time I realized that it was something big. When I went home I saw them on the news, and from that point on it was unbelievable. It just took the country by storm.'

Meanwhile, back in Britain the BBC TV sports programme, *Grandstand*, broke with time-honoured tradition and broadcast an interview with the Fab Four on their February 22 return to London's Heathrow Airport. In June, Dutch TV cameras filmed The Beatles' Amsterdam canal trip, and just a week later Australian newsreels captured the extra-ordinary scenes as an estimated 300,000

52

◀ Brazil, Spain, Italy, Australia – The Beatles' influence really was felt worldwide. The Brazilian mag at far left was different to many of its foreign counterparts in that it consisted of sheets with 96 photos of the '4 Cavalheiros' for fans to separate and then attach to their bedroom walls.

◀ The 'intellectual Beatle' (as the press dubbed him) would often vent his frustration during interviews. Once, John announced that The Beatles would be making no further unscheduled public appearances during their tour – 'We're going to stay in our hotel, except for concerts.' 'Won't this make you feel like caged animals?' came the next question. 'No,' John replied. 'We feed ourselves.'

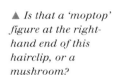

▲ *Is that a 'moptop' figure at the right-hand end of this hairclip, or a mushroom?*

▼ *Today, a bottle of this perfume could cost you anything up to $400 (£265) – so it may be wise to opt for something cheaper, such as Chanel No. 5!*

► *Compiled in 1964 after The Beatles had allowed Bill Adler access to the mountain of fan mail they had received, the book* Love Letters to The Beatles *featured such gems as the contribution of Melissa B. from New York City: 'I have kissed this letter 3,268 times. My lips are sore but I am in heaven!'*

► *During a shopping spree the ideal place to store all those Beatle goodies was in this easy-to-clean white vinyl Beatle handbag.*

people crowded outside the group's hotel in Adelaide. Towards the end of that crazy year, US radio stations even went so far as to broadcast hourly bulletins on Ringo's progress following his tonsillectomy. For, by this time, The Beatles were sufficiently big news to bump almost anyone – and anything – off the front page. Indeed, the *Philadelphia Daily News* even boasted its very own 'Beatle Editor'!

And so it continued through 1965 – Ringo's marriage to Maureen Cox; the group's second full-length feature film, *Help!*; John's second book, *A Spaniard in the Works*; the MBE awards; more hit records and more sellout concerts, including the landmark Shea Stadium performance.

The turning of the tide eventually came in mid-1966. Compared to today's short-term standards, when many stars are knocked off their perches almost as soon as they have climbed to the top, The Beatles had a good run for their money. They received roughly three years of uniformly great publicity, and even after that the condemnation tended to be infrequent. When it came, however, its effects were significant.

It fell to the Philippines – and, more specifically, to the Marcos regime – to start the really bad vibes. When The Beatles landed in Manila on July 3, 1966 the obligatory press conference featured the usual mundane questions and the by-now standard, flippant answers, none of which overly impressed the local media. This was a poor start, but far worse was to follow. The next morning, the group failed to turn up for a pre-arranged meeting with the First Lady, Imelda Marcos, at Malacañang Palace. The fault for this lay not with The Beatles, but with one Ramon Ramos, the promoter of the two shows scheduled for later that day. For, although Ramos had indeed arranged the meeting, he had forgotten to tell The Beatles themselves about it.

As a result, according to the July 5 edition of the *Manila Times*, Imelda Marcos, her three children and a crowd of 400 friends

▶ *Beatlemania, newspaper-style. In what is clearly a staged shot that has been arranged by press cameramen, four young fans are photogenically draped around a lamp-post in London's Piccadilly Circus, prior to the arrival of their idols for the July 29, 1965 première of* Help! *at the London Pavilion cinema. While amused bystanders watch, the girls scream on cue, with the one at top left obviously vying for an Oscar nomination.*

◀ *It may have been compulsory to scream at the Fab Four in concert, but it was also worthwhile listening to their songs! So, what better way to do this than on your very own 4-speed Beatles record player? Approximately 5000 of these were produced at the height of Beatlemania, and if you held onto yours and looked after it, then today it may be worth anywhere up to $1,800 (£1,200) — and more than half again if it is in its original box.*

NOW AVAILABLE IN THE U.S.A.

THE OFFICIAL
BEATLES
record carrying case

DISK·GO·CASE™

THE
BEATLES
© 1966 NEMS Enterprises, Ltd.

▶ *Available in green, yellow, red, blue, brown, lavender and pink, this 'Disk-Go-Case' came in on the tail end of Beatlemania, being manufactured in 1966 by Charter Industries in the US. Not the best way of caring for your discs but, there again, these were the days of auto-stacking record players, which tended to mete out rough treatment to easily-scratched vinyl records.*

were kept waiting. The article, headlined 'Imelda stood up', made it clear that The Beatles alone were to blame, stating that they had 'snubbed the First Lady', while she and her spokespeople pointedly avoided saying otherwise.

Death threats followed, and Brian Epstein's attempt to calm the waters with a hastily recorded TV statement was foiled when a surge of static – uncannily lasting the precise length of the broadcast – rendered inaudible everything he had to say. Subsequent to that, The Beatles were forced to pay tax immediately on earnings which Sr. Ramos had never paid them, and all their security cover was withdrawn so that, on arrival at Manila International Airport, they and their entourage were set upon by an angry mob of 200 Filipinos who kicked and punched their targets while the police simply looked on. Of course, all of this was graphically reported by the *Manila Times*, while President Marcos issued a statement exonerating The Beatles . . . minutes after their plane had departed.

As if the Philippines fiasco was not enough to put The Beatles off touring, a piece by the US teenage magazine, *Datebook*, finally did the trick. In the March 4, 1966 edition of the London *Evening Standard*, John Lennon had prophesied: 'Christianity will go. It will vanish and shrink. I needn't argue with that; I'm right and I will be proved right. We're more popular than Jesus now.'

Lennon's friend Maureen Cleave had conducted the full-page interview as one of a four-part series concentrating on each of The Beatles, and John's observation, lamenting the decline of religion within popular culture, went largely unnoticed by the readers. Not so, however, when *Datebook* got its hands on the piece and sensationalized it nearly five months later. 'I don't know which will go first – rock 'n' roll or Christianity!' announced the front-page teaser on July 29, while inside the magazine a sub-heading misquoted John out of context, implying John had asserted that The Beatles were 'bigger than Jesus'.

To many Americans this was nothing short of blasphemy. Led on by station WAQY in Birmingham, Alabama, 22 radio stations promptly banished all Beatles records from their playlists (even though some of them had never even played the band's music in the first place), and several also organized 'Beatles bonfires', onto which enraged citizens were encouraged to toss the group's records and memorabilia – in full view and hearing of the assembled cameras and microphones of the media, of course.

On the eve of the group's latest – and, as it would turn out, last – tour of the US, Brian Epstein once again entered the fray in an attempt to steady passions and calm a few nerves. Flying to New York on August 6, he held a press conference and read a statement which was, this time around, heard by all but still only accepted by some. Instead, it took a full and formal apology from John himself, in front of a blood-thirsty media gathered at Chicago's Astor Towers Hotel on August 11, finally to lay the issue to rest – although the usual assortment of death threats still followed.

Still, once Beatlemania had subsided, press coverage of the group's professional and personal activities remained mostly positive, if somewhat muted in its enthusiasm. Occasionally, however, it could be nothing less than downright hostile.

Following the December 26, 1967 showing on BBC TV of the ill-conceived *Magical Mystery Tour* film, The Beatles were subjected to their first unanimous slating from the British press – The *Daily Express*, which only three years before had lauded *A Hard Day's Night* as 'gorgeous fun . . . Nothing like it since the Goons on the radio and the Marx Brothers in the 30s. Delightfully loony. Palpitating cinema,' now declared the Fab Four's latest effort to be 'blatant rubbish'.

On the other side of the Atlantic the *Los Angeles Times* announced: 'Beatles Bomb With Yule Film'. In many ways the band, which was stung by the extent and ferocity

▲ Released as an EP in Britain, Magical Mystery Tour *was padded out to album-length in the US. After nine years, and many imports, EMI followed suit and issued it in Britain.*

▼ Want to drink Canada dry? Then try using this long mug, manufactured by North American neighbours of the US.

▶ *During the 1960s there were three series of black and white Beatles bubblegum cards, and one series in colour. There were 165 autographed photos in the former, and 64 pictures in the latter, each with questions and answers on the reverse side.*

▼ *Jimmy Nicol fills in for a tonsil-troubled Ringo as The Beatles tape their best-ever TV appearance, in Holland on June 5, 1964. After answering questions from the audience the band mimed to six songs, were mobbed by the fans, and eventually had to abandon the stage.*

◄ One of a series of four 340-piece jigsaw puzzles which were manufactured in Britain. Utilising various photos of the group as the basis for their composite portrayals of The Beatles, all four puzzles, when assembled, produced life-like images – which is more than can be said for much Beatles-related merchandise.

► There were many countries that the Fab Four never visited, yet they still had to deal with the demands of full-scale Beatlemania. This bathroom rug, for instance, was manufactured in Belgium. Very colourful, but George and Ringo bear a striking resemblance to one another.

of the criticism, never fully recovered from this brief flirtation with failure. The standard of recordings, from *Sgt. Pepper* to *Abbey Road*, may have been brilliant to the end, but after 1967 it was often the botched business deals and internal squabbles – not to mention John's escapades with Yoko – which tended to make the headlines.

John and Yoko's first public 'events' together included planting an acorn for peace at Coventry Cathedral, releasing 365 white helium-filled balloons over London, posing naked on the cover of their avant-garde *Two Virgins* album and 'appearing' in a bag on stage at London's Royal Albert Hall. None of these garnered favourable press and media coverage, and neither did John and George's drug busts, the quick closure of the Apple shops, 'bed-ins', a returned MBE and erotic art exhibitions.

'All we're saying is give peace a chance,' a laid-back John asserted during a break from his and Yoko's eccentricities. 'But if the least we can do is give somebody a laugh, we're willing to be the world's clowns, because we think it's a bit serious at the moment and a bit intellectual.'

On April 1, 1970 – April Fool's Day – John and Yoko issued a hoax press release stating that they had entered the London Clinic to undergo sex-change operations. Nine days later, a press release which Paul distributed with review copies of his first solo album, *McCartney*, was seen as no joke. Citing 'personal differences, business differences, musical differences', he predicted that the most successful band in the history of popular music would never work together again, and he was right.

Once more, The Beatles' names, images, actions and statements were emblazoned across front pages and TV screens around the world, as the fans delivered their eulogies and commentators reached for new platitudes in appraising the band. An unforgettable era had certainly come to an end – but the media's interest in John, Paul, George and Ringo was still far from over.

▶ *The Beatles enjoy a light-hearted break from rehearsals for their final appearance on the weekly TV pop show,* Thank Your Lucky Stars, *on March 28, 1965. The programme featured artists miming to their current hit records and, in January, 1963 it had launched The Beatles on British network TV. Such TV appearances would eventually help to establish them around the world.*

▶ *Many of the fans no doubt kept a diary throughout the Beatlemania years, but it is doubtful whether the four main men actually did, if their own often mistaken recollections are anything to go by. Dates have never been their forté, and so it has been left to researchers and biographers to establish the true facts.*

fads, fashions and cash-ins

'In reality, The Beatles were just as cynical as us, but they'd been pitched as clean-scrubbed and they got the suits and so on, and we were billed as the sort of black version of them.' The words of Mick Jagger in 1988, describing the way in which The Rolling Stones' original manager, Andrew Loog Oldham, cast his young protégés as the direct antithesis of The Beatles, even though neither of the groups' carefully contrived public images exactly coincided with the truth.

The Stones, of course, were never the anarchic ne'er-do-wells that their own publicity made them out to be, while The Beatles had come a long way in a short time from their days of greased-back hair, leather outfits and smoking on stage. As 'moptops', their hair was, in fact, shorter than that of 'Teddy Boys', yet, during the early 60s, it somehow gave the opposite impression due to the way that it hung down just above the eyebrows. (By the end of the decade, The Beatles and their contemporaries would show the world what long hair *really* was.) ▶

A 'Beatles' hairstyle was the height of fashion back in 1964, almost more so than the music. The magazine cover (right) stylishly demonstrates how the 'moptop' could be successfully adapted by women. The 'Beatle bouffants' and 'baby dolls' were somewhat less in tune with prevailing fashion trends. Indeed the same could be said for the hair grease or 'pomade' (below), which The Beatles themselves had not used since their Hamburg days.

DELL 1000 HINTS
07 141-411

BEATLE HAIRDOS
& SETTING PATTERNS

35¢

BEATLE **BANGS,** BOUFFANTS, BUBBLES, **BOBS,** BABY-DOLLS,

PLUS **PICTURES** OF **JOHN, PAUL, GEORGE,** & **RINGO**

THE **BEATLES** HIGHEST QUALITY *Hair* POMADE

10¢ EACH

MANUFACTURED BY H. H. COSMETIC LABORATORY SAN JUAN, RIZAL, PHILIPPINES

◄ The Beatles as they looked when Brian Epstein first saw them in the Cavern on November 9, 1961: leather-clad rockers with 'arty' hairstyles. (Pete Best was the only non-'moptop'). By December 'Eppy' was their manager, and within three months the leather gear would be gone.

◄ Still in leather, but looking altogether smarter. Wearing shirts, ties and overcoats, it is early 1963 and The Beatles are posing with a new drummer who has yet to perfect his 'moptop'. Having dispensed with the greased-back look on joining the group back in August, 1962, Ringo then sported side-parted hair that was too long on top. He finally got it right the following April.

Astrid Kircherr, the girlfriend of Stu Sutcliffe, The Beatles' bassist from their Hamburg days, had been responsible for introducing the group to a hairstyle which was already popular among certain German students who called themselves 'Exis' (Existentialists). Brian Epstein's idea to then replace his clients' leather gear with three-piece suits was even less original, as it was simply his way of making them more presentable by conforming to the then-current taste for clean-cut pop stars. If anything, then, Oldham was the more inventive of the two managers in terms of his feel for presentation, although the Fab Four themselves did break with convention to the extent of smoking in public and admitting to enjoying some Scotch with their Coca-Cola. This may sound ridiculous now, but at the time it was considered *risqué* behaviour for 'responsible' teen idols!

Still, The Beatles were very much the trend-setters of their time. The Pierre Cardin collarless jackets and Cuban-heeled boots which they wore in 1963 were copied and bought in their millions by kids around the world, while later garb such as velvet-collared jackets (as seen in *A Hard Day's Night*), military jackets (as seen in *Help!*) and even *Sgt. Pepper* uniforms would also serve to define style for the young (and, in some cases, not so young).

After 1967, with more freedom to develop their individual tastes, The Beatles no longer dressed exactly alike, but still they had immense fashion influence both in terms of their look – did anyone mention centre-parted hair and granny glasses? – and even in terms of their album sleeves. The elaborate cover of the *Sgt. Pepper* album, designed by Peter Blake, was almost as revolutionary as the record – it even featured lyrics printed on the back of a record cover for the first time. Meanwhile, earlier efforts such as Robert Freeman's photos for the *With The Beatles, A Hard Day's Night, Beatles For Sale* and *Rubber Soul* LPs, as well as Klaus Voorman's fine design for *Revolver*,

One of the most extraordinary aspects of The Beatles' career was the speed and extent of their musical and personal development. These photographs show some of the different fashions they adopted over the years (from left to right, top to bottom); no clues as to which Beatle changed the most during this period! The Fab Four clown with personal tailor, Dougie Millings, in the collarless suits which the band wore from April to October, 1963; stepping out in the Cuban-heeled boots which lasted a little longer; collar-length hair and military-style jackets in 1965; granny glasses, moustaches and elaborate Sgt. Pepper uniforms in May, 1967; and four long-haired, deeply serious individuals in April, 1969.

bee-ooootiful **BEAT-BABES!**

◄ *What was it about 60s films and advertising that obliged them to portray everyone as having an incredibly fab, fun-filled time? Indeed, the item above, from a January, 1964 issue of the British* Fabulous *magazine, features a 'teen' apparently in the throes of ecstasy over her Official Beatles Sweater, while such off-target, snap-happy terms as 'it's absolutely top gear' were straight out of the mouths of middle-aged ad men rather than of those 'bee-ootiful Beat Babes' themselves.*

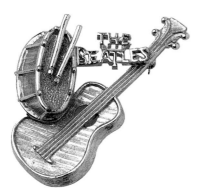

▲ *Everything the well-dressed girl could want: a metal brooch (bottom), a brass necklace (top) and a leather-bound locket (centre) containing 11 fold-out photos of 'the boys'.*

still stand out as classic trend-setting icons of the 60s.

Less than classic in design or musical terms, but still indicative of The Beatles' incredible impact, were the 'novelty' records dedicated to them. No less than 357 of these were produced in the English language alone up to 1981 and, although hardly any of them made any money, the list of well-known personalities who made such records illustrates that few were above making an attempt to cash in on Beatlemania.

Dora Bryan led the way in 1963 with *All I Want For Christmas Is A Beatle*, but once John, Paul, George and Ringo had visited the US a few months later, the floodgates really opened. *Ringo Beat* was the contribution of no less an artist than Ella Fitzgerald, while among others to chip in were Cher – under the guise of Bonnie Jo Mason – with the Phil Spector-produced *Ringo I Love You*; The Vernon Girls with *We Love The Beatles*; Allan Sherman with *I Hate The Beatles* (well, I guess someone had to be a party pooper); Sonny Curtis with *A Beatle I Want To Be*; Rolf Harris with *Ringo For President*, and even cartoon favourite Huckleberry Hound with *Bingo Ringo*!

Of all the songs, only The Carefrees' *We Love You Beatles* broke into the Top 80 in the US (it charted at No.39) and, post-Beatlemania, the flood of 'tribute' records slowed to more of a trickle. Still, in 1967 TV personality Steve Allen felt obliged to jump onto the bandwagon with *Here Comes Sgt. Pepper*, while the sight of John and Yoko in all their naked glory on the cover of their *Two Virgins* album prompted outraged actress-to-be Sissy Spacek (calling herself 'Rainbo') to exclaim *John, You Went Too Far This Time*: 'I loved the things you showed me up till now, John,' she sang enticingly, 'But ever since that picture, I don't think my love will be the same.' Who could blame her?

Clearly, good taste was never a central issue as far as the vinyl entrepreneurs were concerned, and neither was it of paramount importance to any of the merchandisers, some of whom were more than prepared to carry things over the edge. Thus, in addition to the plethora of Beatle dolls, bubblegum cards, wigs, wallpaper and other exciting paraphernalia that could be purchased from all good stores during the Beatlemania years, there were also choice items such as canned 'Beatle Breath' on sale in New York in 1964.

After The Beatles had decamped from the Muehlebach Hotel, Kansas City, on September 18, 1964, the manager sold the 16 sheets and pillow cases on which they had slept to two Chicago businessmen for $750 (£265). The businessmen, in turn, cut the linen into three-inch squares which, mounted on card and with a legal affidavit testifying to their authenticity, they sold for $10 (£3.50) each. A towel used by The Beatles to wipe their faces after leaving the stage of the Hollywood Bowl on August 23 met with a similar fate. So, all in all, there was obviously a considerable amount of money to be made, but the problem for Brian Epstein was trying to ensure that The Beatles got a fair share of what they themselves were generating. Unfortunately – and, perhaps, inevitably – this was not to be.

'Brian was not a good businessman,' John Lennon would later tell *Rolling Stone* magazine. 'He had a flair for presenting things, he was more theatrical than business. He was hyped a lot. He was advised by a gang of crooks, really.'

In truth, however, there was no precedent in 20th century British show business for Brian Epstein to follow. No artists of The Beatles' stature and staying power, no market so desperate to buy up huge quantities of anything vaguely connected to a band of popular idols, had ever existed before. Even Colonel Tom Parker, Elvis' shrewd manager, had never had to deal with marketing on this scale and, as Lennon correctly pointed out, Epstein's strength lay in presentation rather than in pure profit-making. He was no Colonel Tom Parker – though The Beatles would at least have cause to be thankful for that from an artistic standpoint.

At first, when Beatle wigs and woollen Beatle sweaters found their way into British shops, Brian's company, NEMS Enterprises, attempted to keep track of what was being offered to the fans. By Christmas of 1963, however, this was fast becoming impossible, as thousands of items ranging from belts, badges and lockets to pens, puzzles and shoulder bags flooded the market. Besides, how could Epstein prevent the sale of cheap mementoes bearing the intentionally mis-spelt name 'Beetles' together with hand-drawn images of the group, let alone those that *did* infringe copyright?

Hereafter, Nicky Byrne accepted the task of administering The Beatles' world-wide merchandising operation, for which he – together with five partners – set up a company named Stramsact, together with a US subsidiary called Seltaeb (Beatles spelt backwards). Within a short space of time these operations would net a veritable fortune, but the drawback for The Beatles was the contract drawn up between NEMS and Stramsact-Seltaeb, and signed on their behalf by Brian's solicitor, David Jacobs. Jacobs, unfortunately, considered a 10 per cent cut to be a fairly good deal for his clients, even though this meant that the Stramsact-Seltaeb directors would be walking off with the remaining 90 per cent.

Licences were issued in exchange for a cash advance against 10 per cent manufacturing royalties. So it was that the Reliant Shirt Corporation, for example, paid £25,000 ($70,000) – a not inconsiderable sum in 1964 – for the exclusive rights to produce Beatle T-shirts. Within three days of the T-shirts reaching the shops one million had been sold. The *Wall Street Journal* estimated that by the end of the year $5 million- (£1.8 million-) worth of Beatle goods would be purchased in the US alone. In August of 1964, The Beatles' royalty was renegotiated to a more rewarding 46 per cent.

Of equal business significance, meanwhile, was the transformation taking place back in the capital of The Beatles' home country. Granted, the whole phenomenon of 'Swinging London' was as much a figment of media imagination as it was based in reality, but for a while it attracted record numbers of visitors to the once-staid city and generated a boom in the British fashion industry.

Where Paris and Rome had once led the way, London now stepped to the fore. The Kings Road in Chelsea had, until 1965, been best known for its antique shops; that year, however, saw a plethora of small, brightly-coloured clothes stores (or 'boutiques') being established. The King's Road soon became *the* place to spot the 'in-crowd'. This consisted of young actors such as Terence Stamp, models such as Jean Shrimpton and photographers such as David Bailey, all of whom were allotted a celebrity status usually reserved for pop stars, while the real thing – the likes of The Beatles, The Kinks or The Rolling Stones – could also be seen taking a stroll down the Kings Road, together with trendy wives or girlfriends such as Pattie Boyd, Jane Asher, Anita Pallenberg or Marianne Faithfull. Sharing the pavements of 'Swinging London' with them would be crop-headed girls in black and white pop-art mini-dresses and shaggy-haired boys in hipster trousers and button-down shirts, each trying to emulate their idols while soaking in the magic of their presence.

At the same time, in a small, previously nondescript backroad located just behind Regent Street in London's West End, the clothes of designers such as John Stephen and Mary Quant were turning Carnaby Street into a world-famous name and tourist attraction. This was an era when young people's clothes were made to be fun rather than practical and so, as the 60s progressed and the twin cultures of drug experimentation and flower power took over, pin-striped jackets and plain wool dresses gave way to psychedelic shirts, floppy hats, tinted glasses, feather boas and beads. (By this time even the Queen's hemlines were creeping up perilously close to her knees!)

A lampshade was one thing (below), but buying pieces of Beatles' bedsheets was maybe carrying things a little too far. The 1.5in.-square sample shown above came from the Idlewood Hotel in Riviera, New York, where the group stayed on September 20-21, 1964.

▲ Wearing these tennis shoes would certainly be one way of distracting your opponent during the game.

► 'It's New! It's Wild! It's Pink Mild!' was how Colgate advertised its 1965 'Paul' and 'Ringo' bubble bath.

◄ There was no shortage of Beatles-related merchandise for US window-dressers to choose from back in the mid-60s, although in this case it is not quite clear as to what the 'lay-away plan' was all about.

◄ *The Dutch were the specialists when it came to Beatle dresses. However, the purchaser was only supplied with the cut cloth – which was available in a number of different designs – together with instructions on how to make up the outfit.*

► *While the boots worn (and made famous) by The Beatles had 'Cuban' heels and pointed toes, this pair, made in Italy and sold in Canada and with 'RINGO' printed on the inside, were rather more conventional in appearance.*

◄▲ *In the days before such items were fashionable with both sexes, it was mainly girls who wore Official Beatles Bows and headbands.*

◄ *Those well-known trendsetters, Messrs. John Lennon and Paul McCartney, parade the 'in' look of May, 1968, en route to New York in order formally to announce The Beatles' Apple venture. John, already well into his peace-and-love phase, is decked out in white from head to toe, while Paul sports a debonair Pickwick-style jacket and brogue shoes. And to think that just a few years earlier they were wearing scruffy leather outfits!*

While The Beatles and their peers continued to push back the barriers of popular culture and break with time-honoured traditions, so their contemporaries in the world of fashion also felt as if they could get away with anything when capitalizing on the boom within their own industry. 'The more colourful the better' and 'quick change' were the orders of the day and so, to cater to the increased demand, redundant stocks of deck-chair and furniture material were put to good use in the production of Pickwick-style jackets and velveteen dresses.

It was a time when British was best – today, flat-chested supermodel Twiggy, tomorrow, Cockney-accented film star Michael Caine. As if to emphasize this point even the Union Jack became a fashion symbol, adorning everything from skirts and jackets to bags and wall plaques, while fast, brightly coloured Mini cars and Lambretta motor scooters became synonymous with the 'Swinging London' scene, along with clubs such as the Scotch Of St. James, the Bag O' Nails, Sibylla's and Revolution.

In so many ways it was a case of out with the old and in with the new, as the long-established order of things was reassessed and, for a short while at least, the counter-culture threatened to take over. Whereas a clipped, 'Queen's English' voice had formerly been one of the prerequisites for success in the parallel worlds of British film, TV, radio and fashion, suddenly it was acceptable – if not a definite advantage – to be in possession of a Cockney or Liverpudlian accent.

The young appeared to be taking over, and many of the up-and-coming whizz kids – be they photographer David Bailey, actor David Hemmings or designer Mary Quant – were either in their late teens or early 20s. The Beatles, for their part, were an integral part of all that was going on, wearing the clothes, driving the cars and regularly visiting the clubs. Indeed, their unofficial endorsement of a club or boutique was on a par with the Royal seal of approval, for what they did others copied, and where they went others

◀ *Soda pop, sherry, you name it – there were Beatle drinking glasses to suit all tastes, and any occasion.*

▼ *One of the earliest ranges of Beatles merchandise was this popular 1963 collection of crockery, made by Washington Pottery in Britain. It featured famous Dezo Hoffman photos of the group.*

▲ *With her beehive hairdo, fork and Beatle plate at the ready, one happy model smiles prettily for the camera as she tucks into her delicious sausages – one each for John, Paul, George and Ringo . . . Who said that earthy symbolism wasn't alive and kicking back in the 60s?*

◄ Not exactly everyday wear, even in the 'Swinging London' of the late 60s. After opening in a blaze of publicity on December 7, 1967 The Beatles' Apple shop at 94, Baker Street closed down on July 31, 1968. Before closing, the group, wives and friends took their choice of the stock; what remained was snapped up during a two-day free giveaway by people who had to wait in line around the block.

followed. After all, what better means of support could there be for pirate radio than a full-page photo of a ship together with the slogan 'Radio London – Your Number 1 Beatles Station,' appearing in the June, 1967 issue of *The Beatles Book*?

Still, not everyone was prepared to go along for the ride, especially certain old'uns who were fed up with the whole business of 'Swinging London'. When The Beatles' Apple shop opened at 94, Baker Street in December, 1967, the corner building's exterior was decorated with a psychedelic mural which had been conceived and painted by a group calling themselves The Fool. This same band of Dutch artists applied similar skills to John Lennon's piano and gypsy caravan, (a company by the name of J.P. Fallon worked on his Rolls-Royce), while also designing some of the more outlandish Apple shop clothes. However, on the instructions of the local borough council the psychedelic mural was replaced by a coat of plain white paint on May 18, 1968, after numerous complaints from local residents and shopkeepers.

So, clearly, London's populace was not quite as ready to 'swing' as the papers, magazines and TV implied. For, when it came down to it, the young were *not* running the country (or any other part of the world, for that matter), and those holding the positions of power were ready to stamp down on anything that represented a threat – whether real or imagined – to the status quo:

'Nothing happened except that we all dressed up, [John Lennon told *Rolling Stone's* Jan Wenner in 1970.] . . . The same people are running everything, it's exactly the same. They hyped the kids and the generation'

Perhaps Lennon was right. Whatever, the whole idea of a 'swinging' London always seemed a little incongruous – if disarming – set against a backdrop of a palace, a tower, double-decker buses, black cabs, red phone boxes, and plenty of rain. Still, it was fun while it lasted. . .

▲ *Hello austerity, goodbye psychedelia. Apple Music's HQ was located in offices above the shop. A second shop, Apple Tailoring (Civil and Theatrical), at 161, King's Road, also lasted only a few months.*

◄ *The front cover of this 1968 book featured Richard Avedon's solarised photos; these had first appeared in the US magazine,* Look, *on January 9. Soon after, the* Daily Express *issued them as posters.*

granny glasses and cooler vibes

'I think that if The Beatles had continued touring they would have had a whole younger slew of kids running after them. But, once the touring stopped, it then got to be on a more intellectual level. We really started to analyse their records and our attitude towards them changed.' (Life-long Beatles fan Lorraine Davis, speaking in 1994.)

By 1966, The Beatles were not only fast losing interest in playing live, but also they were no longer able to fill every venue at which they performed. Only 45,000 fans, for instance, turned up for their August 23 appearance at New York City's Shea Stadium, whereas all 55,600 tickets had sold out within hours the previous year. Clearly, interest on both sides was beginning to wane.

Indeed, by 1967 the sort of fan worship witnessed earlier in the decade had become distinctly 'un-cool' to kids who were now more concerned with turning on, tuning in, dropping out and getting high to the sounds of Cream, Janis Joplin, Jimi Hendrix...and *Sgt. Pepper's Lonely Hearts Club Band*. The basic ▶

A psychedelic poster inspired by Yellow Submarine, *the superb 1968 feature-length cartoon which was hailed by some critics as 'the best film The Beatles never made'. Indeed, the group had little involvement in its production, yet it stylishly (if falsely) sustained their happy-go-lucky image.*

▼ *One of The Beatles' finest moments was their June 25, 1967 performance of* All You Need Is Love *on the* Our World *TV programme. In attendance at EMI Studios that night were the likes of Mick Jagger, Keith Richard, Marianne Faithfull, Keith Moon, Eric Clapton and Graham Nash, while there were an estimated 350 million viewers worldwide. The peace and love era now had an anthem.*

message was to look, listen and move to the music by all means, but not to scream! Besides, many young people's thoughts were now turning to other, more serious matters.

Apartheid in South Africa, US involvement in Vietnam, mysticism and experimentation with drugs; these were some of the controversial discussion topics of the mid-60s – topics which had largely been forbidden territory to The Beatles as far as Brian Epstein was concerned when the group was still touring, and while Epstein still had a measure of control over their public utterances and activities. Yet, once the concerts stopped it was a different matter altogether. John, Paul, George and Ringo at last had enough time on their hands (and money in their pockets) to take stock of their situation, both as a group and as four individuals. They no longer required their manager either to mould their image or to arrange their work schedule, and with Epstein's role severely diminished they had the freedom to do and say largely as they pleased.

In the latter part of 1966 this involved John filming *How I Won the War* in (what was then) West Germany and in Spain; Paul writing the score for the British movie, *The Family Way*; George flying to India in order to study yoga and take sitar lessons; and Ringo playing the family man at home in Surrey, England.

There was also a change of image, away from fab, smiling, joking, clean-cut mop-tops, to serious, moustachioed faces, deep thoughts and, in the case of John Lennon, circular British National Health 'granny' glasses. And finally, yet another nail in the coffin of Beatlemania was the distinct shift in emphasis from the boy-finds-girl, boy-loses-girl simplicity of the early pop songs. After all, compared to lines like, 'Ooh I need your love babe, guess you know it's true / Hope you need my love babe, just like I need you,' (from *Eight Days A Week*) it was not nearly as easy to sigh and go weak at the knees when hearing George, backed by assorted Indian instruments, try to explain that, 'life goes on

▶ *These headphones date from the Beatlemania years, yet it would have been more appropriate to use them in the late 60s, when fans began listening far more closely to the group's recordings, on the look-out for sound effects and subliminal messages.*

▼ *Made out of papier-mâché, these four* Yellow Submarine *figurines were, in fact, piggy banks, with coin slots located in the back of each Beatle's head. In truth, however, money was not the only thing filling the Fab Four's heads at that time.*

◄ *Two trendy couples – Cynthia and John Lennon, George and Pattie Harrison – step out in style in the 'Swinging London' of late 1967. Clearly ahead in the fashion stakes on this occasion, George sports a 'Pickwick jacket', so named because of its ultra-short, pointy lapels, which date from the era of Charles Dickens, author of* The Pickwick Papers. *As for the women, it is evident that the mini dress was already becoming somewhat* passé.

within you and without you,' (*Within You Without You*), or John imploring the listener to, 'lay down all thought, surrender to the void,' (*Tomorrow Never Knows*).

Lysergic acid diethylamide (LSD) is a hallucinogenic drug which exerted a powerful influence during the mid-60s, both on its users' way of thinking and on the work of a number of popular musical artists, from The Byrds and The Beatles to The Beach Boys and The Rolling Stones. When the rock community first started to experiment with the drug back in 1965, non-medical use of LSD was still legal. Lennon and Harrison subsequently ingested substantial quantities during the recordings of the *Revolver* and *Sgt. Pepper* albums yet, by the time that Paul McCartney publicly admitted – in June, 1967 – that even he had indulged, LSD was acknowledged to be dangerous, and possession of it had been made illegal. The majority of public opinion was by now against McCartney and his colleagues.

As a result, parents, politicians and others in positions of authority who had once either smiled at The Beatles' innocent antics or simply dismissed them as a passing fad, now condemned them out of hand. They held that as The Beatles, and others like them, were idolised by the young, they had a moral duty to act responsibly and to set the right example. The fans emulated their heroes in almost every respect, growing their hair long, sporting the same clothes and mouthing similar opinions. Now, the Fab Four's critics argued, these kids would also follow The Beatles in using dangerous drugs.

In an interview with *Life* magazine, Paul had likened the taking of drugs to 'taking aspirin without a headache.' 'It opened my eyes,' he said, before going on to explain that 'We only use one-tenth of our brains. Just think what we'd accomplish if we could tap that hidden part.'

The response of Britain's *Daily Mail* newspaper was to brand the 'baby-faced' Beatle 'an irresponsible idiot'. And when a TV reporter made the same inference – following

◀ Pepperland Laid Waste – *symbolic of the burgeoning counter-culture movement of the late 60s were the kind of 'underground' publications which fuelled rumours about Paul's supposed death. Meanwhile, in the real world, The Beatles were off on their own trip, and even George's Esher bungalow (below) received the psychedelic treatment.*

an interview with McCartney in which he confirmed that he had taken LSD – McCartney pointed out that the TV network was not obliged to broadcast his statement. 'It's you who've got responsibility not to spread this,' he said. 'If you'll shut up about it, I will!'

The damage had already been done, however, and when all four Beatles – along with Brian Epstein – signed a petition calling for the legalization of marijuana which appeared in *The Times* of July 24, 1967, the group's collective opinion on the subject of drug-taking in general appeared pretty obvious to most adults, and this was bad news.

Still, The Beatles continued to do their own thing, and while this certainly destroyed much of their personable, boys-next-door image and alienated some of their older fans, it nevertheless firmly established them among the chief spokespersons of their generation. None of their contemporaries managed such a drastic, yet successful, transformation. Herman's Hermits, The Dave Clark Five and others like them simply continued on their clean-cut way, with diminishing results in terms of record sales; then there was the Stones' uneasy and (thankfully) brief flirtation with beads, bells and psychedelia, while Bob Dylan utilised the excuse of a near-fatal motorcycle crash to take an extended break from a music scene which had not fully accepted his conversion from folk to electric.

The Beatles, however, had the talent and the strength of personality to pull it off and, while the world around them was rapidly changing, they were somehow intrinsic to these new developments, beating a path and pointing the way for a new generation. So it was that when George and wife Pattie visited the Haight-Ashbury district of San Francisco in August, 1967, this was viewed as some sort of official endorsement of the hippie scene which was then flourishing on the west coast of the US.

Then, when The Beatles decided to study Transcendental Meditation under Maharishi Mahesh Yogi, others soon followed, among them Mick Jagger, Marianne Faithfull, Mike Love, Mia Farrow and that born-again 'flower child', Donovan. And when John penned such numbers as *All You Need Is Love* and *Give Peace A Chance,* they were adopted as anthems by millions of people in a variety of different situations around the globe. Essentially, a social revolution was taking place among the young people of the free world in the late 60s, and The Beatles were helping to lead it.

The war in Vietnam, which was costing thousands of lives on all sides and which prompted huge demonstrations world-wide against what was perceived by many as unwarranted US involvement; the anti-government student riots in Paris in May, 1968; the Soviet invasion of Czechoslovakia the same year; the Berkeley student riots of 1969 – John, Paul and George had views on all of these events, as well as on many other topics. More to the point, whenever they expressed their opinions, either in interviews or in song, the world invariably listened.

Ringo, on the other hand, continued to be his same old self, apparently content to let the others do most of the talking, and going along with the latest craze, but still remaining down-to-earth and essentially his own man. When The Beatles visited the Maharishi's compound in Rishikesh in February, 1968, it was their drummer who left much sooner than anticipated, likening the place to a holiday resort!

So, at least the balance of personalities within the band remained the same, as did the group's tendency to change fashions and ideologies with the wind: 'psychedelic' clothes and album covers in 1967, but then a plain white cover for *The Beatles* album the following year; embracing the Maharishi's teachings in February, 1968 and then denouncing him as a charlatan less than three months later; singing about global harmony one moment and then about revolution the next. But whatever the contradictions, the world persisted in listening to the Fab Four.

▼ Putting 'wow on the wall' was a far cry from the days of Beatle pennants and bubblegum cards. But, there again, so were the images of a psychedelic John, back-to-nature Paul, mystical George and peace-loving Ringo.

The 'Beatlebanner', incidentally, was a Richard Avedon black-and-white group shot which was later to be used on the gatefold sleeve of the popular 1977 Love Songs *double-album compilation.*

▶ *A 1968* Yellow Submarine *watch, conveying not only the time but also, alongside The Beatles' cartoon images, the all-important message of 'Love'.*

▶ *At the court of the Maharishi in Rishikesh, India, February, 1968. Among others with The Beatles were Maureen, Jane Asher, Pattie, Cynthia and (at right) assistant Mal Evans and Beach Boy Mike Love. John wrote* Sexy Sadie *after the giggling guru had reportedly tried to force his none-too-holy charms on actress Mia Farrow.*

The idea of a Yellow Submarine *feature* began to form in late 1966, shortly after The Beatles had recorded the song of the same name. The cartoon went into full production the following year, despite the band's concern that it was being made by the same company that had animated Popeye the Sailor Man.

▼ *The 'Blue Meanie' mask and costume were based on the villainous characters dreamed up by the feature-length cartoon's chief writer, Lee Mintoff.*

◄ *To tie-in with the July, 1968 release of* Yellow Submarine *a wide range of related products, such as this mobile (above) and snowdome were marketed by more than 25 officially licensed merchandisers.*

▶ Yellow Submarine – *you've heard the song, you've seen the movie ... now watch the clock!*

► *The Beatles at a promotional photo-session on July 28, 1968. They are doing their best to spray the camera lenses with water from the drinking fountain, which is located in St. Pancras Old Church and Gardens in north London.*

◄ *Just before 6pm on that same day, The Beatles (and Yoko) mingled with a crowd which had gathered behind railings dividing the church and the gardens. Another of the Don McCullin photos from this session would later be used in black-and-white for the gatefold sleeves of the 1962-1966 and 1967-1970 compilation albums.*

By this time, unsurprisingly, it had also become fashionable for the mainstream press to mock certain members of the group, especially Lennon, 'the controversial one' who had seemingly 'gone weird'. It was certainly true that John courted controversy – from adopting the look of a bespectacled long-haired guru, to leaving his wife and child and posing naked with his 'strange' Japanese girlfriend on the cover of their even stranger *Two Virgins* album, to immersing himself in Yoko's avant-garde art activities, and penning erotic illustrations of what they got up to on their honeymoon. Overall, John seemed to spend much of 1969 either jumping into bags or lying in bed for peace (and love, man!). There was, of course, another side to the widely-shared perception of John's antics, but in the short term they undeniably served to estrange people from the group as a whole.

'Why, oh why, did The Beatles have to change?' asked a girl yearning for the old days in a 1969 letter to *The Beatles Book* monthly magazine just before the group split. 'Why has the fun, the humour, the sheer zest for living all gone?' Well, the simple truth was that they had *had* to change, or be lumbered with a contrived image that they could never have felt comfortable with, and one that would – even as early as 1967 – have made them both look, and sound, dated. This in turn would have destroyed much of The Beatles' artistic credibility and would probably have confined them to a future playing old songs for a dwindling band of still-faithful, and ageing, fans.

Nevertheless, despite the changes of the late 60s many die-hard Beatle People kept the faith through thick and thin, displaying great loyalty even when their heroes' work, statements or actions tended to flow against the tides of mainstream opinion and taste.

'I was thoroughly disgusted to read that *A Day In The Life* had been banned by the BBC "because it could encourage a permissive attitude to drug taking",' wrote an English fan signing herself as (Dizzy Miss)

▶ *This cardboard* Yellow Submarine *display is now worth around $1800 (£1200) in mint condition, due to the fact that most record stores destroyed such items once a promotion was over.*

▼ *'On the first day they fought at the door to get in, thinking there was something, y'know, sexy going on, and they found two people talking about peace,' was how John recalled media reaction to his and Yoko's 1969 Amsterdam Hilton 'bed-in', when talking to TV interviewer Tom Snyder in 1975.*

◄ This record store display, featuring a 1969 photo of The Beatles, was actually devised to promote the Hey Jude *album, a hotch-potch collection of well-known tracks dating from 1964 through to 1969. The album was released in the US (but not in Britain) on February 16, 1970.*

Lizzy Hoey in a letter to *The Beatles Book* in July, 1967. 'It is as daft as saying *Eleanor Rigby* was sick, or something like that.'

And, following the critical and public mauling of the group's *Magical Mystery Tour* TV film, which BBC1 screened on December 26 of that year, 18-year-old Carol McKee, from Newmarket, England, summed up many of her contemporaries' feelings when, in a letter to the same publication, she assured the group that their first self-produced film was 'surely excellent as a first-time experiment'. 'Anyway,' she continued defiantly, 'those doddering old critics should have asked a few Beatle People for their opinion!'

Towards the end, however, even those opinions became divided, as personal and business differences saw the group disintegrate amid considerable acrimony. From mid-1968 onwards, disagreements arose not only between The Beatles but also between their fans, and in truth it was Yoko's disruptive influence which was responsible for much of this. Basically, most fans – and the general public, for that matter – simply did not like her. They were not interested in her avant-garde art projects, and they resented her invasion of a marriage and of a group *ensemble*. A handful of fans, meanwhile, felt duty-bound to support John and his new partner, no matter what. On top of all this, Linda Eastman's March 12, 1969 name-change to Linda McCartney did not help matters either, dashing thousands of women's hopes of ever marrying any of the Fab Four. Linda and Paul's marriage meant that the last bachelor Beatle had now been claimed!

Still, for many of the fans it was a case of once bitten, forever smitten, and to this day many of the original Beatle People continue to play the records, refresh the memories and follow their heroes, while successive generations are gripped by a love that seemingly will never die. 'One thing The Beatles did was to affect people's minds,' John Lennon once asserted. True, but did he ever realise how long this would last?

► *Ringo displays what was, by 1969, fast becoming the usual level of enthusiasm for a day's work in the Apple offices. John and Yoko are in attendance.*

▼ *'I was cursing because I hadn't done it. I wanted to do it, I should have done it', said John regarding Paul's announcement, which was made several months after Lennon's own decision to quit the group.*

▲ *The final Beatles photo-session, in the grounds of John's Tittenhurst Park estate, Friday, August 22, 1969. This took place just two days after John, Paul, George and Ringo had recorded together for the very last time.*

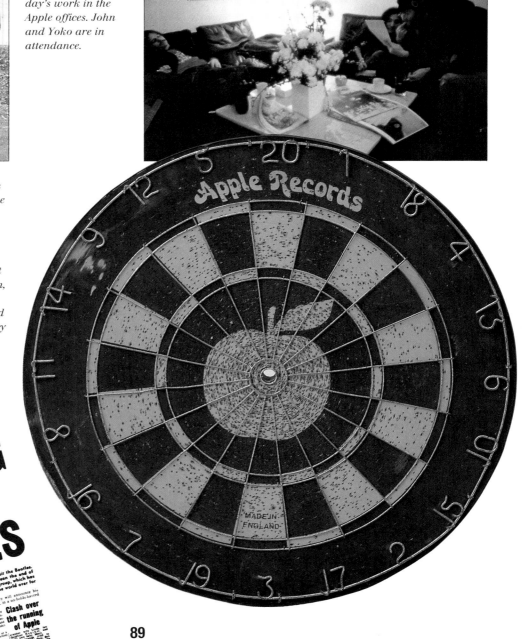

DAILY Mirror

Lennon-McCartney song team splits up

PAUL IS QUITTING THE BEATLES

Swing to Labour .. but Tories are still in command

89

post-beatles beatlemania

'The Beatles – they're a passing phase; symptoms of the uncertainty of the times and the confusion about us.' This prediction by Dr. Billy Graham in 1964 illustrates just how wrong one man could be. For, despite the uncertainties, the 'phase' has yet to pass, and it is one which looks destined to last well into the 21st century.

It was on March 31, 1972 that the Official Beatles' Fan Club closed down, its members having finally given up any vestige of hope that the band would ever re-form. The previous August, Paul McCartney had issued a statement officially informing the Club that he no longer wished to be involved with 'anything that continues the illusion that there is such a thing as the Beatles', and that same month he had also announced the formation of his new group, Wings. Besides, back in 1970 *Melody Maker* had reproduced McCartney's hand-written note categorically asserting that The Beatles were finished. So the dream, as John Lennon had proclaimed in his song, *God*, was clearly over, but ▶

And so it continues . . . whereas the close attention devoted to most of The Beatles' musical contemporaries from the 60s has either faded or died, fan worship and media interest regarding the Fab Four show no signs of abating.

MARK AND CAROL LAPIDOS PROUDLY PRESENT:

BEATLEFEST '94

CELEBRATING THE 30TH ANNIVERSARY OF THE BEATLES ARRIVAL IN AMERICA!!! AND 20 YEARS OF BEATLEFESTS!

N.Y. METRO'S ANNUAL OFFICIAL BEATLES FAN'S CELEBRATION!

FRIDAY, SATURDAY & SUNDAY MARCH 11, 12 & 13 N.J. MEADOWLANDS HILTON HOTEL

"SPLENDID TIME IS GUARANTEED FOR ALL!"

WORLD'S LARGEST BEATLES MAIL ORDER CATALOGUE!!!

TOKYO BEATLES FAN CLUB MAGAZINE

TBFC

25 ANNIVERSARY

ビートルズ来日25周年記念特別企画

東京ビートルズ・ファン・クラブ
Tokyo Beatles Fan Club

No.2
1991. AUTUMN

▲ *Before John Lennon died, this modest tribute to The Beatles, located opposite the derelict site of the old Cavern Club, was all that Liverpool could muster. The angel at right was added after Lennon's murder.*

▶ *EMI's Abbey Road studio complex is also a shrine for fans, yet while they can walk on the famous crossing outside, few see inside Studio 2, where most of The Beatles' music was recorded.*

▲ *Liverpool honoured its four favourite sons in the wake of John's death by building a shopping mall on the former site of the Cavern (above right). Life-sized bronze statues of The Beatles (above) stand in the lobby area.*

▶ The Beatles Memorabilia Price Guide *is the ultimate authority regarding the huge range of Beatles memorabilia – official, unlicensed and counterfeit – that has been produced over the years.*

the problem for all four ex-Fabs was that few of their fans really took them at their word.

Indeed, while The Beatles may have been among the great communicators of their generation, successfully conveying their innermost thoughts through their music, they were somehow unable to get over the message that their joint career would never, ever be resumed. Nobody wanted to listen, least of all the rumour-hungry press, which seemed intent on keeping the Beatle flame flickering.

After the group split in 1970, there were three-year gaps between major outbreaks of 'Beatles reunion' fever. The 1973 album, *Ringo*, started the ball rolling when John, Paul and George all guested on the popular drummer's offering. Yet what may have appeared to be a reconciliation of sorts was actually the opposite, for none of the songs featured all four musicians playing together. (*I'm The Greatest* came closest, with Lennon, Harrison and Starr all participating.)

Still, hopes began to rise further when, a few months later, John told an interviewer, 'I think anything is possible now, and if it happens I'm sure we'll all do something wonderful.' Elsewhere, Paul added that 'We wouldn't get together as The Beatles, but I'd like to see us working together – possibly for recording – and I think we will.' There were no further comments on the subject from George and Ringo, however, and no further developments.

Then, in March, 1976 there was a kind of watered-down Beatlemania mark II, when EMI Records repackaged all 22 of The Beatles' British singles in a box set, together with the first 45 rpm issue of *Yesterday*. Several weeks earlier American promoter Bill Sargent had offered the group $30 million (£20 million) to play a single concert (he increased his inducement to $100 million (£66 million) later in the year) and so, with interest and speculation racing hand in hand, the charts were once again swamped by the Fab Four's songs. Twelve of the singles entered the British Top 60, *Yesterday* made the Top 10

and, amid all the excitement, a spate of 'tribute' magazines hit the news-stands as a new generation succumbed to a mild form of the Beatlemania bug.

There were numerous reports that The Beatles were 'busy recording a new album,' and that the concert had 'tentatively been fixed for July 5, 1976'. The reality, of course, was quite different, George Harrison wryly commenting, 'That man who offered us $5 million dollars each was supposed to also promote a match between a man and a shark. So my suggestion was that he fight the shark and the winner could promote the Beatles concert!'

The strongest of the 'Beatles reunion' rumours, however, was also the last. Paul and Wings headlined an all-star charity concert in aid of Kampuchean refugees and UNICEF at London's Hammersmith Odeon on December 29, 1979, and all day long there were newspaper, radio and TV reports that this was *definitely* it. John Lennon had been 'seen booking into the Dorchester Hotel,' and there was a tremendous buzz among Beatles fans – both young and old – outside the venue beforehand, with tickets changing hands for between £50 to £100 ($75 to $150). Needless to say, the end result was disappointment for the faithful and success for the ticket touts, many of whom had, most likely, been responsible for spreading the rumour in the first place.

Yet despite these setbacks, the loyal fans did – and still do – have other, more rewarding outlets for their enthusiasm: first, there are the fanzines, including *The Beatles Book*, which re-surfaced as *The Beatles Book Appreciation Society Magazine* in May, 1976; and then there are the Beatles Conventions, which began with the event organized by Joe Pope in Boston, Massachusetts in July, 1974. The first British Beatles convention was staged in Norwich a couple of years later.

Today, conventions are held on a regular basis throughout the world, providing fans of all ages with the opportunity to meet, watch films, purchase memorabilia and merchandise, and listen to guest speakers and artists. By far the most successful of these affairs have been the US 'Beatlefests' produced by Mark Lapidos, who placed a two-line ad in a February, 1974 issue of *The Village Voice*, asking those who were interested in attending a New York City convention to write to him. Initially, 200 people responded. Then, within two days of the New York *Daily News* running a story on Lapidos' idea, he received more than 2000 letters.

When Lapidos succeeded in meeting John Lennon and informing him of his plans, the ex-Beatle told him, 'I'm all for it. I'm a Beatle fan, too.' As a result, John and Paul donated signed guitars for the charity auction, George the tabla that he had used on *Sgt. Pepper* and Ringo a set of drumsticks. On September 7 and 8, 1974, over 6000 people turned up at the Commodore Hotel in New York City and, that October, Beatlefest made the cover of *Rolling Stone* magazine.

Since then, annual shows in New York, Chicago and Los Angeles have raised over $200,000 (£135,000) for various charities, and Lapidos asserts that 'I wouldn't have been doing this for 20 years if there wasn't the demand for it. We have fans coming in from all over the world – from Japan, England, Mexico, Brazil – and a lot of them plan their vacations to tie-in with the show. We produce a full-color catalog that features all of the official Beatles merchandise, and we send out 100,000 pieces a year. So, I'm very proud of it and I love what I'm doing.'

The December 8, 1980 assassination of John Lennon, on the other hand, demonstrated what can happen when fan worship is carried to its obsessive extremes. At the same time, it also provoked an international outpouring of grief and outrage – on December 14, some 400,000 people gathered in New York's Central Park to join the rest of the world in ten minutes' silence in memory of John. 'John is smiling across the sky,' asserted Yoko.

This event also provided memorabilia owners with something to smile about: for, almost overnight, they had some extremely valuable assets.

Suddenly, the once-moderate prices of Beatles autographs, clothes, drawings, cars, instruments and other paraphernalia soared through the roof as eagle-eyed businessmen entered the market. Most fans could now only sit and watch as prized possessions went under the hammer at auction houses such as Sotheby's, Christie's and Phillips; even a small, nondescript Lennon doodle which, towards the end of 1980, would have sold for some £125 ($190), was capable of fetching around £12,500 ($19,000) one year later. Plainly, such prices were ludicrous, but on many occasions it was almost as if the bidders had succumbed to a strain of the Beatlemania bug – or perhaps they simply lacked any common sense – as auctions took on a momentum of their own.

To this day, the value of much Beatles-related memorabilia remains vastly inflated, yet of some consolation to the fans has been the fact that the largest purchaser is the Hard Rock Café. This, at least, means that much of the best memorabilia is now freely available for *everyone* to look at in any of the HRC restaurants around the globe.

Yet, while the strength of the continuing interest in The Beatles is indicated by the number of films, documentaries, books, magazines and almost-daily newspaper articles that are published about the group or individual members, it is still their music which is the message. For it was music that brought The Beatles together in the first place; it was their music that won them most international acclaim during their years together; it was their music that helped to inspire the peoples of the Soviet bloc in their struggle against oppressive communist regimes; and it is their music which will live on far into the future, long after the four men themselves – and those who adored them – have gone. 'Nothing is left of The Beatles,' said Paul McCartney in February, 1976, 'only memories.' Maybe, but *what* memories.

▲ *Following the demise of The Beatles, fans from all over the world visited the Apple HQ in London's Savile Row and scrawled graffiti on the front door. Apple, in fact, sold the building in 1976, after which John and Yoko reportedly shipped the famous door back to their apartment in New York City. Here, those well-known Beatle People Vidal Sassoon, Vera Lynn and Lionel Bart, show off the equally fancy replacement just before it was sold at auction in 1982.*

▲ John's 'Bag One' lithographs go under the hammer at Sotheby's in London for £5000 ($7500), and his guitar picks (top right) are snapped up by the Hard Rock Café. No Beatles items were anywhere near as valuable before John's death, but afterwards the prices sky-rocketed as collectors and businessmen entered the market. Still, money had nothing to do with the December 14, 1980 gathering in New York City's Central Park (right), when 400,000 of the real fans paid tribute to a great man.

author's acknowledgements

Firstly, I would like to thank all of the interviewees whose conversations with me, from 1982 until the present, appear in this book.

During the course of this work, two of Mark Lewisohn's authoritative volumes – *The Complete Beatles Chronicle* (Pyramid Books) and *The Beatles: 25 years in the life* (Sidgwick & Jackson) – were, of course, invaluable sources of information, as were *The Beatles Memorabilia Price Guide* by Jeff Augsburger, Marty Eck and Rick Rann (Wallace-Homestead), and *The Beatles' London* by Piet Schreuders, Mark Lewisohn and Adam Smith (Hamlyn).

Other books referred to were: *26 Days That Rocked The World!* by The O'Brien Publishing Company, *The Beatles: It Was Twenty Years Ago . . .* by Michael Press, *Collecting The Beatles* by Barbara Fenick (Pierian Press), *Shout!* by Philip Norman (Elm Tree Books), *Love Letters to The Beatles* as selected by Bill Adler (Anthony Blond Ltd), *I Me Mine* by George Harrison (Simon & Schuster) and *Lennon Remembers – The Rolling Stone Interviews* by Jann Wenner (Penguin Books).

picture credits

The Publishers would like to thank the photo agencies and photographers who have supplied photographs for this book. The photographs are credited by page number and position on the page as follows: (T) Top; (B) Bottom; (BL) Bottom left, etc.

All photographs of memorabilia are copyright Salamander Books Ltd.; these have not been listed below.
Front jacket/cover: John Launois/Black Star; Front and back endpapers: Hulton Deutsch; 2: Photograph by Terence Spencer, Camera Press, London; 4: MSI/*Daily Mirror*; 6: Photofest; 7: Apple Corps Ltd./Hulton Deutsch; 8: London Features; 9: Rex Features (T); MSI/*Daily Mirror* (B); 10: Photograph by Terence Spencer, Camera Press, London; 11: Rex Features; 12: Topham Picture Library; 13: Rex Features; 17: Rex Features (T); Topham Picture Library (B); 19: Rex Features; 20: Hulton Deutsch; 23: MSI/*Daily Mirror* (T); Photograph by Terence Spencer, Camera Press, London (B); 26: Rex Features: 28: Apple Corps Ltd./Hulton Deutsch; 29: Topham Picture Library; 32: Photofest; 33: Rex Features; 35: Photograph by Dezo Hoffmann, Rex Features; 37: Photofest; 41: Beat Publications Ltd.; 43: Rex Features; 45: Rex Features; 48: Hulton Deutsch; 49: Hulton Deutsch; 51: *The Indianapolis News*; 52: London Features; 53: Rex Features; 55: Photofest; 58: Topham Picture Library (T); 59: Rex Features; 61: Rex Features; 64: Phillips Fine Art Auctioneers (T); Rex Features (B); 65: Victoria & Albert Museum, London (TL); Rex Features (TR); Steve Hale Photography/Hulton Deutsch (C); Photofest (BL); Camera Press, London (BR); 66: Rex Features (L); Mirror Syndication International (T); 69: Rex Features; 72: Hulton Deutsch; 73: Rex Features; 74: Rex Features; 75: Photograph by Peter Mitchell, Camera Press, London (T); 78: Rex Features; 80: Hulton Deutsch; 81: Rex Features; 83: Hulton Deutsch; 86: Camera Press, London (T, B); 87: Rex Features; 89: Camera Press, London (TL, TR); MSI/*Daily Mirror* (B); 92: Mark Lapidos (R); Tokyo Beatles Fan Club (B); 92: Richard Buskin (TL, TR, C); 93: Richard Buskin (T); Wallace-Homestead Book Company, Radnor, PA/Jeff Augsburger (B); 94: Topham Picture Library; 95: Rex Features (TL); Richard Buskin (TR); Rex Features (B); back cover/jacket: Camera Press. London.

SPICE
HEALTH HEROES

SPICE
HEALTH HEROES

Natasha MacAller

Photography by Manja Wachsmuth

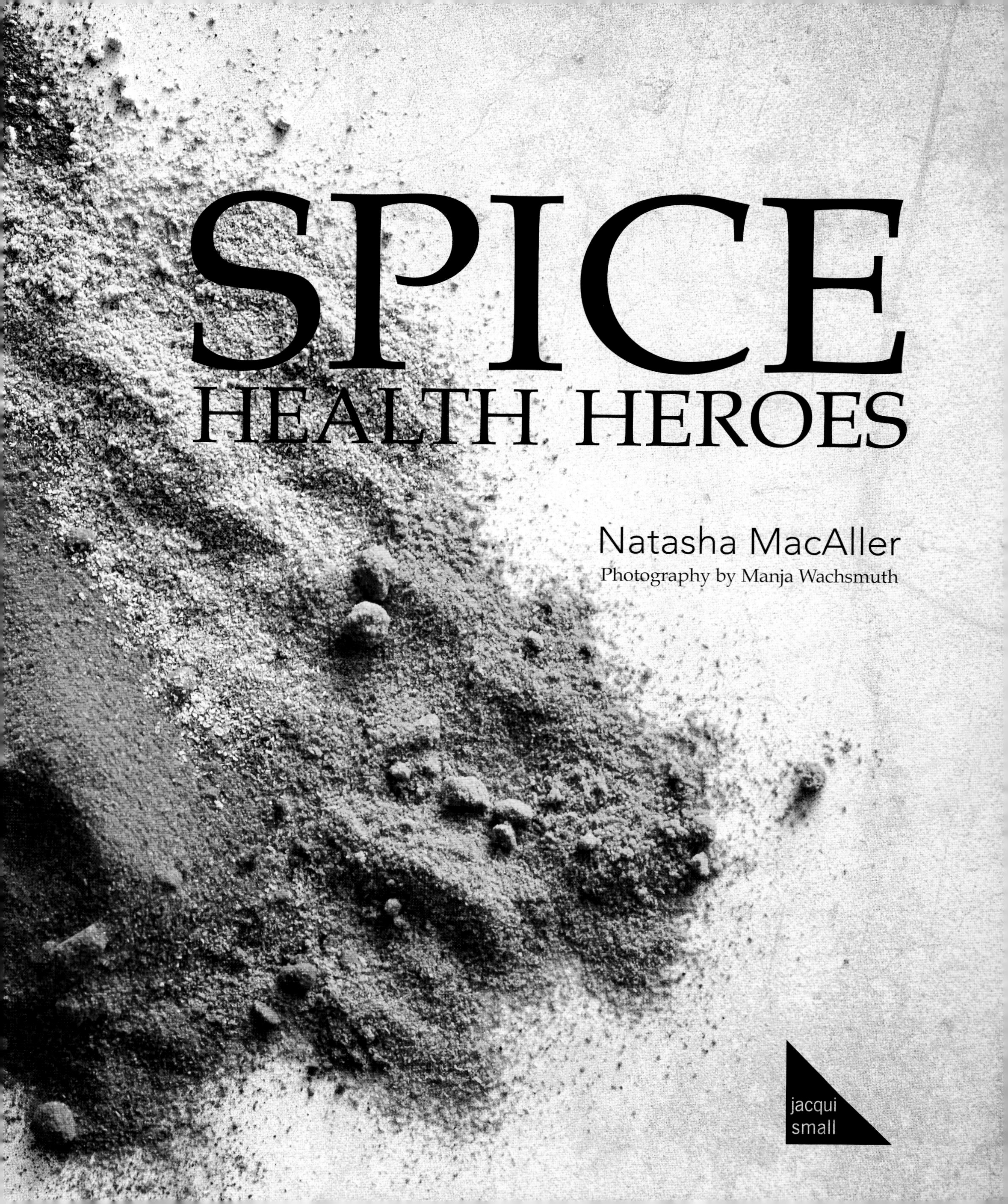

jacqui
small

First published in 2016 by
Jacqui Small LLP
74–77 White Lion Street
London N1 9PF

Publisher: Jacqui Small
Senior Commissioning Editor: Fritha Saunders
Managing Editor: Emma Heyworth-Dunn
Editor: Anne McDowall
Designer: Maggie Town
Production: Maeve Healy

ISBN: 978 1 910254 77 6

A catalogue record for this book
is available from the British Library.

2018 2017 2016
10 9 8 7 6 5 4 3 2 1

Printed in China

For Michael
With all my heart

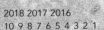

Quarto is the authority on a wide range of topics.
Quarto educates, entertains and enriches the lives
of our readers – enthusiasts and lovers of hands-on living.
www.QuartoKnows.com

Contents

Foreword

My own experience of spices was formed during my childhood in Northern Greece. Nearby was Crocus, a small village in the mountains named after the plant that produces saffron, the most precious and expensive of all spices. In Crocus and the wider area of Kozani where saffron is grown, people often start their day by drinking a cup of tea made of an infusion of just two fine saffron filaments. They understand the potency of this spice and use it sparingly and respectfully in their food and drink.

Spices, earth's refined alchemy, discovered and cherished by our ancestors, enhance the flavour of our food, bringing life to our mealtimes. As this wonderful book shows, we can use spices not only for their culinary delights but also for their impressive healing qualities to support our health, inner balance and wellbeing.

Along with flavour, spices add texture and colour to our plate. Eating a tasty, aromatic, nutritious meal mindfully in a pleasant environment nourishes the mind, body and spirit. When our food satisfies our tongue, then our brain is content and doesn't look for pleasure and satisfaction elsewhere. If our diet is bland or unbalanced, lacking one of the six tastes: sweet, sour, salty, pungent, bitter and astringent, then we can feel something is missing. That's when our body turns to the 'easy' tastes – sugar and salt – and overeating, which, as we know, contributes to obesity and the increasing prevalence of chronic diseases.

Spices, I believe, are the heroes that can save us from disease and poor quality of being. As the title *Spice Health Heroes* suggests, spices have extra-special properties, including recently confirmed antidepressant effects. Trust spices to help us find happiness.

Spice Health Heroes takes us on a journey through history, folklore and science to our kitchen with unique recipes gathered and artfully created by the charismatic Natasha. Her ideas convince us to grab our apron and explore further in our own kitchens these beautiful spice recipes.

In my own 'Medical Kitchen Wisdom' workshops for professionals and 'Cooking on Prescription' groups for the public, people explore how to use 'Food as Medicine'. Hippocrates said that 'The best doctors cure by changing the diet and lifestyle of their patient'. My intention, in my medical practice as a specialist in Nutritional Medicine and Ayurvedic Nutrition, is to help people find what foods suit their 'type', and spices are often the forgotten or unknown ingredient that can help. *Spice Health Heroes* will be on my 'prescription list'.

I love spices and use them everyday in my cooking. My wish is that, by the time you finish reading this book, you too will come to love and respect our spice health heroes.

Eleni Tsiompanou, MD, PGDip, MSc Nutritional Medicine
Founder, Health Being Institute, London, England

Introduction

Spices are the flavour of life and may be the source of wellbeing for life, too.

The word spice, derived from the Latin word species, originally meant 'merchandise, goods, wares or a commodity from the Far East'. The definitions of what constitutes a spice and what constitutes a herb are rather fluid, and opinions differ, with herbs often turning into spices and vice versa. For example, garlic is considered a spice – the garlic clove is a flower bud – but it is also listed as a culinary herb. Plant leaves are the most confusing and argued about: a fresh basil leaf is referred to as a herb, but the moment it is dried it becomes a spice. Therefore, after much researching, analyzing and pondering, I believe that a spice is the seed, berry, bark, root, rhizome (creeping rootstock), branch, leaf, aril (a fleshy coating of some seed varieties e.g. pomegranate) or sap of a plant.

Spice history… in a nutshell

Spices have been part of civilization, culture, myths and medicine for tens of thousands of years. One of the first records of spices being used, dating back to at least 1600BC, was found on the Greek island of Santorini, where frescoes display a scene of young girls and monkeys picking saffron, presumably for medicinal use. The earliest evidence of spices being traded dates back to a pharaoh queen's funerary monument, which depicts spice-trade routes linking the Nile by camel and boat to the Horn of Africa some 3,500 years ago, including voyages to the ancient isle of cinnamon, Sri Lanka.

Thousands of years later, saffron was introduced to Eastern America by German religious groups fleeing persecution, who brought with them their penchant and passion for saffron. By the 1730s, the Pennsylvania Dutch, as they became known, had become famous for cultivating, selling and exporting saffron. Although the acres of crocus are now small kitchen gardens, saffron is still grown there by Mennonite, Amish and Lutheran families. Saffron recipes from centuries back are still made in these devoutly religious communities – and at 10,000 US dollars a pound of stamens, saffron-growing remains a very profitable, albeit labour-intensive, hobby.

Spices have been tasted, traded, stolen and the cause of bloodshed for many millennia all over the world. One of the most bloody and significant battles that rewrote spice history took place over the span of around 200 years, between the 15th and 17th centuries. The battling participants in the murderous Spice Wars included Spain, Portugal, England and Holland as each country fought for dominance and control of the Spice Islands. Two of the Banda islands, a tiny set-apart chain of ten volcanic islands in Indonesia, were the only place where the coveted nutmeg grew and, at that time, the spice was worth its weight in gold because not only was nutmeg thought to be an aphrodisiac but it was also believed to cure the plague.

In countries and climates near and far, other familiar and exotic spices flourished: Middle Eastern Persia and Ancient Greece, Rome and later the first European spice-trade capital of Venice were rich with an abundance of oregano, rosemary, bay leaf and pomegranate, all used for medicines. India, the land of holy basil (tulsi), cardamom, fenugreek, tamarind, cassia cinnamon and today's rock-star turmeric, to this day still grows 15 per cent of the world's spices and leads the way in health studies of turmeric. China has a wealth of flu-fending star anise, star rhizome ginger and super-C citrus, while Africa, a continent of ancient spice routes, where, ironically, no spices actually originate, is the creative hub of some of the world's most popular and colourful spice blends. In the New World, Grenada in the Caribbean now grows the majority of allspice, nutmeg and clove, planted hundreds of years ago from Spice Island seedlings by the British colonialists. Lastly, in the Americas, land of fiery-hot chilies, heart-healthy cocoa and body-cleansing hibiscus, these spices have been revered as healing medicines by the ancient indigenous populations of both North and South America.

Spices for flavour and health

Historically, spices have been used throughout the ages as aromatic flavourings for food and as perfumes to sweeten the scent of battle-weary knights when they were in attendance to the king. However, more importantly, spices have been used throughout the ages as medicine, to heal the body and extend life. Different spices have different talents and can be used to warm, cleanse, restore, soothe, boost energy levels and support the vital body-balancing immune system. Spices are concentrated full of phytonutrients (nutrients and chemicals in addition to vitamins and minerals), which, while not vital for keeping you alive, may help prevent disease in addition to keeping your body systems working at their best.

Spices used as medicine remain relevant as natural sources of active compounds for treating human conditions or disorders, including immune-imbalanced and inflammatory

> *Spices have been used for so many centuries not only as flavour enhancers but as medicine as well. There must be some benefit; there is something more to spices than simply taste.*
>
> Luigi Fontana, MD, PhD

diseases and cancers. There are hundreds, if not thousands, of current cancer-research projects investigating the promising potential of medicinal plants to discover new possible therapies utilizing complementary medicines that lack the toxic effects of chemotherapeutic drugs and may have the same, or better, curative effects as current chemical therapies.

Spice Health Heroes is not a diet book, nor is it a medical treatise. (I am not a doctor, but rather a ballerina-turned-chef with a passionate interest in health and, particularly, in spices.) However, it does include contributions from a number of revered international medical doctors, who are weighing in on the promising research, trials and conclusions relating to the medicinal uses of these 30 spice health heroes, which it is thought may relieve, assist and have genuine benefit to health and wellbeing.

There are also contributions here from 21 lauded international chefs, whose spice stories and recipes began from their very first taste of a spice then developed over years of cooking, creating and tasting into their own individual spice signature.

These two professions, culinary and medical, have come together and are working as a team to bring attention to the simple fact that good food equals good heath. Culinary medicine is not about following a diet, nor is it about removing entire food groups from your life, but rather it consists in eating fresh food that is free from a long list of artificial ingredients: just simple, wholesome, fresh food, full of flavour, health-giving properties – and spice.

'Spices have been used for so many centuries not only as flavour enhancers but as medicine as well. There must be some benefit; there is something more to spices than simply taste', suggests Luigi Fontana, MD, PhD, Professor of Medicine at Washington University and at University of Brescia, Italy. Dr Fontana is a very lean man. This is not so surprising considering one of his areas of study: calorie restriction (CR). 'From yeast to mice, if you reduce calorie intake (without causing starvation), animals are healthier and live much longer! We are now studying this in humans.' As with many matters relating to diet, Dr Fontana and his colleagues are learning that things are never simple. 'We are finding that it is not *just* CR that gives benefit. It is an interaction of many factors, one of which is the friendly bacteria that live in our gut, the microbiome. For example, we recently published a paper showing that mice that are 1) fed turmeric, and 2) contain the microbiome of a human from Bangladesh show an increase in the amount of time the body has to absorb nutrients, compared to mice that are identical except that they have a microbiome from a human from a European country. It is not just turmeric that gives this benefit, it is the interaction of turmeric with the healthful flora that live within us!'

Storing and using spices

Do you open your spice cupboard to a collection of dusty tins, dog-eared paper boxes and no-longer-see-through small glass jars of reddish or brownish powders of… what is that? Spice? Is there any smell to them? Check that neither the colour nor the scent of the spices has faded: if it has, toss it out. Don't keep spices you want to use on a rack above the stovetop: they will perish within weeks. Keeping spices in tightly sealed glass jars will prevent the volatile oils from becoming humid and oxidizing. Stored in a cool dark place, whole spices, including leaves and flowers, will keep for 1–2 years, seeds and roots for 2–3 years and ground spices for 6–12 months.

The single most important tip for ground spices is to buy only what you need for a few months. For the best value for money, purchase spices whole, then toast and grind them as you need them. Freshness is more important than origin, but if possible, choose organic, as many spices come from the tropical climates over long distances and non-organic ones are most likely to have been sprayed or irradiated to prevent pests and extend shelf life.

To warm and release their volatile oils, toast and swirl whole spices over low heat in a small dry pan until they release their scent, then allow to cool before grinding in a mortar and pestle or electric spice grinder. If you need to replace fresh spices with dried ones in a recipe, as a good rule of thumb, allow 1 teaspoon of dried for 1 tablespoon of chopped fresh (though in the case of dried sage, use only ½ teaspoon). The fragrance of fresh spice will fill the kitchen and your soul with its intoxicating aroma.

Spice blends

This international sampling of spice mixes are easy to blend into your favourite foods. Spice mixtures are often the secret and essential ingredient that will transform a so-so plate of food into something deliciously memorable! Use them to add a boost of flavour to anything from a soup to roasted nuts, finely grind your spices and stir into a drink, or invent your own blends as a creative idea for gifts.

1. Tash's Tamale and Taco Spice

A Mexican mix that pairs well with veggie, fish and meat dishes for that authentic 'south of the border' flavour! Hibiscus adds a bit of sour citrus; if unavailable, you can substitute the zest of 2 limes.

2 tbsp chopped fresh sage (or 1 tbsp dried)
2 tbsp mild chili powder
1 tbsp salt flakes
1 tbsp chopped garlic (or 2 tsp garlic powder)
1 tbsp onion powder
1 tbsp dried oregano, crumbled
5 tsp cumin seeds, toasted and ground
2 tsp guajillo chili powder
1 tsp ground cinnamon
1 tsp freshly ground black peppercorns
2 tsp crushed chipotle of chili pepper flakes
2 tsp hibiscus tea or 6–8 calyx petals, ground

Combine all the spices together and mix thoroughly. Store in an airtight container.

2. Homemade Pumpkin Pie Spice

A blend to add healthy sweetness to your morning latte, lunchtime roasted veggie salad or evening dessert.

3 tbsp ground cinnamon
1 tbsp ground ginger
1 tsp ground cloves
1 tsp ground fresh nutmeg
¼ tsp ground cardamom
¼ tsp ground white pepper

Combine all the spices together and mix thoroughly. Store in an airtight container.

3. Somoma Spice Mix

Inspired by California's top wine-growing region, this blend can be added to farmers' market finds, or to pizza or pasta dishes.

2 tbsp dried basil, crumbled
2 tbsp dried marjoram, crumbled
2 tbsp dried oregano, crumbled
1 tbsp dried thyme leaves, rubbed or ground
1 tbsp dried bay leaves, crumbled
4½ tsp dried rosemary needles, ground
2 tsp red pepper flakes
2 tsp fennel seeds, toasted and ground
1½ tsp dried mint, crumbled
1½ tsp garlic powder
1½ tsp onion powder
1 tsp lemon zest

Combine all spices together and mix thoroughly. Store in an airtight container.

1

2

3

4. Rich Curry Blend

A full-flavoured blend for traditional Indian curry dishes, this masala can even be added to poached fruit or nut desserts for a rich, mysterious aroma and taste.

2½ tbsp sweet paprika
2 tbsp cumin seeds, toasted and ground
2 tbsp ground turmeric
1½ tbsp coriander seeds, ground
1 tbsp smoked pimentón
1 tbsp ground fenugreek
1 tbsp mustard seeds, ground
2½ tsp fennel seeds, toasted and ground
2½ tsp ground red pepper flakes
2½ tsp fenugreek leaves
2½ tsp ground cardamon
1 x 5cm (2in.) piece cinnamon stick, charred and ground, or ½ tsp toasted ground cinnamon
¼ tsp ground cloves
¾ tsp dried orange peel

Combine all the spices together and mix thoroughly. Store in an airtight container.

5. Citrus Salt and Pepper Spice

Add a little citrus zing with your pepper-and-salt blend on salads, appetizers or even fresh fruit.

zest of 6 lemons, or 2 tbsp dried chopped peel
zest of 2 oranges, or 1 tbsp dried chopped peel
zest of 6 limes, or 2 tsp dried chopped peel

6 tbsp coarse sea salt
3 tbsp black peppercorns
1 tbsp dried pink peppercorns
1 tbsp dried green peppercorns
2 tsp Aleppo pepper flakes

Spread out all the citrus zest (unless using pre-dried peel) on a lined baking tray. Put into the oven on the lowest setting and leave until completely dried, about 1 hour. When dried, transfer to a bowl, add the salt, peppercorns and pepper flakes and stir until well mixed. Store in a decorative glass jar or salt mill and grind as needed.

6. Oriental Five Spice Plus One Blend

The go-to mixture for stir-fries, clear soups, marinades and chicken wings.

2 tbsp + 1 tsp ground star anise
1 tbsp ground Sichuan pepper or black pepper
1 tbsp ground fennel seed
1 tbsp ground cinnamon
1 tbsp ground cloves
1 tbsp ground ginger or galangal
1 tbsp sea salt (optional)
1 tbsp dried orange zest

Combine all the spices together and mix thoroughly. Store in an airtight container.

Immune spice

Immunity is balanced strength, the ultimate support for bodies and minds. Through an astonishing and elaborate programme of checks and balances, our immune system strives to keep us healthy and well. This handful of spices gives support to the immune system, our body's power-plant protector.

Immune Spice Health Heroes
Turmeric ★ Cumin ★ Clove & Allspice ★ Citrus Zest ★ Star Anise

Some complaints and diseases identified as immunodeficiency diseases (where the ability of the immune system to fight infection is reduced) are assisted by immune-boosting action – the common cold and flu, for instance – while others, such as inflammatory reactive autoimmune diseases (where the immune system displays an increased/abnormal response to tissues or organs in a person's own body) like rheumatoid arthritis and multiple sclerosis, require immune balancers. Immune spice health heroes have qualities that may help support and enhance our body's extremely complex immune system. Complaints from the common cold to serious and life-threatening diseases are defined in a very simplified way as generally due to a disconnect somewhere in the immune system. According to the International Union of Immunological Societies, there exists today a shocking 150 primary immunodeficiency diseases. One of this extraordinary system's many vital functions is to inhibit the activation of cells that can cause cancers to develop, and this handful of spices may offer not only flavour but also immune reinforcement.

Turmeric has a multitude of talents and is thought to help prevent and alleviate the symptoms of rheumatoid arthritis and Alzheimer's disease. Cumin is being studied as a hormonal balancer and black cumin as an anticancer warrior. Clove and star anise both offer anti-inflammatory support, while super-C citrus zest provides protection against common colds and flu.

Other immune spice heroes

Garlic A powerful preventative used for centuries by fighting forces from Ancient Greek battalions to Russian World War II infantry, garlic kept soldiers fighting fit and ready to do battle with its antimicrobial properties. Garlic is thought be have strong anticarcinogenic attributes that help to support the immune system.

Rosemary A must-have for barbecues, rosemary has been well studied, tested and analyzed for its extraordinary ability to nullify the cancer-causing hetrocyclic amines (HCAs) that form when beef, pork, chicken, lamb or any other meat is grilled (broiled), fried, charred, smoked or cooked over an open flame, and thus protects the immune system from having to stave off these easily absorbed chemicals.

Pomegranate Sprinkle a generous handful of fresh pomegranate seeds on grain dishes and fresh salads: not only are these red jewels delicious, but this traditional Persian super-spice, which has been used as a medicine since ancient times, also provides great anti-inflammatory and immune support and shows great promise as an anticancer hero.

Fenugreek Considered a legume and full of protein, the maple-scented fenugreek can create a barrier to assist the immune system in disabling toxins found in our food and drink that are often unwittingly ingested. Fenugreek shows promise in preventing calcium oxalate from accumulating in the kidney and gallbladder, preventing not only kidney and gallstones but also a reactive inflammatory response by the immune system. It is believed that it may keep blood-sugar levels better balanced and lessen the immune system's workload and it shows great therapeutic potential in stunting the growth of cancer cells, notably in the pancreas.

Wasabi Another promising anticancer, antibacterial hero, wasabi is ranked as the strongest antibacterial against *E. coli* and *Staphylococcus aureus*. Wasabi also helps to prevent food poisoning by killing off the bacteria that could be lurking on the fresh raw fish (sashimi) with which it is often served. This green-coloured rhizome has a great concentration of active isothiocyanate (ITC) compounds and may have a chemopreventive effect on cancer.

Mustard These tiny seeds are full of cancer-preventative isothiocyanate (ITC) compounds. In the nutrient-rich and cancer-suppressing brassica family, mustard displays promising results: hundreds of lab studies have demonstrated the chemopreventive potential of this sharply strong-tasting seed.

igliving.com/magazine/articles/IGL_2009-06_AR_Immune-Deficiency-and-Autoimmune-Disease-A-Complicated-Relationship.pdf

Turmeric *The Master Spice*

Some consider turmeric the most powerful spice in the pantry. Not only does this rhizome give curry dishes their distinctive, rich earthy flavour, but turmeric is also possibly the oldest and most scientifically studied spice in the world. Thousands of years ago, it was used as a medical, culinary and sacred spice: archaeological digs in Southern India have unearthed ancient pottery shards with traces of turmeric, garlic and ginger dating back over 4,000 years, while the ancient Indian discipline of natural healing, Ayurveda, describes turmeric as 'one who is victorious over diseases'.

Most of the world's turmeric comes from India; the finest quality with the highest concentration of the active compound curcumin comes from Alleppey, a city in the southern Indian state of Kerala.

Exciting current studies from around the world show promising results for turmeric as an antioxidant and antiseptic with anti-inflammatory and analgesic benefits, and it is thought to support the liver with its LDL- and triglyceride-cholesterol-lowering punch. The active compound that gives turmeric its bright-yellow colour, curcumin (not to be confused with cumin), is also thought to help fend off Alzheimer's disease and is one of the ingredients found in acetaminophen (more commonly known in the US under the brand name Tylenol). Current trials are underway, testing elite Olympic-level athletes, to study curcumin's ability to combat pain, inflammation and joint damage (which can lead to osteoarthritis). As turmeric is not considered a drug, it can be used in competitive sport when drug testing is obligatory.

A kitchen staple in Asia, turmeric is a key spice in an uncountable array of curries and is found, too, in Mexico's chile con carne; Japanese teas, vinegars and noodles; the Moroccan spice blend ras-el-hanout; soups, stews, pickled fruits and vegetables; that bright-yellow American mustard; classic British piccalilli and coronation chicken.

When chopping or grating fresh turmeric root (as in the Tropical Turmeric Smoothie on page 54), it's a very good idea to use gloves: in Asian countries, turmeric is still traditionally used to dye clothing a stunning sunshine orangey-yellow and it will dye your hands as well! Choose roots from a reputable source that are large, smooth-skinned and free of mould. Crisp, well-dried turmeric root is easily grated using a fine-toothed grater such as a microplane and its slightly bitter, peppery earthy flavour will be more prominent.

❝ There is a widespread belief that all inflammation is negative, and must be reduced at all costs. However, there are different types of inflammatory processes, and they are mediated by different chemicals. The gentle 'COX1' inflammation helps to heal tissues from everyday damage – it encourages the maintenance of the stomach and gut lining, for example. 'COX2' inflammation occurs in response to more immediate damage, like strains and arthritic problems. Normal anti-inflammatory drugs such as aspirin and ibuprofen inhibit both reactions, so the recuperative effects of COX1 are reduced alongside the desired loss of pain and swelling.

In practice this causes gastric problems in many people, and can lead to ulcers and indigestion. The loss of the positive COX1 action in joints has been shown to actually increase the rate that cartilage damage occurs – really bad news for hips and knees!

The search for selective COX2 inhibitors has been intense, and disappointing. Several promising drugs have been withdrawn due to serious side effects – and all the time turmeric has been virtually ignored! However turmeric may be just what we are looking for – it shows great promise as an ideal COX2 inhibitor, free from any serious side effects. Research is positive in many areas including arthritis, heart disease, colon cancer and inflammatory bowel disease. It may also reduce the side effects of chemotherapy and long-term anti-inflammatory drug medication.

If you use only one spice, make sure it's turmeric! ❞

Margaret Papoutsis, DO, Raw Dips (SN) (NT), MBANT, CNHC

Cumin *The Global Spice*

This humble, dried, seed-like fruit has been around for so long that historians are unsure where it originated. Related to parsley, dill seed and its look-alike cousin caraway, cumin is a hardy annual grower that is both drought and flood tolerant. Planted from seed in the winter months in countries from Mexico, India, China and Japan to Spain, Italy and Africa, the eight-sided, ridged, khaki-coloured seeds are harvested in summer. The Bible (Isaiah 28:27) speaks of harvested cumin being spread on a cloth and beaten with a rod to extract the drab, dusty seed, which, when toasted and freshly ground, exudes the most alluring aroma.

Ancient records indicate that cumin was an important spice in early Roman and Middle Eastern cuisine. Traditionally, it has been used medicinally for a number of complaints and diseases, including to counteract the bacteria that causes food poisoning, as a poultice for swollen throats and digestive organs and as an aid to reduce stress and lower blood sugar; especially important for those with diabetes. On-going studies also indicate that oil of cumin (cuminaldehyde), which is rich in phytoestrogens, mimics HRT, and it is being tested on a large scale for its antiosteoporotic effects.

This nutty and familiar-smelling spice is welcome in cuisines and dishes throughout the world, from Indian to Mexican, Thai to Middle Eastern, African to Germanic and Caribbean to Cajun and Portuguese, and is particularly prevalent in spice mixes, famously in ras-el hanout, hot Caribbean colombo powder, Madras curry powder, garam masala, baharat, Mexican chili powder and, my favourite, dukkah (see page 206).

It is one of the easiest spices to grind, so purchase whole seeds, toast them lightly in a pan and freshly grind the seeds when cooled.

Black Cumin *The Imperial Spice*

Also known by the names black seed, kalonji, onion seed and nigella, black cumin (*Nigella sativa*) is not biologically related to common cumin but to the flowering Ranunculaceae family. Native to Southern Europe, North Africa and Southern Asia, it is grown in the Middle East, the Mediterranean region and the Indian continent. Matte black in colour when dried, these small, roughly surfaced, wedge-shaped seeds are pricier than common cumin and were once an important spice in Southern and Central Europe. The earliest mention of black cumin relates that it adorned the young Egyptian King Tut's sarcophagus to accompany him to the afterlife, along with fragrant cinnamon and rosemary, generously used as embalming spices.

Black cumin has been revered for centuries in India and the Middle East for its wealth of traditional healing properties and its great support of the immune system. It is considered a natural interferon remedy for autoimmune diseases such as Crohn's disease and immune-mediated diseases like multiple sclerosis. More than 100 health-related compounds are found in the oil extracted from these tiny flavourful seeds, the most powerful and potent of which is thymoquinone. As yet found only in this black seed, thymoquinone is thought to strengthen the immune system by increasing activity in the body's natural killer cells that fend off viruses and disease. Promising studies continue in South Carolina.

The pungent scent, reminiscent of oregano, and slightly bitter flavour of black cumin seed lend themselves to spicy curries, slow-cooked vegetables and sauces. Always used as whole seeds, they can be sprinkled on cakes, breads and lavash, used in dips and lightly toasted then sprinkled over salads and soups.

❛ In recent years, there has been enormous interest in the bioactive constituents and pharmacological activities of cumin. A number of chemicals, such as flavonoids, lignins and other phenolic compounds, have been identified in cumin seeds, as well as fatty acids, vitamins, minerals and dietary fiber. Useful antimicrobial and antifungal activity of cumin has been shown against some gram-positive and gram-negative bacteria and other animal and human pathogens. The anticancer ability of cumin against colon and liver cancer is highlighted in a number of animal studies. Further animal tests have repeatedly shown cumin products to be diuretic and to reduce high blood sugar, plasma and tissue cholesterol and triglycerides. Last but not least, cumin extracts were found to relieve coughs and have anti-epileptic activity. ❜

Eleni Tsiompanou, MD, PGDip, MSc Nutritional Medicine

Clove *The Enchanting Spice*

Derived from the Latin word *clavus,* meaning nail, the tack-shaped clove is the handpicked and carefully dried flower bud of a tree belonging to the myrtle family.

Discovered in the Moluccas, the exotic Spice Islands now known as Maluku, Indonesia, where nutmeg, mace and pepper once flourished, cloves are cultivated commercially today in Sri Lanka, Brazil, Tanzania, Mauritius and Madagascar, where these elegant trees with their shiny evergreen leaves and pink clove buds scent the tropical island air with a pungent sweet fragrance. The trees grow slowly – they take at least eight years before blooming – and the buds are harvested by hand just as they are beginning to turn bright pink.

This ancient spice arrived in the European kitchen in abundance during the Middle Ages, enchanting kings and commoners alike, who soon discovered the many medicinal and culinary uses of this tiny dried flower bud. Huge demand for this valuable spice soon made the seafaring explorers unimaginably wealthy – and eventually sparked the bloody Spice Wars.

For centuries, cloves have had numerous medicinal uses as well as acting as a food preservative. Ancient Chinese medicine from the third century used clove to treat a number of ills, including indigestion, nausea and toothache. The active compound in clove, eugenol, has powerful antioxidant, antibacterial and antifungal properties. Today's increasing bacterial resistance to antibiotics is concerning and on-going studies with essential oils, such as clove, to kill bacteria without creating resistance could hold a solution to this problem.

The tiny but powerfully fragrant clove is now well known in nearly every cuisine and wields great results in both sweet and savoury dishes. It is also a component of numerous spice blends, pastes and beverages throughout the world, including China's five-spice, France's quatre épices, India's garam masala, Morocco's ras-el-hanout, Britain's mulled wine spice and America's pumpkin pie spice.

The finest quality cloves are the Penang variety from Malaysia. Look for this spice with the buds intact. Store sealed in a cool, dark pantry and use them whole in stews, sauces, compotes and for studding the Christmas ham, but remember to remove before serving.

❝ Clove has been revered not only for its culinary delight but also for its medicinal qualities. Historically, it has been used as a breath freshener and is still used in some chewing gums today. From a nutrient perspective, clove houses key minerals (potassium, selenium manganese, magnesium and iron) and vitamins (A, C, K, pyridoxine, thiamin, riboflavin). Traditionally, clove has been used for a spectrum of benefits as an anti-inflammatory and antiflatulent when taken orally, and as a rubefacient (warming and calming) when applied topically to muscles and joints. Moreover, it is noted to have properties that serve as a robust antioxidant, antiseptic and local anesthetic. This is often credited to its essential oil, eugenol, which has been in therapeutic use in dentistry as a local anesthetic and antiseptic for teeth and gum health. Eugenol also has been found to reduce blood-sugar levels in animal studies when compared to placebo and thus may have benefits in diabetics, but further studies are needed to determine its future role in therapeutics. ❞

Param Dedhia, MD

Allspice *The Awesome Spice*

First 'discovered' by Christopher Columbus in Jamaica growing from an evergreen tree, allspice was mistakenly thought to be the prized and pricey black peppercorn and was named *pimenta* (Jamaican pepper).

From Europe to the Middle East, Africa to the Americas, Scandinavia to the Caribbean, allspice glides effortlessly from savoury to sweet and is a must in pickled vegetables, sauces, fish dishes and desserts.

Although they were discovered thousands of miles apart, allspice and clove are often confused because they share the active compound eugenol, a warming and powerful antioxidant and antiseptic. This single berry does triple duty in place of traditional cupboard-spice blends such as mixed spice, English spice and pumpkin pie spice. It is a bit more peppery than clove, but with a complex sweetness, and softer in fragrance, with a hint of toasted orange peel.

Most of the flavour and compounds are found in the shell. Dried berries will last 2–4 years; ground allspice considerably less time – six months at the most – so purchase a little at a time for the freshest flavour.

Citrus Zest *The Zing Spice*

Not only is a bit of citrus zest often the secret ingredient in a salad dressing, carrot and coriander soup or a sauce for fish, but it also contains compounds that can help fight a number of complaints and diseases, from aching feet to, according to new studies, cancer. The flavonoids (organic componds) in citrus fruits, particularly in the peel, are being used in tandem with chemotherapy in several cancer studies, including to treat prostate cancer.

The range of citrus varieties and peel preparations are numerous. Orange, tangerine and mandarin peel are traditionally used in liqueurs, confectionary, pastries and cakes, and smell of winter holidays when added to warming mulled wine. Lemon is the most popular citrus fruit, for both its juice and peel, and there are thousands of varieties around the globe. Thought to have originated in Northern India or China, the lemon was introduced into Sicily in 200AD, and to the Middle East a few hundred years later. My favourite lemon-zest variety is the curious-looking but exquisitely fragranced Buddha's Hand Lemon, or Fingered Citron, a citrus variety composed nearly entirely of peel, used for flavouring savoury dishes, desserts, cocktail infusions and for making preserves. In Chinese tradition, it symbolizes happiness and long life, while in Japan, it is believed to bestow good fortune.

But the scent of a tropical lime is an all-time citrus favourite. Originating in Southeast Asia, it is one of the few citrus fruits that is grown from seed rather than being grafted and is happiest in tropical climes, being more prone to frost damage than other kinds of citrus. Lime peel is generally thinner and more delicate than lemon, orange and grapefruit. Loomi, also known as dried or black limes, are a traditional Persian and Indian spice. The limes are preserved by boiling whole green limes in brine then smoking and/or drying them in the sun. Added to Middle Eastern dishes, these rock-hard balls impart a citrusy, smoky flavour and are the perfect addition to legume dishes.

Buy organic fruit, as the peel of non-organic citrus is sprayed before transport with any number of chemicals. If not available, wash thoroughly with a natural plant-based fruit wash (ironically, most are derived from citrus oil!). Using a potato peeler or zester, remove the peel from the pith and use it right away or tightly wrap it in cling film (plastic wrap) and refrigerate to prevent it from drying out and becoming brittle. Or make this easy preserved lemon peel recipe: thinly peel the zest from 4 unwaxed lemons, drop into a small pan of boiling water and blanch for 1 minute. Strain, discard the water and repeat with fresh water. Rinse in cold water, then pat dry. Transfer to a small storage container with a tight-fitting lid, add 2 tablespoons of salt flakes, 3 tablespoons of sugar and 6 thyme sprigs. Mix well then cover and chill for a week, shaking the container daily. Scrape the preserving mix off the peel you want to use, then, using the tip of a knife, slice the peel into thin matchsticks. Garnish dishes, adding additional thyme leaves to finish. Substitute Valencia orange or pink grapefruit peel for a twist on the classic lemon taste.

www.citrusvariety.ucr.edu/citrus/buddha.html / www.ncbi.nlm.nih.gov/pubmed/23673480

' Citrus zest is fun to say, use and taste: it's the essence of the fruit, distilled into a squiggle.

Zest is a part of the peel, and the peel is powerful medicine. In an Arizona study, those who reported drinking both hot black tea and citrus peel had an 88 per cent reduced risk of squamous cell carcinoma of the skin; people who drank iced tea with citrus peel had a 42 per cent reduced risk of skin cancer. Both groups were compared with those who did not drink tea or eat citrus peel. And people who just ate the fruit or drank the juice did not have the same anticancer effect.

Why do tea and citrus zest seem to knock back the risk of skin cancer? Tea's polyphenols [protective antioxidant compounds] may protect against the carcinogenic effect of UV radiation. The theaflavins of black tea is one class of those plant chemicals, which may work by stopping cancer cells from starting.

Gram for gram, citrus zest has much more vitamin C than the juice or pulp, and more of the plant chemicals that are likely protective against cancer formation: d-limonene, hesperidin, naringin and auraptene. D-limonene, which constitutes the vast majority of citrus oil, works on cancer cells directly. Several other components of citrus peel are being studied as anticancer agents. '

John La Puma, MD

http://www.ncbi.nlm.nih.gov/pmc/articles/PMC45584/; http://www.ncbi.nlm.nih.gov/pubmed/18072821; http://www.ncbi.nlm.nih.gov/pubmed/11142088

Star Anise *The Sultry Fighter Spice*

Considered the most important spice used in Chinese cuisine, this photogenic spice, with its eight starry-tipped points, is also a wealth of health. Long used as a traditional Chinese medicine to treat inflammation, nervousness, insomnia and pain, star anise (*Anisi stellati fructus*) has been demonstrated to possess antibacterial, antifungal and antioxidant activities. There's also an active flu-fighter component in star anise called shikimic acid. Slowly extracted from the seeds over the course of several months, this acid becomes part of the recipe for a vital modern-day vaccine.

Plucked just before they are ripe from a small evergreen tree native to Southern China and Vietnam, the green flower-shaped fruits are then sun dried.

The major flavour component in traditional Chinese five-spice powder, a centuries-old Chinese-spice blend, star anise has flavour layers of cinnamon, citrus, clove and peppercorn and the pungent flavour is found only in the pod's pericarp or shell, not in the seeds. Stars can be added whole to long-cooking dishes (see April Bloomfield's Adobo on page 78 or the Blackcurrant Consommé on page 46) or ground in Garam Masala Bastilla (see page 28). Some popular recipes that use star anise include the Vietnamese soup pho, Chinese pork ribs and Peking duck, curries, Jamaica jerk chicken and masala chai tea. Add a bit of star anise powder and a little orange or mandarin orange zest to hot cocoa to enjoy a heavenly after-meal beverage.

Strangely enough, star anise, cultivated in Southern China thousands of years ago, and anise or anise seed, primarily from Spain, contain the same essential oil, anethole, but are botanically unrelated. In traditional recipes from Italy to Scandiniva, anise and the slightly grassier-flavoured fennel seed are the favourites. Today, however, star anise has the spotlight, as it has become less expensive and has a complex richer flavour. Similar-flavoured spices and herbs include fennel seed, licorice and tarragon, all of which also contain anethole. Ground star anise can be substituted for an equal measure of ground anise seed in most recipes.

Because this spice has an extremely long shelf life of several years, merchants may keep it on the shelf for too long. Check that it smells lightly of licorice; it should not smell musty or have no scent at all.

If grinding star anise at home, use a mortar and pestle or a rolling pin to rough grind it then grind finely in an electric grinder or high-powered single-serve high-speed blender.

❝ Star anise has been popularized for its flavour and for its medicinal qualities. Containing minerals (calcium, potassium, iron, copper, manganese, magnesium and zinc) and vitamins (A, C, thiamin, riboflavin, pyridoxine and niacin), it has been used in traditional medicine as an antiseptic, antispasmodic, digestive, expectorant, balancing tonic and stimulant. The seeds have been chewed after meals for generations in the subcontinent to refresh the breath and promote digestion. Its key oils include thymol, terpineol and anethole, which have been used to treat chest infections and coughs.

Modern research has noted star anise's activity as an antioxidant: it has been found to reduce the amount of cancer development after exposure to carcinogens. In a most intriguing study, antibacterial properties from anise showed benefit when tested against dozens of strains of drug-resistant bacteria. Most celebrated is its effective use against several types of viruses by preventing viral replication. Shikimic acid is the ingredient extracted from Chinese star anise to develop the drug oseltamivir, which is prescribed to treat (but not to prevent) the influenza virus.

On-going research is looking at anethole, an essential oil found in star anise, for its anti-inflammatory properties. An experiment conducted with animals showed anethole compounds as effective as the powerful anti-inflammatory drug indomethacin. Anethole is also an antioxidant and has been demonstrated to kill fungus. (Safety note: Star anise should not be fed to infants.) ❞

Param Dedhia, MD

CUMIN AND GOATS' CHEESE STICKS

Nutty, toasty cumin paired with earthy, calcium-rich goats' cheese make these crumbly sticks not only delicious but also good for your bones: the active compound in cumin is rich in phytoestrogens that helps stave off bone loss.

MAKES ABOUT 12 (1.5–2CM/½–¾IN. WIDE) STICKS

100g (3½oz./generous ¾ cup) plain (all-purpose) flour	½ tsp dried thyme leaves
55g (2oz./½ stick) unsalted butter, softened	1 tbsp fresh thyme leaves, plus extra to garnish
140g (5oz.) goats' cheese, cold	1 egg white, beaten, to glaze
½ tsp toasted ground cumin	1 tsp cumin seeds
pinch sea salt	sea salt and freshly ground black pepper, for sprinkling on top

Preheat the oven to 190°C (375°F/gas mark 5). Pulse the flour, butter, goats' cheese, ground cumin, fresh and dried thyme and a pinch of salt in a food processor until the mixture appears crumbly.

Turn out onto a lightly floured board or marble and press into a dough. Roll out a square or rectangle about 5mm (¼in.) thick on cling film (plastic wrap). Slice into thin strips approximately 1.5cm (½in.) wide and cover with cling film (plastic wrap). Chill in the fridge until firm.

Place the sticks on ungreased parchment paper or a silicone-lined baking tray and brush lightly with egg-white wash. Scatter with the cumin seeds, salt and pepper and bake for about 15 minutes, until golden brown.

COURGETTE AND RED PEPPER PARCELS

A simple light starter or tray pass/hors d'oeuvre to celebrate the humble and prolific courgette (zucchini) and luscious buratta mozzarella, seasoned with thyme, peppercorn and citrus zest: a winning combination of flavour and colour. Add a drizzle of your favorite olive oil or fresh thyme oil (see page 194).

SERVES 4

1 red (bell) pepper (about 140g/5oz.)	15g (½oz.) preserved lemon or peel of ¼ lemon, shredded into thin strips
4 courgettes (zucchini), (about 165g/5¾oz. each)	extra virgin olive oil, to drizzle
2 tsp thyme oil, for brushing (see page 194)	12 small thyme sprigs
250g (9oz.) fresh buratta or buffalo mozzarella	a few grinds freshly ground black pepper
2 tbsp capers	

Roast the (bell) pepper over a gas flame or on a barbecue, or place under a hot grill (broiler) on the top shelf of the oven, until blackened. Put in small bowl, cover tightly with cling film (plastic wrap) and leave for about 20 minutes, then peel away the skin. Slice in half, discard core and seeds and cut into 12 wide strips. Set aside. Thinly slice the courgettes (zucchini) lengthways into 5mm (¼in.) thick strips, 24 in total. Brush with a little thyme oil then grill in a pan or on the barbecue for 1–2 minutes on each side until soft and supple. Set aside on a plate. Slice the mozzarella into 12 equal portions. Place two courgette (zucchini) slices lengthways on a plate, just overlapping one another. Lay a slice of mozzarella a third of the way up then place a pepper strip on top. Roll the remaining short end of the courgette (zucchini) over both, then fold the longer end over the top and tuck under. Place three parcels on each plate and sprinkle with capers and preserved lemon peel. Drizzle with olive oil, scatter over the thyme sprigs and add a few grinds of black pepper on top.

STAR ANISE, GARLIC, WASABI

THAT '70s MANDARIN CHICKEN SALAD

This dish was all the rage in California at the time I was dancing with the Koniklijk Ballet van Vlaanderen in Belgium and I made it for a dinner party and invited a few of my Flemish ballet colleagues. Much to my embarrassment, a husband and wife from what was then Yugoslavia tasted this New World dish and refused to take another bite. I was firmly told that one does not mix fruit and meat! Clearly they had not sampled dishes from their medieval ancestors, who mixed fruit, meat and spices in many a recipe. All the more for us then! Star anise has been used in Chinese medicine for centuries to combat a host of complaints and is also the secret spice used to combat the avian flu – how extraordinary!

SERVES 4 AS A MAIN OR 6 AS A STARTER

2 chicken breasts, with skin, bone in

10g (¼oz.) peeled fresh ginger, cut into 4 pieces

1 star anise

2 kaffir lime leaves (optional)

½ tsp black peppercorns

3 spring onions (scallions), green and white parts separated

approx. 500ml (2 cups) vegetable or chicken stock or water

100g (3½oz.) cellophane noodles

oil for flash frying

400g (14oz.) Chinese cabbage, shredded

150g (5½oz.) kale, shredded

175g (6oz.) sugar snap peas or 115g (4oz.) edamame beans

2 or 3 Mandarin oranges (350g/12oz.), peeled and segmented

85g (3oz./¾ cup) cashew nuts, toasted and roughly chopped

For the Five-spice Sesame Dressing:

90ml (6 tbsp) kecap manis (thick sweet soy sauce)

60ml (¼ cup) lime juice

3 tbsp freshly grated ginger

2 tbsp sesame seeds

2 tbsp grapeseed oil

2 tbsp black or clear rice wine vinegar

1 tbsp wasabi powder

1 tbsp five-spice powder

1 tbsp sesame oil

1 tbsp minced garlic

1 tbsp soy sauce

¾ tsp chili paste

Add the chicken breasts to a large deep sauté pan. Add the ginger, star anise, kaffir lime leaf, peppercorns and the green tops of the spring onions (scallions). Slice the white part of the onions on the diagonal, measure out 55g (2oz./½ cup) and set aside. Cover the chicken with the stock or water and bring to a gentle simmer. Poach until tender and cooked to the bone, about 20 minutes. Turn off the heat and set aside until cool enough to debone. Discard the bones, skin and liquid. Cover the chicken meat and cool, then break up into bite-sized pieces and chill until ready to use.

While the chicken is cooking, whisk together the dressing ingredients, cover and chill until ready to use.

Pour oil into a wok or deep pan to a depth of 3cm (1¼in.) and heat to 180°C (360°F). Flash fry the noodles in four batches and drain on kitchen paper.

Put the Chinese cabbage, kale, sugar snap peas, mandarin orange segments, chopped cashew nuts, reserved spring onion (scallion) and chicken into a large bowl, pour over the dressing and lightly toss. Gently add the noodles and serve immediately.

★

CLOVE, ALLSPICE, CUMIN, CITRUS ZEST

GARAM MASALA BASTILLA

This rich but vegetarian take on a medieval 'greyte pye' includes an unorthodox garam masala that is really more like a medieval spice blend. In this modern version, vegetables, dried fruit and pulses replace the traditional game or fowl, enabling these once exotic and sought-after fragrant spices to be savoured in a new way.

SERVES 4

2 or 3 small sweet potatoes, peeled and thinly sliced

400g (14oz.) can white cannellini beans or chickpeas, rinsed and drained well

70g (2½oz./½ cup) sultanas (golden raisins)

2 pieces preserved lemon peel, shredded (see page 20) or zest of ½ lemon

100g (3½oz./¾ stick + 1 tbsp) butter

about 5 tsp Garam Masala Spice Blend (see below)

6 filo (phyllo) pastry sheets, opened out flat, covered with a damp cloth

½ quantity Turmeric Melted Onions (see page 146)

200g (7oz.) baby spinach, rinsed and patted dry

3 large eggs

100g (3½oz.) punnet ricotta (or farmer's cheese or cottage cheese)

13 cherry tomatoes, with stalks

Preheat the oven to 190°C (375°F/gas mark 5). Lightly oil a 30 x 15cm (12 x 6in.) baking dish.

Blanch the sweet potato slices in boiling salted water until al dente, about 2 minutes. Drain well and set aside.

Mix the beans, sultanas (golden raisins) and lemon peel or zest together in a bowl and set aside.

Melt the butter with 2 teaspoons of the spice mix. Brush two filo (phyllo) pastry sheets with this spiced butter, fold them in half and lay them side by side in the bottom of the baking dish so that they just overlap in the centre and the edges hang over the sides of the dish.

Layer the potato slices over the bottom of the dish, then add an evenly spread layer of the Turmeric Melted Onions and sprinkle over ½ teaspoon of spice blend. Next add an even layer of the bean and sultana (golden raisin) mix then sprinkle with a further ½ teaspoon of the spice blend. Cover with the spinach.

Beat the eggs with 1 teaspoon of spice mix. Pour over the spinach and gently shake the pan to settle. Spoon dollops of ricotta on top. Fold the edges of the filo (phyllo) just inside the edges of the dish.

Brush spice butter on the remaining filo (phyllo) sheets, fold in half, then cut into a grid of eight rectangles. Scrunch the filo rectangles into kerchiefs and arrange over the top. Pierce each tomato then tuck randomly on top, scattering a big pinch of spice blend over all. Sprinkle salt flakes on top if you like.

Bake in the oven for 30 minutes, until filo (phyllo) is browned and vegetables bubbling. Serve hot or at room temperature with a nice flagon of wine or ale!

GARAM MASALA SPICE BLEND

2 tbsp cardamom seeds, toasted and ground

4 tsp coriander seeds, toasted and ground

4 tsp ground cinnamon (or 1½ cinnamon sticks, charred and ground)

1 tbsp fennel seeds, toasted and ground

1 tbsp ground nutmeg

2 tsp ground allspice

2 tsp cumin seeds, toasted and ground

2 tsp chili powder

1 tsp ground cloves

1 tsp licorice powder (optional)

½ tsp fenugreek powder

Blend the spices in a mortar and pestle and transfer to a jar.

DIVER SCALLOPS
WITH SWEET POTATO PURÉE AND PRESERVED CITRUS PEEL
Suzanne Goin

'In the Southern California winter, citrus comes on strong and stays for the long haul, so I am constantly challenged to come up with new ways to use the whole fruit. We use a lot of citrus peel, often candied, in desserts, so I thought it would be interesting to incorporate it into a savoury dish.' SG

SERVES 6 AS A MAIN COURSE

1.3kg (3lb.) Jewel or Garnet sweet potatoes
25g (1oz.) tamarind block
1 lemon, plus 1 tbsp finely grated lemon zest
1 lime
1 orange
½ grapefruit
½ cinnamon stick, or ½ tsp ground cinnamon
½ tsp curry powder
1 chili de árbol or Thai chili (small red dried chili), crumbled
¼ tsp ground cardamom

2.5 x 2.5cm (1 x 1in.) piece fresh ginger, peeled and thinly sliced
3 tbsp honey
85g (3oz./¾ stick) unsalted butter, cut into small cubes
2 tbsp whole milk, plus more as needed
18 Maine diver scallops, about 55g (2oz.) each
1 tbsp thyme leaves
3 tbsp extra-virgin olive oil
Kosher salt and freshly ground black pepper
12 dandelion or baby rocket (arugula) leaves to garnish

Preheat the oven to 200°C (400°F/gas mark 6). Prick the sweet potatoes all over with a fork, place on a baking tray and bake for about 1–1 ½ hours (depending on their size) until tender when poked with a paring knife.

Using your hands, break the tamarind apart into small pieces and place it in a small bowl. Pour 120ml (½ cup) of boiling water over the tamarind and let it sit for 5 minutes. Stir the tamarind vigorously with a small whisk or spoon to loosen all the pulp and emulsify it with the water.

Using a vegetable peeler, peel strips of zest about 2.5cm (1in.) wide from all the citrus fruits. (Use a light hand to avoid the bitter white pith.) Place the zest strips in a small pan, cover with cold water and bring to the boil. Boil for 1 minute, drain and rinse with cool water. Repeat the process twice more.

Juice all the citrus fruits (you should have about 240ml/1 cup) and put the juice and the blanched zest in a non-reactive (earthenware, glass or stainless-steel) pan that is small enough for all the zest to be submerged. Add the cinnamon, curry powder, chili, cardamom, ginger, honey and ½ teaspoon of salt. Strain 2 tablespoons of 'tamarind water' from the bowl of soaking tamarind and add it to the pan. Bring the mixture to the boil, turn down the heat to medium–low and simmer for 12–15 minutes until the sauce thickens and looks glossy. Set aside.

When the sweet potatoes cool enough to handle, cut them in half. Cut away any burnt pieces and scoop the hot sweet-potato flesh into the bowl of a food processor fitted with a metal blade. Add the butter, 1 teaspoon of salt and a few grinds of pepper and purée to a smooth consistency. With the blade spinning, add in 2 tablespoons of milk (plus a little more if needed for the potatoes to move fluidly around the bowl). Season to taste.

Season the scallops with the lemon zest, thyme, salt and pepper. Heat a large sauté pan over high heat for 2 minutes. Swirl in 3 tablespoons of olive oil and carefully lay the scallops in the pan. (You may need to cook them in batches or in two pans.) It will smoke, but resist the temptation to move the scallops. Cook for about 3 minutes until browned, then turn them over and turn off the heat. The scallops should be a nice medium–rare.

To serve, spoon the hot sweet-potato purée onto the centre of six dinner plates and place two dandelion or baby rocket (arugula) leaves, overlapping the stems, on each plate. Arrange the scallops on top of the purée. Spoon some of the warm preserved citrus peel and some of the juices over the scallops and around the plate.

★

CALIFORNIA GIRL PRAWN CURRY
WITH SAMBALS

Growing up on the 'So Cal' coast, it was normal for us to have enchiladas, sukiyaki or 'authentically British' fish and chips for dinner, but a curry? Sally-Mom would make a curry from scratch – including all the sambals – when we had company. The scent of a curry cooking was mysterious but alluring to us kids and we knew those little dishes – 'sambals' – of coconut, toasted chopped peanuts, diced bananas, cashew nuts, olives, pineapple, golden raisins, jars of Major Grey's, with 'Sunday-best' spoons placed carefully aside, would soon appear on the table. What a treat! We would pile plates high with rice, a little curry, mild chutney and lots of our favourite sambals.

SERVES 6

90ml (6 tbsp) peanut oil	**For the So Cal garam masala:**
1 large onion, chopped	1½ tsp cumin seeds
1 large garlic clove, minced	2 whole cloves
1 tsp finely freshly grated ginger	½ tsp black peppercorns
175ml (¾ cup) shellfish or vegetable stock	½ tsp black cardamom pods
375ml (1⅔ cups) coconut milk	½ tsp green cardamom pods
1.3kg (3lb.) prawns (shrimp), peeled, cleaned and deveined	2 tbsp coriander seeds
1 tsp lemon juice, or to taste	½ cinnamon stick
handful (about 25g/1oz.) roughly chopped coriander (cilantro)	¼ tsp ground chipotle powder – a So Cal addition!
	1 tsp ground turmeric

To serve:

Sambals should include salty, sweet, sour and savoury flavours. Choose 8–12 of the following and serve, finely chopped, in an array of small bowls: salted roasted peanuts, spring onions (scallions), hard-boiled eggs, raisins and/or sultanas (golden raisins), dried apricots, sugared crystallized ginger, shredded coconut, kumquats (or small Valencia oranges seeded, finely chopped, with skins), black and/or green olives, spicy lemon pickle or zested lemon rind, watermelon pickle, radishes, fresh pineapple, apple, banana, flaked (shredded) almonds, salted walnuts, pears, cashew nuts, crystallized violets, etc.

Chutneys: Major Grey's, lime-garlic, mango-ginger or other Indian relishes and chutneys.

First make the garam masala. Turmeric adds that grand yellow curry colour, while coriander (cilantro) adds the real curry flavour. Toasting the spices adds intensity to their flavour. Toast the spices, stirring often, until they turn a few shades darker and give off a sweet, smoky aroma. Do not raise the heat to quicken the process, or the spices will brown too quickly or burn. Toast the cumin and cloves in a dry heavy frying pan (skillet) over a medium heat, remove to a small bowl then toast the coriander seeds, cardamoms, peppercorns and cinnamon stick. Once the spices are cool, transfer them to a mortar and pestle (or spice mill or coffee grinder) and grind to a powder. Stir in the chipotle powder and ground turmeric.

Heat the oil in a large pan, then add the onion and cook over medium heat until translucent and lightly browned. Add the garlic and ginger and cook for a few more minutes.

Add the spice blend and stir gently for a minutes over medium–low heat until you can smell the spices cooking. Add 60ml (¼ cup) of water, the stock and 175ml (¾ cup) of the coconut milk. Cover and simmer for 20 minutes, stirring occasionally.

Remove the lid, turn the heat to low and add the remaining 200ml (scant 1 cup) of coconut milk. Bring to a simmer, add the prawns (shrimp) and cook for 4 or 5 minutes. Stir in the lemon juice, chopped coriander (cilantro) and salt and black pepper to taste.

Mound a ladleful of the curry on steamy seasoned rice, sprinkle on the sambals, spoon on your favourite chutney and enjoy!

TURMERIC, CUMIN, CLOVE, GARLIC

CREAMY CHICKEN TIKKA
(HALDI ZAFRAN AUR ELIACHIWALI MURG TIKKA)
Cyrus Todiwala

'The word "tikka" originates in Persia and has been adopted globally, but seldom do people know its meaning, often assuming it refers to a sauce. In fact, the word simply means "cube"! This tikka, which is surprisingly creamy and mild, is spiced with saffron, cardamom and turmeric, enhanced with puréed nuts, yogurt and cream and served with a simple, yet very delicious Pulao Rice and a sauce created with the leftover marinade.' CT

SERVES 4

800g–1kg (1lb. 12oz.–2lb. 4oz.) boneless chicken leg or breast, cut into 2.5cm (1in.) cubes

For the marinade:

2 tsp ground turmeric

juice of 1 lime

2 tsp sea salt

1 handful raw cashew nuts

1 handful skinned unroasted almonds

handsome pinch saffron threads (I favour Iranian saffron)

1 level tsp ground green cardamom

1 level tsp ground mace

2 fresh slender green chilies, chopped

4 garlic cloves, chopped

7.5cm (3in) piece fresh ginger, peeled and chopped

200g (7oz./¾ cup) Greek-style yogurt

50ml (scant ¼ cup) extra virgin rapeseed oil (or other vegetable oil but not olive oil)

100ml (scant ½ cup) single (light) cream

salt to taste

For the sauce:

1 heaped tbsp butter

7.5cm (3in) piece cinnamon stick, broken into 2 or 3

2 medium onions

reserved marinade (see method)

1 x 450ml (15floz.) can coconut milk

1 tbsp chopped coriander (cilantro), optional

To serve:

Pulao Rice (see opposite)

thinly sliced pink shallots, chopped fresh mint and coriander (cilantro), dash of lime juice and salt, to serve (optional)

Blend the turmeric, sea salt and lime juice in a large bowl. Add the chicken pieces and turn to coat well, using a rubber spatula to avoid staining your hands. Transfer to a lidded container and refrigerate for at least 2 hours while you prepare the rest of the marinade.

Put the cashews and almonds in a bowl and pour over boiling hot water until the nuts are submerged. Cover and set aside for a couple of hours to allow the nuts to soften. (If you don't soak them well they don't purée well.)

Preheat the oven to 130°C (275°F/gas mark 1). Put the saffron threads into a small ovenproof bowl and put into the oven, then turn off the heat and leave for 10–15 minutes until just crisp. Crumble the threads gently between your finger and thumb then add a tablespoon or so of warm water, cover the bowl and set aside for the saffron to infuse.

Drain the cashew nuts and almonds, put in a blender and pulse to crush them as finely as you can. Add the saffron, cardamom, mace, chili, garlic, ginger, yogurt, rapeseed (or vegetable) oil and cream and purée. Pulse for a few seconds then scrape down the sides and check. You want a smooth texture but, but if you keep the blender running continuously, the contents will get hot and the cream may separate, so do take care.

Add this marinade to the partially marinated chicken and stir to mix well. Taste the marinade and add more seasoning if needed. Place in an airtight container and refrigerate for a few hours before using.

Scrape off and reserve the excess marinade before roasting, grilling (broiling) or barbecuing the chicken.

To roast the chicken, preheat the oven to 220°C (425°F/gas mark 7). Lay the chicken pieces on a silicone sheet on a baking tray and place on the top shelf of the oven. Cook for 8–10 minutes, turning the pieces halfway through cooking.

Alternatively, cook them under the grill (broiler) in your oven. Place them on the wire rack and place under the grill (broiler) and turn every 2–3 minutes until the chicken is cooked through and is nicely coloured all over.

If you want to barbecue the chicken, don't place the pieces directly onto the grill as the tikka will stick to it. Instead, skewer the pieces and hold them just above the flames: they will cook and colour perfectly.

To make the sauce: heat the butter with the cinnamon stick in a medium pan over a low heat for about 2 minutes, then add the onions and sauté gently until the onions are soft and pale.

Add the leftover marinade and increase the heat slightly. If it starts to stick to the bottom of the pan, loosen the sauce with some water and continue cooking until the fat separates. Add the coconut milk, bring to the boil, reduce the heat and simmer for 2–3 minutes. Turn off the heat and remove and reserve the cinnamon sticks.

Purée the sauce using either a stick blender or a blender (cool the sauce slightly first if using the latter), starting off on a low speed to ensure it doesn't spill out. Return the sauce to the pan, add the reserved cinnamon sticks and bring to the boil. Check the seasoning and add a tablespoonful of fresh chopped coriander (cilantro) if wished.

Serve the chicken tikka with the sauce, Pulao Rice and – if you really want to impress – a salad made from thinly sliced pink shallots and fresh mint and coriander mixed in with a dash of lime juice and salt.

PULAO RICE

'We Indians say pulao or palav but you may know this rice dish as pilaf or pilav. If you already have a favourite recipe, feel free to use it, but make sure you include some sultanas (golden raisins) and/or dried cranberries and some chopped cashew nuts and almonds. My version is a simple one that seldom fails.' CT

SERVES 4–6

1 tbsp butter	2 or 3 cloves
1 tbsp rapeseed oil	2 or 3 black peppercorns
50g (1¾oz.) whole raw almonds, skin on, cut into 5 or 6 pieces	1 tsp cumin seeds
	2 or 3 green cardamom pods, flattened to open
100g (3½oz.) barberries (available in some supermarkets, specialty shops or online), or 150g (5½oz.) dried cranberries, chopped	1 medium onion, halved and thinly sliced
	1 litre (4¼ cups) clear stock or water
	500g (1lb. 2oz./2⅓ cups) basmati rice

Preheat the oven to 130°C (275°F/gas mark 1).

In a wide casserole that will fit into centre of your oven with its lid on, heat the butter and oil over a low heat. Add the chopped almonds and barberries or cranberries and fry until the almonds have coloured slightly. Remove using a slotted spoon.

Add the whole spices to the fat (adding more and reheating if necessary) and cook for a few seconds until the cloves have begun to swell and the cumin to colour. Add the sliced onion and sauté until soft and pale. Add the stock or water and season with salt to taste. Bring to the boil, then add the rice and stir well.

Cover the casserole but check it regularly to ensure the rice doesn't stick to the bottom. (The best way to prevent this is to stir it from the bottom up so that you keep the heated rice at the top.) Simmer until the water is nearly absorbed, then clean down the sides, cover the casserole and place it in the oven.

After 10 minutes, turn off the oven. Leave the casserole in the oven for a further 30 minutes then remove it and loosen the rice gently. Stir in the almonds and cranberries or barberries.

If necessary, you can heat the rice up before serving it: put it in a glass bowl in the microwave and reheat on full power for 3–4 minutes until the rice is very hot.

Illustrated on pages 34–5

CUMIN, TURMERIC, GARLIC

SLOW-ROASTED LAMB SHOULDER
WITH QUINCE, CUMIN AND CORIANDER

The aromas from the slow-roasting cumin, quince and onions create a wordless way to introduce your family to the secrets of combining spices to create a mouth-watering main! The fat and spices melt down into the onion-carrot bed, which can be served alongside the meat. This is also great with farro or couscous and seasonal wilted greens.

SERVES 4

3 large onions (350g/12oz.), unpeeled, sliced into rounds

3 large carrots (225g/8oz.), peeled and cut into 5cm (2in.) rounds

3kg (6lb.10oz.) lamb shoulder, bone in, lightly trimmed of fat

2 tbsp coriander seeds

2 tbsp cumin seeds

2 tbsp black peppercorns

1 tsp cardamom seeds

3 bay leaves, torn

1 tsp ground turmeric

6 garlic cloves

2 tbsp salt flakes

2 tbsp olive oil

8 thyme sprigs

3 quince (or tart, firm apples), peeled, cored and cut into sixths

3 tbsp brown sugar

3 tbsp rice wine vinegar

cooked farro or couscous, to serve (optional)

seasonal wilted greens, to serve (optional)

Preheat the oven to 160°C (325°F/gas mark 3). Scatter the onion and carrot rounds on the bottom of an oiled roasting pan. Trim and lightly score the fat on the lamb shoulder and place on top of the bed of vegetables.

Dry-toast the coriander, cumin, peppercorns and cardamom in a frying pan until the aromas are released, then crush with a mortar and pestle. Add the bay leaves, turmeric, garlic, salt and oil to the mortar and crush to a paste. Massage this paste all over the lamb. Scatter with thyme sprigs and tuck quince pieces around the meat.

Sprinkle the sugar and vinegar over the top, then pour 100ml (scant ½ cup) of water into the side of the roasting pan. Tightly cover the roasting pan with thick foil and slow-roast for 4 hours.

Raise the oven temperature to 180°C (350°F/gas mark 4). Remove the foil, skim off the fat and add more water if needed. Baste the lamb then return it, uncovered, to the oven. Cook for a further 35 minutes or until fork tender.

PORK CHILE VERDE

Anne Conness

'I can't speak for the scientific connection between spice and health, but what I do know is that eating spicy things makes me feel happy and satisfied. And when I feel happy, I feel less stressed, and that makes my doctor happy!' AC

SERVES 4

1 tbsp cumin seeds	1 head garlic, cloves separated and peeled
1 tsp black peppercorns	60ml (¼ cup) canola oil
½ tsp cloves	2 tbsp lime juice
½ tsp ground cinnamon	1½ bunches coriander (cilantro)
½ tsp cayenne pepper	2 tsp cumin
2 tsp paprika	½ tsp cloves
2 tbsp salt	¼ tsp cayenne pepper
1.6kg (3.5lb.) pork shoulder, cut into 2cm (¾in.) cubes, most of fat removed	2 tsp paprika
	¼ tsp cinnamon
1.2 litres (5 cups) chicken stock	1 tsp salt
For the corn:	350ml (1½ cups) reserved cooking jus (see method)
3 ears of corn	**To serve:**
2 tbsp butter	1 tbsp sauce from chilies in adobo or chipotle paste mixed with 115g (4oz./½ cup) sour cream
30g (1oz./¼ cup) grated Monterey Jack or mild Cheddar cheese	
For the sauce:	1 dash Tajin (a classic Mexican dry seasoning of dried lime juice, chili powder and salt)
1 tomatillo, halved and stem removed	
1 onion, roughly chopped	4 lime wedges
2 jalapeños, halved and stems removed	150g (5½oz./1 cup) pico de gallo (Mexican fresh tomato salsa)
2 Anaheim chilies, halved and stems removed	small handful micro-coriander (cilantro) leaves

Preheat the oven to 180°C (350°F/gas mark 4).

Toast the whole spices, cool, then grind to a powder. Stir in the cinnamon, cayenne pepper, paprika and salt.

Toss the pork in the spice mixture and put in a roasting pan. Pour over the chicken stock, cover tightly with foil, put in the oven and cook until tender, about 1½ hours.

Strain the jus, skimming off the fat, and reserve 350ml (1½ cups) for the sauce. Break up the meat if necessary.

Char the sweetcorn: shuck the corn and remove the silks. Place the corn cobs on a baking tray on the top shelf of the oven or under the grill (broiler) on a high heat until charred. Leave to cool then place the corn cob in a cereal bowl and, using a sharp knife, cut the kernels from the cob in a downward motion; the kernels will collect in the bowl. Set aside.

For the sauce, toss the tomatillo, onion, jalapeños and Anaheim chilies and garlic in a bowl with the oil. Spread out on two baking trays and roast until caramelized, about 30 minutes at a medium–high heat. Leave to cool.

Blend the caramelized veggies in batches with the lime juice, coriander (cilantro), spices and strained cooking jus. Check the flavour and season to taste.

Put the pork in a pan with this sauce and heat up.

Melt the butter in a hot ovenproof pan then add the charred corn. Season with salt and pepper. Sprinkle cheese on top and put in the oven just long enough to melt the cheese.

To serve, put the pork on a plate and top with the corn. Garnish with the chipotle cream, a sprinkle of Tajin, a lime wedge and some pico de gallo. Finish with the coriander (cilantro).

CLOVE, STAR ANISE, ALLSPICE

SPICED PICKLED PLUMS

Served with a traditional Sunday supper of roast meats, these spiced pickled plums, full of the sweet comforting spices of autumn and winter, are readily transformed into a chutney for cheese and charcuterie (see recipe below).

MAKES 1KG (2LB. 4OZ.)

750ml (3¼ cups) apple cider vinegar	2 star anise
5g (⅛oz.) blade mace	10g (1½ tsp) orange zest
5 allspice berries	¾ tsp sea salt
2 tsp yellow mustard seeds	200g (7oz./1 cup) brown sugar
5 whole cloves	700g (1lb. 9oz.) pitted plums, quartered
1 cinnamon stick, charred	

Clean and sterilize one 1-litre (1-quart) or two ½-litre (½-quart) canning jars.

Put all the ingredients except the plums in a 1-litre (1-quart) pan and bring to a simmer for 3 minutes.

Put the plums in the sterilized jars then pour the liquid and spices over. Seal tightly with lids and set on the work surface until at room temperature. (You will hear the lids compress and create a vacuum.)

Store in a cool dark place for 2 weeks before using. The pickle will keep for up to a year unopened. Store opened jars in the fridge. Once opened, it will keep, chilled, for 6 months.

CLOVE, STAR ANISE, ALLSPICE

PICKLED PLUM AND SHALLOT CHUTNEY

A nice accompaniment for a cheese board, as pictured here, this chutney also makes a simple but tasty addition to a selection of cured meats and is delicious spread in a ploughman's ham and cheese sandwich.

MAKES 350G (12OZ./1 HEAPED CUP)

150g (5½oz.) shallots, unpeeled	1 tbsp vinegar from jar of Spiced Pickled Plums
2 tbsp extra virgin olive oil	1 tbsp honey
5 thyme sprigs	1 tbsp Vanilla Honey Mustard (see page 164)
2 tbsp port	1 tsp freshly grated ginger
30g (1oz.) sultanas (golden raisins)	1 sprig fresh thyme
200g (7oz.) Spiced Pickled Plums (see above), chopped into bite-sized pieces	

Preheat the oven to 180°C (350°F/gas mark 4). Trim the shallot root ends, leaving the papery skin attached.

Place in a small foil-lined baking tin and drizzle with olive oil. Top with thyme sprigs and roast in the oven for about 30–35 minutes, or until soft when pierced with the tip of a knife and golden brown.

When cooled, peel, discard the skins and slice the shallots lengthways into sixths.

Warm the port, add the sultanas (golden raisins) and leave to soak for about 10 minutes. Mix in the shallots and remaining ingredients and combine well.

Serve with your favourite cheeses and biscuits. The chutney will keep for 1 month chilled.

ALLSPICE, CITRUS ZEST

FLOATING SPICE ISLANDS
WITH LIME, RASPBERRY AND COCONUT JAM

A tropical-island tribute to the French classic, île flottante, a light, humble farmhouse dessert. Here, the 'islands' are baked in moulds then floated in a passion fruit-orange-pineapple (POP) 'sea' finished with citrus and nutmeg.

SERVES 4–6

For the lime, raspberry and coconut jam:
240ml (1 cup) coconut cream
1 vanilla pod (bean), split in half and cut into 4 pieces
4 large egg yolks
1 tbsp cornflour (cornstarch)
100g (3½oz./½ cup) palm sugar, or raw or white sugar
100g (3½oz.) frozen raspberries
6 whole allspice berries, toasted and cracked
zest and juice of 1 lime

For the POP crème anglaise:
175g (¾ cup) passion-fruit pulp seeded (about 8 passion fruit)
120ml (½ cup) orange juice
zest of 1 orange
100g (3½oz.) fresh or frozen pineapple chunks

1 tsp freshly grated ginger
100g (3½oz./½ cup) caster (superfine) or coconut sugar
4 large egg yolks
475ml (2 cups) full-fat (whole) milk

For the meringue:
1 tsp coconut oil or butter, for greasing molds
4 large egg whites, at room temperature
⅛ tsp cream of tartar
150g (5½oz./¾ cup) caster (superfine) sugar
1 tsp vanilla extract

To garnish:
2 kaffir lime leaves, cut into thin strips
½ tsp freeze-dried raspberry dust (optional)
large pinch freshly grated nutmeg

To make the lime, raspberry and coconut jam, in a medium pan, whisk the coconut cream, four pieces of the vanilla pod (bean), the egg yolks, cornflour (cornstarch) and sugar with a pinch of salt. Add the raspberries, allspice and lime zest and juice and cook over medium heat, scraping down the sides occasionally and gently stirring until the mixture is thick and custard-like, coating the back of a spoon, and has reached 70°C (160°F). Strain through a fine mesh sieve into a bowl set in an ice bath to cool the jam then chill.

To make the POP crème anglaise, in a saucepan over low heat, warm the passion-fruit pulp, orange juice and zest and pineapple chunks with the ginger, remaining four pieces of vanilla and 1 tablespoon of the sugar. Simmer for 10 minutes. Cool briefly, then using a bar or stick blender, purée until smooth. Set aside to cool. In a small bowl, beat the egg yolks with the remaining sugar. In a medium pan, warm the milk over medium heat. When the milk steams, slowly stream in the yolks, whisking until incorporated, then stir with a wooden spoon until the sauce thickens and coats the back of the spoon. Strain into a bowl inside an ice bath and whisk to stop it from cooking further. When cold, fold in the juice purée. Cover and chill until ready to serve.

To make the meringue, preheat the oven to 160°C (325°F/gas mark 3). Very lightly brush 16 dariole moulds or a mini-muffin tin with coconut oil or butter. Set aside. In the bowl of a stand mixer or electric mixer with the whip/whisk attachment, beat the egg whites with the cream of tartar and a large pinch of salt on medium speed until frothy. Increase the speed and add the sugar 1 tablespoon at a time. Add the vanilla and whip until the whites form shiny stiff peaks. Using a piping bag with a star tip, pipe the meringue into each mould until two thirds full. Place in a casserole or cake tin and place in the oven. Pour boiling water into the corner of the pan to come halfway up the moulds. Bake in the oven for 7–10 minutes until set, or until a temperature probe reaches 63–66°C (145–150°F). Remove the moulds from the water bath and unmould onto a parchment-lined baking tray.

To serve, arrange three or four meringues on the bottom of each flat-bottomed bowl. Fill a jug with the POP crème anglaise then carefully pour equally into each bowl. Spoon the jam into quenelles around the meringues and garnish with kaffir lime leaf strips, a sprinkling of raspberry dust (if using) and a grating of nutmeg.

CLOVE, STAR ANISE, CITRUS ZEST

BLACKCURRANT CABERNET CONSOMMÉ
WITH VANILLA MILK CUBES, CLOVE–CARAMEL APPLE AND CHOCOLATE 'NOODLES'

This divine consommé contains not only eugenol-packed clove but also delicious deep-purple blackcurrants,
which are known to contain high levels of anthocyanins for optimum brain health.

SERVES 4–6

For the consommé:
1 star anise
½ tsp peppercorns
500g (1lb. 2oz./5 cups) blackcurrants, fresh or frozen
peel of 1 orange
700ml (3 cups) apple juice or water
250g (9oz./¾ cup) golden or cane syrup
60ml (¼ cup) Cabernet wine
2 tbsp fresh Key or Tahitian lime juice
For the vanilla milk cubes:
2 gold gelatin leaves (see page 86, or 1½ tsp powdered gelatin)
120ml (½ cup) double cream
120ml (½ cup) full-fat milk
2 tbsp golden or cane syrup

½ vanilla pod (bean), split and scraped, or ½ tsp vanilla paste
¾ tsp amaretto
For the clove-caramel apple:
1 crisp red apple
240ml (1 cup) apple juice or water
200g (7oz./1 generous cup) golden or cane syrup
10g (¼oz.) fresh ginger, peeled and cut into 4 pieces
½ tsp ground cloves
For the chocolate 'noodles':
1½ tsp agar agar powder (or 3 tbsp agar agar flakes)
85g (3oz.) dark chocolate (72% cocoa solids), chopped
1 tbsp cognac
To serve:
about 2 tbsp toasted sliced almonds

To make the consommé, toast the star anise and peppercorns and rough grind using a mortar and pestle. Put into a 2-litre (2-quart) pan with the blackcurrants, orange peel, apple juice, syrup and a pinch of salt and bring to a low simmer. Cook for 5 minutes then take off the heat, whisk in the wine and lime juice and infuse for 20 minutes.

Using a stick or bar blender, purée the liquid then strain and discard the pulp and spices. Strain again using a fine mesh strainer or cheesecloth. Chill the consommé until ready to serve.

To make the vanilla milk cubes, line a small rectangular plastic container with cling film (plastic wrap).

Put the gelatin leaves in a bowl, cover with cold water and leave to soften. (If using powdered gelatin, see page 86.) In a small jug, whisk together the cream, milk, syrup, vanilla, amaretto and a pinch of salt until smooth.

Squeeze out the water from the gelatin leaves then add the gelatin to a small pan and warm to melt. Whisk immediately into the cream mixture until dissolved, then pour into the prepared container. Place on a flat surface in the fridge until set, about 30 minutes, then cut into cubes.

To make the clove-caramel apple, slice the apple horizontally wafer thin using a mandoline or sharp knife. Pour the apple juice or water into a small pan, add the syrup, ginger and cloves and bring to a simmer. Add the apple slices and simmer gently until they are almost translucent. Cool, then chill and cover until needed.

Remove the ginger pieces, then simmer and reduce the cooking liquid until it is of a caramel consistency.

To make the chocolate 'noodles', dissolve the agar agar in 175ml (¾ cup) of water and bring to a simmer. Turn down the heat and add the chocolate and cognac, stirring to blend smooth. Pour into a plastic squeezy bottle with a small tip opening. Secure the top. Let the liquid chocolate thicken to a soft custard-like consistency.

Prepare an ice-water bath in a rectangular container. Gently squeeze the chocolate from the bottle to create squiggles over the ice bath, a bit at a time. Gently scoop the 'noodles' out of the bath using your hands and drain on baking paper. Repeat until you have four small piles of noodles.

To serve, divide the vanilla milk cubes amongst flat-bottomed bowls. Carefully ladle the consommé around them. Garnish with the apples, chocolate noodles, a drizzle of clove caramel and some toasted sliced almonds.

SWISS BERRY QUILT CAKE
WITH CARAMELIZED PEACH COULIS AND LEMON VERBENA SABAYON

Always a popular light dessert during long Indian Summer days – a reminder of autumn, but not yet – this is a low-gluten and, excluding the sabayon, dairy-free dessert.

SERVES 8–10

140g (5oz./1¼ cups) plain (all purpose) flour, sifted

¼ tsp ground cloves

280g (10oz./1½ packed cups) soft light brown sugar

14 large egg whites, at room temperature

1½ tsp cream of tartar

2 tsp orange zest

For the Swiss Berry Coulis:

450g (1lb.) blackberries

500g (1lb. 2oz.) raspberries

200g (7oz./1 cup) caster (superfine) sugar

2 allspice berries, toasted and ground

2 cloves, toasted and ground

1 tsp fresh lemon juice

To serve:

Lemon Verbena Sabayon (see opposite)

Caramelized Peach Coulis (see opposite)

fresh berries

edible flowers and/or lemon verbena or mint leaves

Preheat the oven to 180°C (350°F/gas mark 4). In a bowl, combine the flour with the ground cloves and half of the brown sugar. Place a piece of waxed or parchment paper on a flat surface. Sift the flour mixture onto the parchment, then sift again back into the bowl. Repeat then set aside.

In a stand mixer with a whisk attachment on medium speed, or in large bowl using a whisk, beat the egg whites until foamy. Ensure all equipment is clean, dry and grease-free. Sprinkle in the cream of tartar then continue to beat the whites until tripled in volume. Sprinkle the remaining sugar over the whites 1 tablespoon at a time and continue beating until the sugar is incorporated and the whites are thick and glossy. Turn the speed to medium–low and fold in the flour and sugar mixture in three additions. Finally, add the orange zest.

Spoon the cake batter into an unbuttered 25cm (10in.) angel-cake tin with a removable bottom. Run a knife through the batter to break up any air bubbles. Bake for 45 minutes, until golden and the cake springs back when you lightly press the surface. Invert, in its tin, onto a cooling rack and cool completely, at least 1 hour.

While the cake is cooling, make the coulis. Rinse and drain the berries, reserving about a quarter of each. Add the remaining berries to a large pan. Over low heat, add the sugar and spices and bring to a low simmer, stirring the sauce to break down the berries. Use a food mill or sieve to strain out the seeds then stir in the lemon juice. Cover and chill the coulis and reserved berries until needed.

Turn the cake right side up, then run a knife around the sides and centre tube of the tin. Release from the sides, then run a knife around the bottom to release. Slice the cake vertically into 2cm (¾in.) slices. Set aside.

Have a spring-form pan, reserved berries and berry coulis ready. Lightly moisten the pan then line with cling film (plastic wrap), letting the side of the film (plastic) fall over the edges. Sprinkle a third of the reserved berries in the bottom of the pan then add a ladleful of sauce. Press a layer of cake slices onto the bottom, filling in the cracks to make a 'patchwork-quilt' layer. Repeat these layers two or three times, finishing with a little more sauce on top. Tuck the cling film (plastic wrap) over the top then add another layer of film over the top. Weight the cake with a flat plate and a 500g (1lb.) weight or can on top. Chill in the fridge for at least 3 hours or overnight.

Make the Lemon Verbena Sabayon and Caramelized Peach Coulis (see opposite).

To assemble, peel away the cling film (plastic wrap) from the top of the cake tin and cover with a cake plate. Flip over onto the plate then release the sides then the top of the spring-form pan. Peel away the film. Cut the cake in wedges and place on individual plates. Spread a generous spoonful of peach coulis onto each plate then spoon the sabayon over the edge of the cake. Garnish with fresh berries and edible flowers and/or verbena or mint leaves.

LEMON VERBENA SABAYON

This sabayon is made with lemon verbena, but you can use the same technique for infusing cream with all sorts of spices and herbs.

SERVES 8–10

240ml (1 cup) double (heavy) cream

10–12 fresh lemon verbena leaves, roughly chopped

¼ vanilla pod (bean), split, or ¼ tsp paste

3 large yolks, at room temperature

55g (2oz./¼ cup) caster (superfine) sugar

120ml (½ cup) sparkling wine

Put the cream, lemon verbena leaves and vanilla pod (bean) into a pan and heat to a gentle simmer, stirring. Let cool, then cover and infuse for at least 2 hours or overnight.

To finish the sabayon, place the egg yolks in a heatproof bowl set over barely simmering water and whisk well. Slowly add the sugar a little at a time, then gradually add the sparkling wine and vigorously and continuously whisk for about 10 minutes until light yellow and fluffy. Have an ice bath ready. Transfer to the bowl to the ice bath and continue to whisk the mixture until completely cooled. You may set aside the mixture at this point until service, but keep it chilled.

When ready to serve, strain the leaves from the chilled cream, then whip the cream into soft peaks.

Fold the cream into the egg mixture in three stages, gently mixing until combined. You can make this up to 3 hours in advance, covering and chilling until needed.

Serve a generous spoonful over each wedge of quilt cake.

CARAMELIZED PEACH COULIS

SERVES 8–10

450g (1lb.) fresh yellow peaches (or apricots), pitted and quartered

2 tbsp brown sugar

2 tsp freshly grated ginger

¼ tsp ground allspice

1 tbsp grapeseed oil

large pinch salt

¼ tsp ground white pepper

Preheat the oven to 180°C (350°F/gas mark 4). Put the peach quarters in a large bowl, sprinkle in the sugar, ginger and allspice and toss to coat.

Oil a baking tray and arrange the peaches on it, cut side up. Sprinkle with the salt and white pepper. Bake on the middle rack of the oven for 30 minutes, until bubbly and caramelized.

When cool, run through a food mill to purée. Adjust seasonings, cover and chill until needed.

Illustrated on pages 48–9

MANDARIN POPPY-SEED POUND CAKE

Zesty with mandarin, lime, the sweet crunch of poppy seeds and the tang of turmeric, this simple cake is delicious, can be adapted for any occasion and pairs perfectly with a steamy cup of Cardamom Chai Tisane (see page 208). If you can't find mandarin purée (available from specialty food shops), you can make your own by gently simmering and reducing 475ml (2 cups) of tangerine or orange juice by about three quarters to yield approximately 150ml (²⁄₃ cup) of purée. Leave to cool before using.

MAKES ONE BUNDT CAKE OR 12–14 SMALL CAKES

For the cake:

3 tbsp poppy seeds, plus 2 tsp for lining moulds

240g (8½oz./2 cups) plain (all-purpose) flour

2 tbsp cornflour (cornstarch)

½ tsp sea salt

225g (8oz./2 sticks) butter, softened

¾ tsp ground turmeric

200g (7oz./1 cup) castor (superfine) sugar

zest of 3 tangerines (or 2 oranges) and 1 lime

5 large eggs

80ml (⅓ cup) mandarin purée or orange juice concentrate (see recipe introduction)

For the icing:

60ml (¼ cup) mandarin purée

2 tbsp boiling water

250g (9oz./2 cups) icing (confectioner's) sugar

30g (1oz./2 tbsp) butter

pinch salt

Preheat the oven to 160°C (325°F/gas mark 3). Grease a ring cake mould (Bundt pan) or individual dariole moulds and line with the 2 teaspoons of poppy seeds, then place on a baking tray.

Sift the flours with the salt and 3 tablespoons of poppy seeds and set aside.

In the bowl of a stand mixer with a paddle attachment, or in a bowl using a spoon, cream the butter with the turmeric and sugar until light but not over beaten; about 2 minutes. Add the zest, then fold in the eggs one at a time on medium speed until blended, scraping down sides between additions. Add the purée and the flour mixture until just combined. Scrape down the sides and bottom of the bowl to blend well. Do not over mix. Spoon into the prepared cake tin or moulds, smoothing the top, and bake in the oven for 18–20 minutes for the small cakes, or about 50 minutes for the large one, until a knife or toothpick comes out clean.

To make the icing, in a small bowl, add the mandarin purée and water to the sugar. Beat with a whisk until smooth. Beat in the butter with a pinch of salt until combined.

To finish, cool the cake(s) for 10 minutes in the tin, then turn out on to a wire cooling rack. When completely cool, cover to keep from drying out. Glaze with the icing and allow to dry.

TURMERIC, CITRUS ZEST

TROPICAL TURMERIC SMOOTHIE

The combination of fruit and spice and rich-but-healthy coconut or cashew milk is my favourite before a workout or just as a get-to-work beverage! If you prefer, you can use papaya instead of mango and add three leaves of coriander (cilantro). For a thicker smoothie, freeze the coconut milk in cubes before blending.

SERVES 1

85g (3oz.) pineapple	¼ tsp cardamom seeds, toasted and ground
115g (4oz.) fresh frozen mango	1 tbsp fresh lime juice
2.5 x 5cm (1 x 2in.) strip orange peel	240ml (1 cup) coconut milk
5cm (2in.) piece (20g/¾oz.) turmeric root, or ¼ tsp ground turmeric	4–6 ice cubes
⅛ tsp cracked black pepper	1 tsp chia seeds

Put all the ingredients except the chia seeds into a high-speed single-serve blender-juicer and blend until smooth. Sprinkle chia seeds on top and serve.

TURMERIC, CLOVE, STAR ANISE, CITRUS ZEST

SPICED TURMERIC TISANE

This warming drink is spicy, aromatic and does not contain any caffeine or dairy. It is recommended that you add a little fat to any recipe containing turmeric as this helps activate turmeric's health properties. The alliance of peppercorn and turmeric makes for a powerful spice team!

SERVES 2

5cm (2in.) piece fresh turmeric, peeled and cut into 'coins', chopped	5 whole cloves
2.5cm (1in.) piece fresh ginger, peeled and chopped	3 green cardamom pods, crushed to release seeds
1 cinnamon stick, toasted	2 x 2.5cm (1in.) wide strips orange peel
6 black peppercorns	1 tbsp honey, or to taste
1 star anise	240ml (1 cup) coconut milk

Put the turmeric, ginger, cinnamon stick, peppercorns, star anise, cloves, cardamom and orange peel into a pan with 240ml (1 cup) of water and bring to the boil. Reduce the heat and simmer for 3–5 minutes or until fragrant. Turn the heat to low and steep for a further 3–5 minutes.

Remove from the heat and stir in the honey. Strain and discard solids.

Warm and froth the coconut milk, or other milk of your choice, and gently pour it into the tisane. Serve immediately.

Cleansing spice

The body's versatile and clever natural detoxification or cleansing systems have evolved over millennia to adjust to the increasingly hostile sphere we exist upon: Earth. These cleansing spices show promising ability to provide support to our natural detoxification systems, helping to cleanse the body and clear the mind.

Cleansing Spice Health Heroes

Cinnamon ★ Rosemary ★ Oregano ★ Bay Leaf ★ Hibiscus

Air, water and soil are necessary for survival, but many parts of the planet's surfaces and oceans are no longer considered clean; finding a pristine lake or ocean reef not affected by the disruptive human footprint has sadly become the exception. Despite our body's remarkable and sophisticated workings, ill health, disease or symptoms may present themselves at any time for any number of reasons, including ones we don't clearly understand.

Spices in this chapter abound with plentiful antioxidants, the most powerful support to fend off free radicals and aid in flushing out toxins. Rosemary can help focus our short- and long-term memory and aid us with complex brain tasks. Sweet-tasting cinnamon may provide additional support for the liver, pancreas and digestive system by aiding in balancing blood sugar. Very topically, oregano checks in to support the system's PH acid-alkali balance, which is constantly being challenged by the effects of stress, an unhealthy diet and exposures to pollutants. The humble and ancient-storied bay leaf, brimming with nutrients, including vitamin C, is an oxidation reducer and LDL-cholesterol fighter. Last but not least, the pink-party-girl hibiscus is thought to be a formidable foe in the war on cleansing and clearing the digestive system of excess fat and carbohydrates by blocking fat absorption and flushing it out of your system.

Other cleansing spice heroes

Turmeric With an encyclopaedic amount of promising healing capabilities, this extensively studied spice also shows benefit for suppressing fat-cell growth and provides tremendous liver-strengthening support. Research studies suggest that active turmeric compounds can lower LDL-cholesterol levels with their lipid-blocking properties, thereby aiding weight loss by reducing fat tissues overall.

Pomegranate This jewelled fruit aids in flushing out free radicals with its high levels of antioxidant polyphenols, the disease-fighting antioxidants found in plants. All parts of a pomegranate – the fresh or dried seeds, the leathery skin, the pulp, flowers and roots – are full of goodness and packed with a variety of powerful polyphenols ready to be utilized to aid in clearing the system.

Coriander The concentrated free-radical-fighting antioxidant compounds in coriander seeds may help to protect, cleanse and regenerate liver tissue damaged by lifestyle behaviours and a number of diseases, including NAFLD (non-alcoholic fatty liver disease). The cell-protecting antioxidant oils contain large amounts of linalool and geranyl acetate, which play a huge part in clearing the body of unwelcome bacteria and may also be helpful in clearing bladder and urinary tract infections.

Thyme The active oil of thyme, thymol, has a commanding antibacterial presence with its protective and clearing properties in the war on MRSA (methicillin-resistant *Staphylococcus aureus* – most well-known as the hospital skin-eating antibiotic-resistant staph infection) and other resistant bacterial strains. Thyme may also provide hangover relief with its detoxifying talents.

Tamarind It is thought that high-fibre tamarind binds to toxins that include cancer-promoting chemicals that may unknowingly be found in our food, thereby reducing their exposure to the digestive system and lessening the risk of colon cancer. Tamarind fibre also binds to bile salts, which are a component of the liquid secreted from the gallbladder during digestion to process the cholesterol-laden lipids and reduce their re-entry into the body via the colon. This process lowers LDL, 'lousy' cholesterol, which can form plaques in blood vessels.

Sage The polyphenol compounds in sage are packed full of antioxidants that may fend off the loss of natural enzyme acetylcholine, the primary neurotransmitter of the brain, giving it significant potential to help with memory, prevent Alzheimer's disease and increase cognition retention and focus in younger adults.

Cinnamon *The Good Sweet Spice*

Do you ever sprinkle cinnamon on your morning cappuccino? Or add a dash in your afternoon chai? Maybe you should. Not only does cinnamon add a bit of zing, it also gives our taste buds the suggestion of sweetness. On-going studies continue to make the connection between cinnamon and lowering blood sugar, which is of vital concern to those needing to reduce their sugar intake, especially as so many processed foods contain added sugar. How apt that this frequently used, sweet-tasting spice may actually *lower* blood sugar!

Loaded with powerful anti-inflammatory polyphenols, cinnamon is thought to help lower blood pressure and current research studies suggest that it may also help those afflicted with Alzheimer's and Parkinson's diseases. It is also thought to have skin-tightening and wound-healing properties and may boost libido in both men and women.

All parts (flowers, bark and leaves) contain cinnamaldehyde, and Ceylon cinnamon also contains eugenol; its leaves have a scented hint of clove.

During the Middle Ages, fantastical myths were born surrounding the indigenous 'true' cinnamon from Ceylon: devious explorers claimed that birds living on the Nile used cinnamon sticks to build their nests and only the Arab traders had the skills to shoo the birds away. The quest continued to find, acquire and trade this enchanting spice, which changed history as 15th-century explorers, including Christopher Columbus (who did find the other rougher cassia variety of cinnamon in Cuba), desperately searched to find the cinnamon that would make them, too, rich.

Cinnamon is found in an international array of dishes: in North America and Northern Europe, it is primarily added to baked-fruit desserts, cakes, bread, cookies and pastry. In Spain and Mexico, it is added to chocolate dishes, whereas Middle Eastern cinnamon is a common addition to dishes such as meat-based tagines and traditional chicken and brick-pastry *bastilla*. In India, China and Vietnam, it is laced through a multitude of spice mixes and dishes.

Cinnamon of both culinary varieties (see below) is best purchased as sticks (or quills). Cassia, with its strong sweet and familiar aroma, is brownish red and has quite a thick bark. It is generally pre-cut to fit in a spice jar. Ceylon (true) cinnamon is lighter brown and is made up of multiple paper-like layers. Its scent is mild and sweet. Cinnamon sticks will keep for about 3 years. Ground cinnamon loses fragrance easily in a few months so grind or buy only what you need. Toast cinnamon sticks in a pan over medium–low heat, turning occasionally until you can smell it; it will take about 5–7 minutes. Once toasted and cooled, it will be easy to grind in a spice or coffee grinder.

Bear in mind that ground cinnamon absorbs liquid very easily, so, when baking, if you want to add more cinnamon, add a little cinnamon oil rather than more ground cinnamon, which may either clump into a paste or make your finished recipe very dry.

❛The cinnamon you buy at the grocery store is cassia (*Cinnamomum cassia*), aka Chinese cinnamon. It's warming and fragrant, and it also happens to lower blood sugar in people with diabetes and pre-diabetes.

Cinnamon is sort of magic: it helpfully changes your insulin receptors, alters the way the liver metabolizes blood sugar and even affects how your intestinal enzymes digest sugar. But it also contains a lot of coumarin, which can poison the liver... and might be responsible for each of the blood-sugar-beneficial effects! One good solution is Ceylon cinnamon (*Cinnamomum zeylanicum*), or "true" cinnamon. Ceylon cinnamon has a lot less coumarin than cassia, plus a sweet taste, delicate aroma and papery bark. Try a Ceylon cinnamon infusion: coumarin is oil soluble and will be left behind... though some of the blood sugar benefits may be as well.

By the way, cinnamon has even more antioxidants than mint, anise, licorice, vanilla, ginger or nutmeg, all of which are stocked with them.❜

John La Puma, MD

http://www.ncbi.nlm.nih.gov/pubmed/26475130; http://www.ncbi.nlm.nih.gov/pubmed/24148965

Rosemary *The Remember-me Spice*

'There's rosemary, that's for remembrance; pray you, love, remember.' This timeless phrase spoken by Ophelia in Shakespeare's *Hamlet* rings true even today, when this remarkably powerful spice remains much written about and discussed by both the complementary and clinical medical communities.

Rosemary is a member of the mint family and indigenous to the Mediterranean region, but it grows over much of the world in moderately temperate climes. Strong and prolific with delicate flower blossoms of blue, pink or purple, rosemary takes hold easily, whether planted in containers or as vast hedges, and is drought tolerant and frost resistant. It is one of the most important spices medicinally, dating back to antiquity. Records of rosemary abound in ancient Greek and Roman legends and, in past centuries, this bountifully aromatic spice was touted for its importance medically far in excess of its use as a flavouring ingredient. Medicine men of the past who adhered to 'the four humours', a holistic Hippocratic medical discipline, believed, as many do today, that rosemary fortifies brain function, especially memory. (I am sniffing rosemary leaves as I write this!) The active compound in rosemary, cineole, which releases a piney-floral-eucalyptus aroma, may be the key to memory performance while another component, carnosic acid, is believed to be beneficial in fighting free-radical damage in the brain and the slow aging of the brain. Pretty heady stuff growing from a garden pot!

Rosemary's spiky leaves sprouting from strong solid stems make great skewers for barbecue or stovetop grilling (broiling) of lamb, chicken and even pineapple pieces. Rosemary is used in both sweet and savoury dishes, including alongside the familiar flavours of roast lamb, chicken, goats' cheese, preserved and fresh lemon peel, olive, garlic and tomato. In sweet dishes, it is wonderful in rosemary-infused olive oil polenta cake, rosemary and orange chocolate sorbet and in the rosemary-crusted Apple and Walnut Galette on page 88. As a teatime treat during pre-exam cramming, mix 1½ teaspoons of dried rosemary or 1 tablespoon of fresh chopped leaves with 2 teaspoons of cocoa powder in a cup. Stir in one cup of boiling water, cover and let steep for 5–7 minutes. Add a squeeze of orange juice and a little zest and/or sweeten if you like, then sip and study! The rosemary will help with clarity and the cocoa with energy.

❝ Rosemary leaf (the needles are the leaves!) is approved officially by Germany's Commission E, which is the US FDA somewhat-equivalent. Rosemary is approved for upset stomachs and has been widely studied – in Iran for improving occupational burnout, in the US for boosting cognitive function, in Scotland for reversing hair loss.

What we know is this: when you use a meat marinade containing rosemary, it both reduces the bacterial count in raw meat and drops the risk of intestinal and breast cancers from charred or overcooked meat.

Dried rosemary powder has reduced heterocyclic amine formation (a cancer-causing chemical created by high-heat cooking of meat and by charring) by up to 77 per cent in ground beef burgers grilled [broiled] at temperatures up to 200°C (400°F).

How? Whether it is powder-activating-detoxifying enzymes in the liver, or the scent triggering free-radical-scavenging activity, which is your body's healthy reaction to clean out damaging, inflammatory chemicals, or its powerful antioxidant and anti-inflammatory ability is not known. It is known that rosemary is delicious, easy to use and grow and widely available. ❞

John La Puma, MD

http://www.ncbi.nlm.nih.gov/pubmed/20492265; http://www.ncbi.nlm.nih.gov/pubmed/26579115

Oregano *The Pungent Spice*

Oregano, the 'pizza spice', is indigenous to the Mediterranean but is so hardy it will grow easily in temperate climates. This strongly scented beauty of the mint family has small oval-shaped green leaves, thrives in full sun and slightly acidic soil and has been used in food and medicine since ancient times.

Oregano's pungent, aromatic and slightly bitter flavour is available fresh, and oregano grows easily in most kitchen gardens, but it is best known and most commonly used in its concentrated dry form – look at that big plastic container of dried oregano leaves at the local pizzeria! The American craze for Italian-style food – pizza, spaghetti and garlic bread – began when World War II soldiers returning from Europe could not get enough of this pizza spice!

Oregano is often mistaken for marjoram, which is understandably confusing given that oregano is also known as wild marjoram, but the presence of a thyme aroma in the smaller leaves of true Greek or Italian oregano gives it a stronger flavour than the more delicate marjoram. It should also not be confused with Mexican oregano, which is related to the lemon verbena family, has a stronger flavour, with hints of citrus, and is frequently used in Mexican cuisine.

Oregano's primary essential oils, contained in its fuzzy leaves and stems, are thymol and carvacol. Oregano and its oil were used as health remedies not only by Hippocrates but also in numerous European, Asian and South American cultures and continue to yield many promising health features: there have been studies into using oregano oil as a possible LDL- and triglyceride-cholesterol-lowering aid, to slow or reverse the build-up of artery-constricting plaque and as a helpful cleanser/body rebalancer for thrush and other yeast infections. Make an orange-oregano infusion by pouring a cup of water over 1 tablespoon of chopped fresh (or 2 teaspoons of dried) oregano, a piece of orange peel and a clove for sweetness (optional). Cover and let steep for 5–8 minutes, then curl up and enjoy.

The pungent leaves are added, dried, to pizza-spice blends and used fresh or dried in Greek salad dressing, Chimichurri Argentina (see page 162) and Turkish lamb marinade. You can also enjoy it in the Stuffed Chicken Breasts with Artichoke Quinoa on page 76.

If drying your own oregano, air or sun dry it, as the low heat of an oven will reduce the strength of its active oils. Dried oregano leaves will keep tightly sealed in the pantry for about a year.

❝ Oregano is so much more than that dried herb you dust all over your pizza. In my practice, oil of oregano is one of my go-to medicines for respiratory and gastrointestinal infections.

It's the volatile oils in this spice, thymol and carvacrol, that have been shown to inhibit the growth of bacteria, including *Helicobacter pylori*, a bacteria that can cause gastric ulcers and reflux disease. The oils also serve as antivirals; I often recommend a few drops of oil of oregano in boiling water, and inhaling the steam for colds and upper respiratory infections. A recent study showed that a spray containing aromatic essential oils from five different plants, including oregano, was found to significantly relieve symptoms in those with upper respiratory infections.

It is also a good source of calcium and vitamin K, and has more antioxidant activity than blueberries! ❞

Geeta Maker-Clark, MD

Lambert RJ, Skandamis PN, Coote PJ, Nychas GJ, 'A study of the minimum inhibitory concentration and mode of action of oregano essential oil, thymol and carvacrol'. J Appl Microbiol 2001 Sep; 91(3):453-62. 2001. PMID:12450.
Evid Based Complement Alternat Med. 2011;2011:690346.

Bay Leaf *The Noble Spice*

Native to the Mediterranean, bay laurel (*Laurus nobilis*) belongs to the family Lauraceae, which also includes cassia cinnamon, Ceylon cinnamon, sassafras and the avocado. Bay varieties abound, including the California bay, which does not contain the cineole essential oils of the bay laurel, while bay leaves in India are likely to be cassia cinnamon leaves. An evergreen tree with hardy shiny tapered leaves, richly green on top and paler underneath, bay laurel grows in moderately temperate climates but manages quite well on many a London balcony. Bay leaf is probably the most used spice in the pantry.

During the Olympics in Ancient Greece, no gold, silver or bronze medals were awarded to the winners; instead, the Olympian was lauded with a prize of olive or laurel branches woven into a crown called *kotinos*. Bay leaves were sacred to the Greek god Apollo – the symbol of triumph – and the fresh crown of laurels was also awarded to poets, scholars and heroes, and still today is symbolic of great physical or mental accomplishment. The title baccalaureate ('bacca' meaning berry plus 'laurel', signifying the berry-laden branches) came into being during the Renaissance, when a newly graduated student was awarded a berry-laden laurel branch with their doctorate degree but had only moments to enjoy 'sitting on their laurels' before the challenging work of a doctor began!

The active compound found in laurel bay oil, cineole, is known as a strong antioxidant. Stronger than other naturally derived chemicals, such as vitamin C, the antioxidant compounds in bay leaves are released as the scent of bay infuses your food. Encouraging studies indicate that consuming bay leaf may help combat diabetes 2 by lowering blood sugar and LDL-cholesterol.

Bay leaf has a sweet aroma and a bitter taste but becomes creamy and luxurious when added to any number of recipes. One of the few leaf spices that retains its flavour and nutrients when dried, it lends itself to slow-cooking soups, stews and sauces. An essential component of bouquet garni, the classic blend of herbs (also including thyme and parsley) used to flavour meat and vegetable broths and stocks, bay leaf is also an essential ingredient in court bouillon for poaching fish, and is always a friend at a seaside lobster, clam or mussels boil picnic. Bay is also obligatory in pickling spices, an often-requested addition to marinade- and potato-based recipes and features in classic cream- or egg-based sauces such as Hollandaise and white sauce. The fragrance of bay leaves complements many an English custard or milk pudding and I often add bay to ice creams and panna cotta: the creaminess of bay enhances the rich mouthfeel of dairy.

www.ncbi.nlm.nih.gov/pmc/articles/PMC2613499/

> There are many different types of plants whose leaves are referred to as "bay leaves", so it's important to distinguish that a true bay leaf is scientifically known as *Laurus nobilis*, from the bay laurel tree. This leaf is very nutrient rich, unlike its imitators.
>
> Bay leaves have been a part of culinary and medicinal culture for thousands of years, dating back at least to Roman times, and likely far beyond.
>
> Bay leaves are powerful medicine for the gastrointestinal system; they are very effective for settling upset stomachs, soothing irritable bowel syndrome or even lessening the symptoms of inflammatory bowel diseases. Unique enzymes found in bay leaves help to improve digestion and nutrient intake, so they are wonderful to add to high-protein meals that might be harder to digest.
>
> The essential oil of bay leaves has a strong aromatherapeutic effect and can even be mixed into a salve and applied to the chest to help alleviate congestion from colds.

Geeta Maker-Clark, MD

Hibiscus *The Refreshing Red Spice*

Many types and colours of hibiscus grow prolifically in tropical, sub-tropical and moderately warm regions of the world, but only *Hibiscus sabdariffa*, the sour tea spice also known as roselle, Jamaica sorrel and karkade, has the concentrated health characteristics and benefits that have been known about and exploited in traditional medicine for centuries. Native to Africa, where it is still cultivated, *Hibiscus sabdariffa* is thought to have been domesticated in the Sudan region over 6,000 years ago. This beautiful hibiscus variety has large white, yellow, pink or red petals and a bright pink-red centre or calyx. The soft calyx (sepals), the red covering that protects the seedpod, is picked by hand in the morning hours, before it begins to harden, and is then dried in the sun.

Hibiscus is most often enjoyed as 'sour spice tea' and has been celebrated for its beneficial nutrients and traditional cures from Egypt to Mexico, Thailand to Brazil and Jamaica to China for millennia.

Hibiscus sabdariffa is being studied as a remedy for a number of conditions, including irritable bowel syndrome, fatty liver disease and metabolic syndrome. It has also gained an enormous amount of attention recently as a weight-loss spice because the active hibiscus acid (hydroxycitric acid) inhibits the production of amylase, an enzyme produced by the salivary glands and the pancreas to help the body digest carbohydrates. Where there is an excessive amount of unused carbs not needed as energy, the leftovers get stored as fat and it is thought that the hibiscus acid may allow this excess to pass through the system rather than being stored as fat. The stems and pectin-laden leaves of hibiscus are also thought to have possible anticancer benefit. Hibiscus contains very high levels of vitamin C and is considered to be a natural antiseptic, a diuretic, a gentle laxative and a natural body coolant.

This bright-red flowerbud is added to several fruit-tea blends and used as a natural food colouring and to give a rush of tart flavour to food and drink. The popular refreshing Mexican drink agua de flor de Jamaica is a blend of hibiscus boiled with water and sugar then cooled and served over ice. For a healthier option, replace the sugar with fresh fruit and fruit juices and add a few lime wedges for colour. This creative, colourful spice (doctors advise that we should 'eat a rainbow everyday') will inspire you to add a measure to food and drink, whether in a marinade for pork, sprinkled on crusted shellfish, as a seasoning for ceviche, in a sauce for poached fish or in a salad dressing or mixed into tonics, teas and martinis!

www.ncbi.nlm.nih.gov/pmc/articles/PMC2742648/; www.ncbi.nlm.nih.gov/pmc/articles/PMC4581252/; www.ncbi.nlm.nih.gov/pmc/articles/PMC3303862/

> ❝ Hibiscus is a really light and pleasant-tasting spice known for its deep-red colour, which infuses into beautiful teas. It owes this lovely colour to the plant pigment quercetin, which is an antioxidant, scavenging particles in the body known as free radicals, which damage cell membranes, alter the DNA and can cause cell death. By neutralizing free radicals, it may reduce or even help prevent some of the damage free radicals cause.
>
> Hibiscus is also very rich in plant acids, including citric acid, malic acid, tartaric acid and hibiscus acid, which is unique to hibiscus.
>
> The scientific evidence has grown over the years supporting the ancient use of hibiscus in many countries for blood-pressure control. On a recent trip to Senegal, I enjoyed many cups of hibiscus tea, which, I was told, was to support my "blood". A Cochrane review of hibiscus's effects on blood pressure published in 2010 included randomized controlled trials of three to 12 weeks in duration that compared hibiscus to either placebo or no intervention at all. All five of these studies found hibiscus had a blood-pressure-maintenance effect. Some of these trials look at hibiscus in tea form and others in extract. The best aspect? The safety profile of hibiscus is excellent, with no proven adverse reactions. ❞

Geeta Maker-Clark, MD

Ngamjarus c, Pattanittum P, Somboonporn C. Cochrane Database Syst Rev. 2010; Jan 20(1):CD007894.

HIPPOCRATES' HEALING BROTH

A comforting cleansing broth from Dr Eleni Tsiompanou, who reveals bay's health secret: 'Most of the ingredients in this recipe go back to antiquity, and Hippocrates would have used whatever meat was available according to season. For unwell people at the peak of their illness, he would have used just barley without meat in the soup and, as the patient got better, he would have given it in less dilute form. When you prepare the soup, chop the leeks, onions and garlic at least ten minutes before cooking them in order to stimulate their active ingredients. (If you use them in cooking immediately after they are chopped, they will have their characteristic taste and smell but not their anti-inflammatory properties.) This is a cheap and easy but highly nutritious dish that requires little preparation time. However, it works better if you cook it slowly over 4–8 hours.'

MAKES 700ML–1 LITRE (3–4¼ CUPS)

chicken wings or the carcass/bones of a roast chicken	1 celery stick
1.5kg (3lb. 5oz.) oxtail	1 or 2 leeks, roughly chopped
1 garlic clove, chopped	1 onion, finely chopped
2–4 bay leaves	115g (4oz./1 cup) chopped cabbage (optional)
2–4 thyme sprigs	175g (6oz./scant 1 cup) barley
2–4 parsley sprigs, finely chopped	pinch sweet paprika (optional)
1 tsp black peppercorns	dash of lemon or lime juice (optional)
1 tsp allspice berries	chopped fresh parsley (optional)
2 carrots, peeled and chopped	

Put the chicken wings or carcass and the oxtail in a large heavy-based cooking pot and pour over enough water to cover them. Bring to the boil slowly then skim the foam (which is mainly fat) from the surface.

Add the garlic, bay leaves, thyme, parsley, black peppercorns and allspice berries and simmer, covered, over a low heat for 2–4 hours. (The longer and more slowly you cook it the better.)

Remove the pan from the heat and strain the broth through a sieve or colander into a large glass bowl. Pick the meat from the oxtail and the chicken wings or carcass and either return some of it to the broth or keep it for another dish. Discard the bones, spices and herbs.

Add the vegetables and barley to the pan and season with coarse sea salt and pepper and sweet paprika if wished. Return to the heat and simmer slowly for a further 1–2 hours.

For a lovely Mediterranean sour twist, add a dash of fresh lemon or lime juice and sprinkle in some chopped parsley just before serving.

OREGANO

JERUSALEM ARTICHOKE DIP

This root vegetable, also known as sunchoke in the US, has nothing to do with Jerusalem but is derived instead from the Italian word for sunflower, girasole, *which sounds quite similar. This creamy appetizer dish can be made well ahead. It's beautiful simply on its own, but for a bit more rich nuttiness, add freshly grated Parmesan.*

SERVES 4–6

475ml (2 cups) vegetable stock
450g (1lb.) Jerusalem artichokes, peeled and sliced
2 garlic cloves
30ml (2 tbsp) lemon juice

1–2 whole chipotle peppers in adobo or 1 tbsp chipotle paste, or to taste
1 tbsp chopped fresh or 1 tsp dried oregano
120g (4¼oz./1 cup) grated Parmesan (optional)

Heat the stock to a simmer in small saucepan. Add the Jerusalem artichokes and garlic and cook until tender, about 20 minutes. Drain, reserving the cooking liquid.

Put the Jerusalem artichokes, garlic, lemon juice, chipotle peppers and oregano in a food processor and process until smooth, adding reserved stock as needed – it should have a hummus-like consistency.

Spoon into a bowl and fold in the Parmesan to combine (if using). Serve warm or at room temperature with breadsticks or crudités.

ROSEMARY, OREGANO, BAY LEAF, THYME

HERB AND SPICE OLIVES

For school lunchboxes, my creative Mum, Sally, would make black olive and cream cheese sandwiches, which my sister hated and I loved. This mélange is a long way from second grade!

MAKES 3 CUPS

4 whole anchovy fillets, drained
2 garlic cloves, thinly sliced
1 tsp orange zest
2 tsp lemon zest
60ml (¼ cup) extra virgin olive oil
2 tsp fresh lemon juice
2 bay leaves
2 oregano sprigs

2 rosemary sprigs
2 thyme sprigs
350g (12oz./2 cups) mixed green and black olives
12–16 piquante or sweet-cherry peppers
2 strips lemon peel
4 strips orange peel
½ tsp chili flakes, or to taste
240ml (1 cup) extra virgin olive oil

Using a mortar and pestle, grind the anchovies, garlic and orange and lemon zest. Fold in the olive oil, lemon juice, bay leaves, oregano, rosemary and thyme. Stir in the olives, piquante peppers and citrus peel. Season to taste with chili flakes.

Spoon into a decorative container with a tight-fitting lid, top up with olive oil, cover and refrigerate. The olives will keep chilled for up to a month.

HIBISCUS AND CITRUS-CRUSTED PRAWNS
WITH TART TUSCAN MELON

Tangy hibiscus flower buds or hibiscus tea, which can be purchased at health or specialty food shops or online, are full of vitamin C and anthocyanins. In this dish, the tart concentrated flavour of the deep-pink hibiscus calyx buds or dried hibiscus tea balances the rich prawns (shrimp) and delicately scented melon.

SERVES 6

½ Tuscan-style cantaloupe melon, peeled, sliced and cut into triangular pieces

zest and juice of 4 lemons

zest and juice of 4 limes

1½ jalapeños, minced

2 tsp dried hibiscus flower buds or tea, finely chopped or crumbled

55g (2oz./generous ½ cup) dry breadcrumbs

¾ tsp sea salt

65g (2⅓oz./⅓ cup) palm or soft brown sugar

4 tsp minced fresh ginger

3 tbsp dark rum

24 large prawns (shrimp), peeled, cleaned and deveined and butterflied

6 tsp grapeseed oil

2 spring onions (scallions), sliced on the bias, to garnish

1 handful micro-greens, to garnish (optional)

Put the cut melon in a medium bowl and set aside.

In another bowl, stir together the lemon and lime zests, jalapeño, hibiscus tea, breadcrumbs and salt. Set aside.

In a small saucepan, warm the lemon and lime juice with the sugar, ginger and 120ml (½ cup) water and heat until reduced to 120ml (½ cup). Add the rum and cook for 1 minute then remove from the heat, pour over the melon and toss together. Set aside.

Pat the prawns (shrimp) dry then coat with 2 teaspoons of the grapeseed oil. Heat the remaining 4 teaspoons of oil in a sauté pan over medium–high heat. Coat the prawns (shrimp) thoroughly in the prepared crust mixture, then sear in the oil in batches, adding more oil if necessary. Cook for 2 minutes then turn.

Spoon the melon and sauce onto individual plates or a serving platter, arrange the prawns (shrimp) on top and scatter with the spring onions (scallions) and micro-greens, if using.

ARCTIC CHAR
WITH HIBISCUS AND CELERY
Michael Kempf

'A light and vitalizing dish with a variety of consistencies and textures. When cooked, the char should have the consistency of a medium-boiled egg yolk. Sansho pepper is a very fresh, slightly spicy, citrus-like seasoning.' MK

SERVES 4

250g (9oz.) char, or brook trout, fillet

150g (5½oz./1⅓ sticks) butter

1 tbsp ground hibiscus

3 thyme sprigs

1 x 40–48g (1½–1¾oz.) jar char, brook trout or lumpfish caviar

1 tbsp walnuts

1 tbsp egg white

a little piment d'Espelette

For the celeriac confit:

150g (5½oz.) celeriac, peeled and roughly chopped

40g (1½oz./2¾ tbsp) salted butter

2 shallots, finely diced

1 tsp freshly grated ginger

salt and sansho pepper (Japanese pepper)

juice and zest of 1 lemon

For the celery emulsion:

150g (5½oz.) celery, leaves removed and reserved

4 parsley and 4 mint sprigs

2 pinches xanthan gum

1 tbsp hazelnut oil

1 tbsp rapeseed oil

1 tsp freshly grated ginger

½ Granny Smith apple, peeled, cored and finely chopped

salt and white pepper, to taste

For the celeriac rolls:

100g (3½oz.) celeriac

1 tbsp rapeseed oil

1 tbsp hazelnut oil

3 pinches sansho pepper

1 thyme sprig

First make the celeriac confit. Lightly salt the celeriac, place it in a plastic bag with the butter and vacuum seal. Put in a pan of lightly boiling water and cook for about 10 minutes. Remove from the bag and allow to drain, reserving the liquid. Cook the shallot down with the reserved cooking liquid until fully reduced. Mash the celeriac with a fork and add to the shallots. Season with the ginger, salt, sansho pepper and lemon zest and juice.

To make the celery emulsion, juice the celery with the parsley and mint and strain through a fine sieve. Blend 50ml (scant ¼ cup) of this liquid with the xanthan using an immersion blender, then blend this with the two oils and the remaining juice. Season with the ginger and a little salt and pepper. Stir the apple into the sauce and leave to stand. Season again to taste just before serving.

To make the celeriac rolls, peel the celeriac and slice thinly with a slicer, then cut into strips about 2 x 8cm (¾ x 3in.), three per person. Reserve the remaining pieces. Blanch the strips in strongly salted water, shock in an ice-water bath and drain well. Juice the remaining celeriac and strain the juice through a fine sieve. Mix with the two oils and season with salt and pepper to create a marinade. Add the celeriac strips and thyme to the marinade in a plastic bag and vacuum seal. Just before serving, remove the strips from the bag and form into rolls.

Lightly salt the char fillets, wrap in foil and refrigerate. Brown the butter slowly, stirring occasionally. Allow to cool, then slowly stir in the hibiscus until dissolved. Portion the char and place in a deep baking dish. Spread the hibiscus butter over it and place the thyme between the fillets. Bake in the oven at its lowest setting for about 10–12 minutes, until translucent. Sprinkle with coarse sea salt. Turn the oven up to 160°C (325°F/gas mark 3). Beat the egg with the piment d'Espelette and coat the nuts in this mixture. Using a slotted spatula or your hands, lift the coated nuts to a baking tray lined with baking paper and roast at for about 8 minutes, until golden.

To serve, portion the celeriac confit onto each plate. Arrange three celery rolls, three celery leaves and some walnuts on top. Pour the emulsion into the centre, place the char next to it and arrange a quenelle of caviar on top.

OREGANO, CINNAMON

STUFFED CHICKEN BREASTS
WITH ARTICHOKE QUINOA

My good chef friend Kathy Kordalis shares her oregano-centric spice blend recipe, passed down through generations in her Greek-Australian family, as the seasoning for this moreish chicken and artichoke dish.

SERVES 4

4 x 170g (6oz.) boneless chicken breasts, skin on

1 tbsp butter or olive oil

For the Kordalis spice marinade (makes 200ml):

30g (1oz./¼ cup) fresh oregano leaves

2 tbsp chopped flat-leaf parsley

2 tbsp chopped mint

3 garlic cloves, sliced

1 tsp sea salt

1 tsp cracked black pepper

¼ tsp chili flakes

¼ tsp ground cinnamon

175ml (¾ cup) extra virgin olive oil

juice and zest of 1 lemon and 1 orange

drizzle (½ tsp) honey (optional)

For the artichoke quinoa:

4 whole artichokes (approx. 450g/1lb. each)

350g (12oz./2 cups) quinoa, rinsed well and drained

415ml (1¾ cups) chicken or vegetable stock

4 tbsp Kordalis spice marinade (see above)

¼ tsp salt

50g (1¾oz.) preserved lemon peel (see page 20)

For the chicken filling:

12 crushed green olives

8 sundried tomatoes, thinly sliced

1½ chopped artichokes (see above)

2 strips preserved lemon peel (see page 20), chopped

4 tbsp Kordalis spice marinade (see above)

4 sliced halloumi, grilled (broiled)

Whizz the marinade ingredients in a food processor or blender until smooth. Reserve 4 tablespoons of the marinade for the quinoa (see below), then submerge the chicken breasts in the remainder. Cover and chill for at least 2 hours.

Make the artichoke quinoa. Trim the artichoke stems and the leaves of thorns, then cut in half. Using a teaspoon, remove the feathery choke and discard. Put the artichokes in a large pan, add 2 tablespoons of the Kordalis marinade, then cover with salted water and bring to a simmer. Cover the artichokes with a plate to keep submerged and simmer for 20–30 minutes until the stem is fork tender. Strain and cool, reserving 60ml (¼ cup) of cooking water. Remove and discard the leaves from the artichoke, revealing the cup-shaped heart. Reserve 1½ artichoke hearts for the filling and roughly chop the remainder. Drizzle with a little olive oil and set aside.

Put the quinoa into a 2-litre (2-quart) pan (with a lid) and warm over medium heat, swirling the pan and stirring until dry-toasted. Add the stock, reserved cooking liquid and salt and bring to the boil. Lower to a gentle simmer, cover and cook for about 17 minutes. Remove the pan from the heat, leaving the lid on and let steam for 5 minutes. Test for doneness: if still crunchy or liquid remains, return to low heat and cook covered for a few minutes longer. Add the artichoke hearts, preserved lemon peel and the remaining 2 tablespoons of Kordalis marinade and heat through. Fluff with a fork, season to taste and keep warm.

Drain the chicken breasts, reserving the marinade. Combine all the chicken filling ingredients except the halloumi together in a small bowl. Cut a horizontal slit in each chicken breast, making a pocket, and stuff the filling inside. Slide a piece of grilled (broiled) halloumi into each and secure with kitchen twine.

Preheat the oven to 180°C (350°F/gas mark 5). Heat the butter or olive oil in a large ovenproof frying pan (skillet) or roasting pan over medium–high heat. Add the chicken parcels to the pan and sear until browned on all sides.

In a small pan, warm the remaining marinade to a simmer then pour into a little serving bowl.

Remove the kitchen twine, slice the chicken parcels in half and serve on a generous spoonful of Artichoke Quinoa. Drizzle the pan juices over the chicken and serve with remaining marinade.

CHICKEN ADOBO

April Bloomfield

'I've always been a big fan of bay leaves – the flavour goes well in pretty much everything – and I like using fresh ones for this dish. The cinnamon hiding in here adds just a touch of intrigue, but it's not too overpowering. The balance between the vinegar, soy and all these spice flavours simmering together has an unexpected, refreshing effect.' AB

SERVES 6

60ml (¼ cup) peanut (groundnut), grapeseed or canola oil

2.3kg (5lb.) bone-in, skin-on chicken legs and thighs

2 heads garlic, cloves separated but not peeled

1 large Spanish onion, peeled and cut into 8 wedges

55g (2oz./½ cup) fresh ginger, unpeeled, thinly sliced

10 black peppercorns, lightly toasted

2 star anise, lightly toasted

1 cinnamon stick, lightly toasted

4 fresh bay leaves, bruised, or 2 dried bay leaves

350ml (1½ cups) white cane vinegar or unseasoned rice vinegar

120ml (½ cup) soy sauce

rice, to serve

Heat the oil in a large pan that has a lid over high heat until it starts to smoke. Add half the chicken (so you don't crowd the pan), skin side down, into the hot oil and cook, turning the pieces over occasionally, until golden brown all over, 10–15 minutes. Transfer to a plate and repeat with the remaining pieces of chicken, then add those to the plate.

Add the garlic, onion, ginger, peppercorns, star anise, cinnamon stick and bay leaves to the pan. Cook, stirring every now and again, until the onion turns translucent, about 10 minutes. You'll start to see lovely, sticky brown bits on the bottom of the pan. Add the chicken, then the vinegar and soy. Raise the heat to bring the liquid to a boil, scraping the pan to release the sweet brown bits.

Cover the pan, lower the heat to maintain a gentle simmer and cook, stirring occasionally, until the chicken is very tender (it will come apart with a spoon), about 45 minutes. Serve in large bowls over rice.

★

ROSEMARY, OREGANO, CINNAMON, THYME

ALLAN'S MARINATED LAMB SKEWERS
WITH CAULIFLOWER 'STEAK' SHAWARMA

Often used as a barbecue spice, rosemary contains a compound that offsets the toxicity of charred and cooked meat. Using rosemary branches as skewers creates clever healthy handles!

SERVES 4

600g (1lb. 5oz.) lamb (saddle or rump), trimmed and diced

1 large onion, cut into 8 segments

8 rosemary 'skewers' for grilling (broiling) lamb

For the marinade:

60ml (¼ cup) lemon juice

4 tsp Dijon mustard

4 tsp soft brown sugar

2 tbsp Worcestershire sauce

1 garlic clove, minced

2 x 10cm (4in.) rosemary sprigs

4 thyme sprigs

4 tsp port

1 tbsp olive oil

For the cauliflower 'steak' shawarma:

1 large cauliflower (approx. 1kg/2lb. 4oz.)

4–8 tsp Shawarma Spice Paste (see below), or to taste

Combine the marinade ingredients together in a large shallow dish. Marinate the lamb for 4 hours or overnight.

Preheat the oven to 200°C (400°F/gas mark 6).

Peel the leaves from the cauliflower and discard. Trim the stem, leaving the core intact. Put core side down on a work surface and, using a large knife, trim each end to create a flat edge, then cut in half through the centre and stem. Cut each half in half horizontally to give you four 'steaks'. Carefully arrange these slices in a steamer and cook until knife tender, about 6–8 minutes.

Carefully transfer the cauliflower to a foil-lined, oiled baking tray and brush the top and sides of each 'steak' with 1–2 teaspoons of Shawarma Spice Paste, or to taste. Sprinkle with salt flakes, place in the oven and roast for 10 minutes until golden brown.

Separate each wedge of onion into three or four layers. Thread two pieces of lamb onto rosemary skewers alternately with sections of onion. Season with salt and pepper. Lay the skewers on the hot grill or barbecue and cook for 10–15 minutes, turning two or three times, until the lamb is medium–rare, 8–10 minutes. Alternately, place the skewers on a baking tray and cook in the oven 10 minutes ahead of cooking the cauliflower, turning the skewers over as you add the cauliflower to finish in the oven.

Serve two lamb skewers and one cauliflower 'steak' per person.

SHAWARMA SPICE PASTE

This makes more than you need for the cauliflower steaks but you can store the remainder in a jar with a tightly fitting lid – it will keep chilled for 1 month – and add it to baked or sautéed potatoes or other vegetables, or brush it onto seafood or chicken.

1 tbsp fresh oregano leaves

3 garlic cloves, crushed

60ml (¼ cup) grapeseed or extra virgin olive oil

1 tbsp cumin seeds, toasted and ground

1 tbsp coriander seeds, toasted and ground

1 tsp peppercorns, toasted and ground

½ tbsp ground mild or smoked paprika

½ tsp ground turmeric

½ tsp ground cinnamon

¼ tsp ground fenugreek

¼ tsp ground cloves

Put all the ingredients into a mortar and grind into a paste with a pestle.

CINNAMON, ROSEMARY, OREGANO, BAY LEAF

MARINATED VENISON
WITH DASHI COCONUT CUSTARD AND CINNAMON TEA BROTH
Neil Brazier

'A spice presented to kings, queens and gods as presents through the ages, cinnamon does everything: its sweet scent is used for oil and for medicine and it's a spice that goes in wine, liqueur, chocolate, desserts, curries, buns and pastry as well as in savoury dishes, including this venison recipe. It really is a spice that knows no boundaries and can be used anywhere! My earliest memories of venison are ones of Christmas, roaring log fires and long winter nights.' NB

SERVES 4

300g (10½oz.) venison

quince paste, cut into cubes, to serve (optional)

For the venison marinade:

500ml (2 cups + 2 tbsp) red wine

90g (3¼oz./scant ½ cup) granulated sugar

40g (1½oz./2⅔ tbsp) salt

zest of 1 orange

zest of 1 lemon

4 bay leaves

2 rosemary sprigs

2 thyme sprigs

2 oregano sprigs

2 cinnamon sticks

3 garlic cloves, peeled and sliced

5 black peppercorns, lightly crushed

1 tsp juniper berries, lightly crushed

For the cinnamon tea broth:

60g (2¼oz.) cinnamon sticks

100g (3½oz./½ cup) granulated sugar

pinch salt

pinch cayenne pepper

For the coconut and dashi custard:

500ml (2 cups + 2 tbsp) coconut cream

300ml (1¼ cups) dashi

1 packet (12.5g) agar agar

For the coleslaw:

50g (1¾oz.) carrot

50g (1¾oz.) apple

50g (1¾oz.) celeriac

50g (1¾oz.) quince

4 tsp lemon juice

60ml (¼ cup) olive oil

For the marinade, put all the ingredients into a pan and bring to the boil. Remove from the heat and leave to cool. Place the venison in the marinade for 1–4 days in a sealed container, turning it over after 12 hours. Remove the venison from the marinade and slice, then place on to plates.

For the cinnamon tea broth, preheat the oven to 170°C (350°F/gas mark 4) and roast the cinnamon sticks for 4 minutes. Pour 600ml (2½ cups) of water into a medium pan, stir in the sugar, salt and cayenne pepper and bring to the boil. Add the cinnamon sticks then take it off the heat. Transfer the hot liquid into a plastic container and cover with a lid or cling film (plastic wrap). You can use it straight away or leave it in the fridge for 2–3 days. Strain the liquid through a sieve. Before use, dilute the cinnamon tea with two parts to one of water, then warm and serve.

To make the coconut and dashi custard, put the coconut cream and dashi in a pan and bring to the boil, then add the agar agar and mix well using a whisk. Cook for a further 3–4 minutes, then take off the heat, allow to cool and leave in the fridge to set overnight. Once set, blitz in a blender, adding water as required to create a custard-like consistency. Transfer to a piping bag. The custard will provide a creamy mayonnaise texture.

Julienne the carrot, apple, celeriac and quince for the coleslaw and dress lightly with the lemon juice, olive oil and a pinch of flaky salt.

To assemble, place venison pieces around each plate, spoon a coleslaw stack on one side, add some quince paste cubes, then pipe some custard dollops around the plate. When everything is on the plate, pour over the warm cinnamon tea, at the table if possible as the aroma of the cinnamon is fantastic.

BAY LEAF, CORIANDER

SYLVIA'S SAUERKRAUT

According to my friend Sylvia, who brought this naturally fermented recipe to New Zealand with her from her native Germany, classic Bavarian sauerkraut always includes caraway. This is my take on her classic staple.

MAKES ABOUT 1 LITRE (1 QUART)

1kg (2lb. 4oz.) cabbage, halved, cored and thinly sliced

1 large red onion, halved, cored and thinly sliced

2 tart green apples, peeled, cored and thinly sliced

2 tbsp salt

1 tbsp yellow mustard seeds

2 tsp caraway seeds, toasted

1 tsp coriander seeds, toasted

5 allspice berries

2 bay leaves

½ tsp sugar

¼ tsp crushed red pepper flakes

In a large mixing bowl, combine the cabbage, apple and onion. Sprinkle with salt and, using your hands, toss and squeeze the mixture. Add the mustard, caraway and coriander seeds, allspice berries, bay leaves, sugar and crushed red pepper flakes, mixing well. Set aside for 15 minutes.

Transfer to a non-reactive (earthenware, glass or stainless-steel) bowl and press the mixture down. Add a weighted plate just inside the container edges to keep the cabbage submerged in liquid. Cover with a clean cloth and store in a dark place at about 19–22°C (65–72°F).

Check the mixture daily, skimming off the scum that rises to the surface. Make sure the cabbage remains submerged. Taste after 5 days. For a stronger flavour, leave for a few more days. When ready, transfer the sauerkraut to a clean glass container, seal with a tight-fitting lid and store in the fridge for up to 3 months.

CINNAMON, BAY LEAF, CORIANDER

FERMENTED RAINBOW CARROTS

Thinly slice and add to salads, soups or main courses, or just enjoy them on their own – delicious!

MAKES ENOUGH TO FILL A 1-LITRE (1-QUART) JAR

3 tbsp kosher or flake sea salt dissolved in 700ml (3 cups) filtered water

1 bunch baby rainbow carrots (enough to fit snugly in a 1-litre/1-quart canning/mason jar)

3 fresh bay leaves

1 cinnamon stick, charred

¾ tsp coriander seeds, toasted

½ tsp cumin seeds, toasted

¼ tsp chili flakes

Dissolve the salt in cold water and set aside. Decoratively arrange the carrots in the jar and wedge in the bay leaves and cinnamon stick. Make sure the carrot tops are at least 1cm (½in.) below the rim. Place the jar on a tray or plate. Sprinkle in the remaining spices and fill the jar with brine, making sure the carrots are totally submerged. Cover with a small weighted plate that sits just inside the container edges – a water-filled jam jar on the plate works great.

Store in a dark place at about 19–22°C (65–72°F), covered with a cloth. Check daily, topping up with more brine if needed. After 5–10 days, taste the carrots (they will continue to ferment). When the flavour is to your liking, cover with a tight-fitting lid and refrigerate to stop the fermentation process.

COCONUT, MANGO AND LIME MOUSSE
WITH HIBISCUS GELÉE

Inspired by the beauty of a lotus flower opening and the taste of ruby-red hibiscus-flower tea, this rich but healthy, eye-catching dessert celebrates the superb benefits of hibiscus, whose clean taste is balanced with creamy mango, coconut, ginger and lime.

SERVES 4

For the hibiscus immersion and gelée:
8g (¼oz.) dried red hibiscus flowers or 3 hibiscus tea bags
6 tbsp sugar or agave syrup
60ml (¼ cup) lime juice
2½ gold gelatin leaves (see note, or 2 tsp powdered gelatin)

For the mango-lime mousse:
1½ gold gelatin leaves (see note, or 1¼ tsp powdered gelatin)
140g (5oz.) fresh or frozen mango pieces
100ml (scant ½ cup) thick coconut cream
2 tbsp lime juice
1 tbsp caster (superfine) sugar

1 tsp freshly grated ginger
½ tsp ground cardamom
½ tsp pure vanilla extract

For the coconut-lime mousse:
1½ gold gelatin leaves (see note, or 1¼ tsp powdered gelatin)
200ml (scant 1 cup) thick coconut cream
7 tbsp lime juice
5 tbsp caster (superfine) sugar

To serve:
toasted coconut shards

Wedge four flat-bottomed glasses snugly at an angle in a container on the shelf of the fridge. Set aside.

First make the hibiscus immersion. Boil 240ml (1 cup) water and hydrate the hibiscus flowers (or tea) until soft and the water is bright red. Add the sugar and lime juice and stir to dissolve. Cover and chill until needed.

To make the mango-lime mousse, soften the gelatin leaves in cold water. In a small bowl, using a stick blender, purée the mango with the coconut cream, lime juice, sugar, ginger, cardamom and vanilla. Squeeze the water from the gelatin, place in small bowl and heat in a microwave until dissolved, about 8 seconds, or melt in a small pan. Whisk into the mango mousse. Gently spoon into the corner base of each glass (see opposite). Chill until set.

To make the hibiscus gelée, soften the gelatin leaves in cold water. Dissolve as above, and stir into the cooled hibiscus immersion. Strain the flowers and set aside. (You can suspend them in the softly set gelée if you wish.) Remove the glasses from the fridge and place the glasses level. Carefully pour the hibiscus gelée equally into the glasses as shown. Chill until set.

For the coconut-lime mousse, soften, then dissolve the gelatin as above. Combine the coconut cream, lime juice and sugar to dissolve then whisk in the gelatin as above. Pour on top of the set hibiscus gelée and chill until set.

Garnish with toasted coconut shards to serve.

Note: If gold leaf gelatin (200 bloom) is unavailable, use the lower bloom strength silver (160) or bronze (140) but increase the amount you use. Use less platinum leaf as its set is stronger (250). All varieties are available online.

HEIRLOOM ORGANIC APPLE AND WALNUT GALETTE

If you love apples, you'll love not only eating but also making this galette: its simplicity itself with its free-form pastry, sliced apple halves and easy homemade apple butter and it can be chilled and ready to bake when you like! Rosemary is a surprising pairing with apples, walnuts and cinnamon, but it adds a distinctive pine-citrus aroma and is believed to have antioxidant and memory-strengthening benefits, too. You may not need to use all the apple butter for this galette, but it's also great on pork or yogurt or your favourite hot cereal!

SERVES 6

200g (7oz./1¾ cups) plain (all-purpose) flour

1 tsp granulated sugar

1 tbsp rosemary leaves, minced

2 tsp ground cinnamon

large pinch salt

115g (4oz./1 stick) cold butter, cut into small cubes

2 tbsp iced water

500g (1lb. 2oz.) mixed crisp organic eating apples
(e.g. Granny Smith, Monty's Surprise, Canadien du Reinette)

30g (1oz./¼ cup) chopped walnuts, preferably organic

55g (2oz./½ stick) butter, melted and browned and mixed with ¼ tsp ground cinnamon

3 tbsp dark brown sugar, roughly chopped

1 egg, beaten, for glazing

1 tbsp cinnamon sugar (1 tbsp sugar, ½ tsp cinnamon, large pinch salt)

For the apple butter (makes 115g/4oz./½ cup):

2 tbsp salted butter

½ cinnamon stick, charred

leaves of 1 small rosemary sprig, or ¼ tsp dried rosemary

225g (8oz.) apples, peeled, cored and chopped

½ tsp lemon juice

1 tbsp caster (superfine) sugar

Whisk together the flour, sugar, rosemary and cinnamon with a big pinch of salt. Crumble in the cold butter using your fingertips or a pastry cutter until pea-sized. Drizzle in the iced water, tossing gently with a fork or your fingers to combine. If it doesn't hold, add a little more water, but don't overwork the dough.

Turn the dough out onto a lightly flour-dusted board and gather into a ball. Pat out and fold over twice. Wrap tightly in cling film (plastic wrap) and chill for an hour.

Make the apple butter. Melt the butter with the cinnamon and rosemary on medium heat in a 500ml (½-quart) pot. Simmer until you can smell the spices, about 3–4 minutes. Add the apples, lemon juice, sugar and 1 tablespoon of water, give it a stir, cover and cook until the apples are mushy, about 10–15 minutes. Remove the lid and cook down to a thick paste, stirring occasionally. Discard the cinnamon stick, then push the apples through a sieve until smooth. Cool the apple butter.

Cut the apples into quarters around the core then slice each chunk into thin slices, stacking together. Set aside.

Turn the dough out onto parchment paper then roll or pat out into a free-from tart about 5mm (¼in.) thick. Transfer to a baking tray, letting the paper edges hang over. Spread the apple butter onto the dough, leaving about 4cm (1½in.) around the edge. Add the apple stacks on top of the apple butter and fold the pastry edges over. Return to the fridge to chill. Preheat the oven to 190°C (375°F/gas mark 5).

Remove the galette from the fridge, sprinkle with the walnuts, then drizzle the brown cinnamon butter over all. Scatter the brown sugar on top. Glaze the crust with egg wash then sprinkle cinnamon sugar on the edges. Bake for 25–30 minutes until the crust is golden brown.

Energy spice

Energy is life: with it we swim; without it we sink. A big boost of these spices can help spark the system to strengthen and optimize the body's inherent stores of energy, whether for aiding digestion, increasing quality brain activity or stepping up physical exertion.

Energy Spice Health Heroes
Black Peppercorn ★ Coriander ★ Cocoa ★ Nutmeg ★ Tamarind

When systems in the body are in balance with proper nutrients – and not disturbed by too much stress, poor eating habits and lack of sleep – the body will be prompted to utilize its energetic vitality to best effect. However, when body and mind are out of sync, we become a reactive unthinking machine, turning to fast-working stimulants such as jam doughnuts or triple-shot lattes, which result in an instant sugar high or a caffeine buzz that soon has the body and brain feeling the consequences of those energy-crashing deficits.

These heroes are energy boosters for physical and mental activity, supporting body and mind for the challenges of a suduko puzzle or a successful workout! Peppercorn, the king of spice, is a super energy burner and may aid in weight loss with its ability to increase circulation. Coriander can help stimulate digestive energy, helping to ease gastric complaints and diseases of the digestive organs. Cocoa, full of long-staying nutrients, gives an energy boost during workouts and is a decadent heart-healthy treat. Nutmeg and mace stimulate the nervous system and focus the brain with their active compound myristicin and are thought to help eliminate toxins in the body through supporting liver and gallbladder functions. Tamarind, full of strong flavour and stronger benefit, contains a wealth of vitamins and minerals, including thiamine (B1) for energy and strength, energy-rich potassium and an active compound that may energetically inhibit fat formation.

Other energy spice heroes

Cinnamon A dash of cinnamon can help to keep your energy levels sure and steady because of the blood-sugar-balancing qualities it provides. It is also a primary ingredient in certain analgesic balms for external pain relief to warm and invigorate muscle tissue and increase blood flow to tired and aching muscles.

Clove These tiny dried flower buds boost energy through reducing inflammation and increasing circulation and have long been known and used as traditional medicine and an aphrodisiac to increase sex drive and libido. Clove has been studied for its natural energy-regulating properties, especially a concern for those with diabetic disease. The natural sweet-licorice flavour of the active compound eugenol adds a bit of sweet energy without the sugar.

Chili Pepper The active plant compound in chili pepper is capsaicin, which is good for the heart, arteries, blood and digestive system and also helps boost metabolism. Applied topically in an ointment, capsaicin rushes blood to the area and reduces pain by increasing blood circulation and stimulating endorphins.

Star Anise A hormonal stimulant for both men and women taken as a tea, star anise may increase sexual drive and may help lift the spirits when you're feeling tired or depressed. Star anise tea has a mild oestrogenic effect, so it may help regulate the menstrual cycle in women, too.

Mint A natural stimulant, mint clears 'brain fog', giving the brain a positive physical boost and enabling you to be more alert, retentive and focused. The scent of its essential oils is enough to recharge your energy levels, but whether mint is eaten, drunk or its diluted essential oil is applied to the skin, it can be enough to get your brain and body functioning on a high level again.

Horseradish Brimming with large amounts of vitamins, minerals and protein, horseradish has few calories and no fat. The proteins are immediately metabolized into useful energy and may help to fend off illness, disarm toxins and increase energy for physical activities. The sharp strong active compound in horseradish, sinigrin, may raise concentration levels to help you feel more intensely focused.

Black Peppercorn *The King Spice*

This most-used culinary spice, second only to salt, has been fought over for centuries on land and sea as the world's demand for this spice changed history.

The unassuming pepper plant (*Piper nigrum*) is a climbing vine that grows almost exclusively in equatorial tropical rainforests, primarily in India and Southeast Asia. Slow to mature, peppercorn clusters take years to appear. Peppercorns are actually a tiny fruit, of the drupe variety, a fruit with a single seed in the middle in tiny grape-like bunches. The tough woody vine and the clusters of tiny green peppercorns have no distinctive aroma (similar to the scentless fresh vanilla pod/bean) until dried, cured and processed, when they reveal their familiar pungent rich scent.

The finest black pepper, still grown on the Malabar Coast of India, contains the highest amount of piperine, the magic curative compound that many traditional folk healers, (Indian) Ayurvedic masters and modern-day Western medical professionals laud for its numerous healing properties. (It's this active compound in pepper that's the reason we sneeze when breathing the stuff!) It is believed to aid healing of a formidable number of diseases and complaints and is considered an energy booster and a possible weight-loss enabler. Piperine is considered and well-known as a thermogenic: it increases the body's metabolic stimulant rate, producing heat and therefore optimizing the body's ability to increase its calorie-burning capabilities.

However, pepper's most astonishing quality, drawing the most attention and analysis, is its ability to act as a bio-enabler or bio-enhancer: a substance that when paired with nutrients or even medicine can maximize absorption and longevity of the nutrients or medicine in the bloodstream. The centuries-old Indian healing art Ayurveda has often prescribed a spice mixture of pepper, long pepper and ginger called trikatu, thought to enhance the effects of medicines in this very way.

Green peppercorns are simply unripened black peppercorns. They have a more complex but milder, fresh taste and are most often purchased in little glass jars, preserved in brine or pickled. Firm but easily crushed or chopped, green peppercorns are added to salad dressings, stews and cocktails and give the pungent finish to a classic steak sauce (see page 121).

White peppercorns are one of the ingredients in the classic quatre épices spice mix. The peppercorns are allowed to ripen on the vine and picked when the skin of the berries turns red. The red berries are soaked in water to peel away the tough outer shell, revealing the tiny greyish white pepper 'corn'. Aromatic white pepper is generally sold as a finely ground powder and used in numerous classic dishes from white sauce to mashed potatoes and omelettes, as well as in Chinese and Scandinavian dishes.

Pink peppercorns are not true peppercorns but the ripe berries of a Brazilian peppertree and a member of the cashew family. Pink peppercorn has a milder taste and is encased in a bright-pink paper-like shell that is easily crushed between finger and thumb to release its delicate peppery aroma. True red peppercorns, which are picked at the same time as white ones, are very rarely available outside of their growing regions and are usually sold fresh so have a short shelf life. A recipe calling for red peppercorns usually means pink peppercorns.

‘ Black pepper, known as 'black gold' in ancient times, is one of the most important healing spices, which has been used for thousands of years. Its main ingredient is piperine, which gives it its spicy and hot properties. Piperine is a bio-availability enhancer, which means it helps to increase the properties of other spices such as turmeric. It has been found to increase anti-inflammatory cytokines in the body and improve lung and joint health as well as reduce pain. It has been used in Ayurveda medicine to enhance digestion and circulation and for its antimicrobial properties to treat diarrheal diseases, stomach and gut problems. It is shown to be useful in the prevention of obesity and studies are looking at its effect on weight reduction, dyslipidemia [an abnormal amount of lipids in the blood] and diabetes. Exciting new research sheds light on its ability to improve circulation to the brain and for the prevention and treatment of Alzheimer's disease. ’

Eleni Tsiompanou, MD, PGDip, MSc Nutritional Medicine

Coriander *The Gentle Giant Spice*

How can a seed and a leaf from the same plant, which is related to parsley and carrot, taste so dramatically different? The leaves of *Coriandrum sativum* have been passionately argued about for years; as with Marmite, you either love or hate the taste, and many people even believe there is a coriander-leaf genetic predisposition (but that's for another book!). The leaf is not a spice but a soft herb and is used only fresh. Also known as cilantro or Chinese parsley, it is the must-have darling of Asian, Indian, Middle Eastern, South American, Mexican and Thai cuisine with its distinctive powerful love-it-or-leave-it smell. Used primarily as a garnish or added to a dish at the end of cooking, the coriander (cilantro) leaf has little to do with the traditional curative benefits of its spherical-shaped fruit-seed sister.

Coriander seed is one of the world's oldest spices, discovered in archaeological digs dating back to about 7000BC. It was also found in King Tut's tomb alongside other precious and medically valued spices of that period.

Coriander seed's remarkable gift of health is shrouded in its quiet and gentle scent. Its powerful antioxidants may help protect the liver from the damages wrought by fatty liver disease, chirrosis of the liver and hepatitis C. Its active phytonutrients stimulate the power of digestion and it is helpful in soothing complaints of flatulence, intestinal spasms and symptoms of irritable bowel syndrome. It is also being analysed as a protective agent against colon cancer and it has been noted that coriander extract could be beneficial in cases of lead exposure, due to its strong antioxidant compounds, as well as in stunting the common yeast infection *Candida albicans*. Further studies continue. The German official government agency 'Commission E', a government body composed of scientists, doctors, pharmacists and toxicologists tasked to study and report on more than 300 herbs and spices, has approved the seed of *Coriandrum sativum* for gastrointestinal complaints, including indigestion and loss of appetite and has stated no side effects, contraindications or drug interactions. All pretty remarkable for a little brown sweetly scented seed!

Coriander seed is an essential component of many spice blends, most notably India's garam masala, Ethiopan berbere, ras-el-hanout and baharat from Morocco and in European pickling spices, marinade mixes and gin. Its sweet, nutty, citrus flavour reminds me of my Nana's kitchen and it easily lends itself to the sweet side in dried- and fresh-fruit compotes, breads, cakes and cookies, as well as being perfect for popcorn (see page 114)! Coriander essential oil is used as a flavouring for the French Chartreuse and Benedictine liqueurs and makes a gently scented tea or tonic.

buecher.heilpflanzen-welt.de/BGA-Commission-E-Monographs/

❛ "Coriander is hot and astringent; it stops heartburn, and when eaten last also causes sleep", wrote the father of medicine Hippocrates 2,500 years ago. Coriander is considered laxative, diuretic and good for the stomach in Ayurveda and traditional medicine. Modern science is interested in the bioactive constituents and pharmacological activities of coriander seeds and fresh herb. Studies have shown this spice to have diuretic, antibacterial, anti-inflammatory, anticancer, neuroprotective and other medicinal properties. The positive influence of coriander on the gut and its antimicrobial properties make it especially interesting in the 21st century, where research on gut microbiota and drug-resistant bacteria has opened up new avenues of understanding and treating illnesses. ❜

Eleni Tsiompanou, MD, PGDip, MSc Nutritional Medicine

Cocoa *The Food of the Gods Spice*

Ahhh, lovely luxurious cocoa. It's all about the flavanols (naturally occurring antioxidants found in various types of plants and in significant amounts in cocoa beans): good for the heart, good for the soul. Don't confuse cocoa with sugary milky or white chocolate bars: choose chocolate that contains a minimum of 72 per cent cocoa solids. The higher the percentage, the darker and less sugary it is and the more flavanols it contains.

The 18th-century biologist and chocolate aficionado Carl Linnaeus named this favoured spice *Theobroma cacao*, the 'Food of the Gods'. Rich, decadent and packed full of antioxidants, cocoa also contains the feel-good amino acid tryptophan, used by the brain to make serotonin, which produces feelings of happiness. The naturally occurring chemical phenylethylalanine in chocolate is the 'love drug' and acts as an antidepressant in tandem with dopamine, one of the many brain balancers, plus the energy-giving theobromine, a stimulant that gives you that 'cocoa buzz'.

There are 22 species of cocoa trees, all indigenous to South and Central America, whose pods are picked and processed, and a growing percentage of which are being sold as single-origin chocolate. Only a handful – well actually a large bucketful, as the ripe colourful cocoa pods are the size of large oval footballs – grow on a single tree trunk per season. The 6–12m (20–40ft) tall cocoa tree must be grown in shade to thrive and is also vulnerable to fungi and pests, though new cross-bred resistant varieties are now being grown to slake the world's hunger for chocolate.

www.ncbi.nlm.nih.gov/pmc/articles/PMC4807961/

In the ancient Mayan culture, hot chocolate was never sweetened, instead this sacred and ceremonial drink was begun by roasting the bitter cocoa beans over the open fire, then boiling them in water and finally spicing them up with vanilla, cinnamon sticks and hellfire-hot chilies!

Since the 1930s, the British Royal Navy has been known for its traditional hot-cocoa beverage kye or kai, supposedly made from a massive block of unsweetened chocolate with the addition of boiling water from a below-deck steam pipe and either sweetened-condensed milk or custard powder. It was rigorously stirred and then supped during the late-night watches (with the occasional addition of Pusser's Rum!).

The terms for cocoa and cacao are interchangeable in today's chocolate market. Traditional cocoa is the powder left after the raw cocoa beans have been fermented and roasted (in a similar process to that for roasting coffee beans) and the cocoa butter has been extracted from the cocoa mass. Raw chocolate and cocoa is also made from fermented beans but left unroasted.

Raw chocolate and cocoa powder generally have a stronger and more astringent flavour and contain more of the active flavanol compounds than traditional chocolate, however there is still an enormous health benefit in adding unsweetened cocoa powder and dark (bittersweet) or semi-sweet chocolate to your day!

❛ While cocoa is now thought of as an indulgence, historically it was used as a medicine in the Mayan and Aztec civilizations, and still is used as such in many indigenous populations of Central and South America. Cocoa is especially rich in polyphenols, a group of protective antioxidant compounds found in many plant foods like red wine and tea, whose benefits for cardiovascular health have been extensively studied. These specific polyphenols make an important chemical called nitric oxide more available, which may explain the potential beneficial effects of cocoa on blood pressure, insulin resistance and blood lipids. An elixir indeed! ❜

Geeta Maker-Clark, MD

Roberto Corti, MD; Andreas J. Flammer, MD; Norman K. Hollenberg, MD, PhD; Thomas F. Lüscher, MD, 'Cocoa and Cardiovascular Health', *Contemporary Reviews in Cardiovascular Medicine*

Nutmeg *The Golden Globe Spice*

This is the only tropical fruit that is the source of two different spices: the grey-brown woodlike nugget nutmeg and its elegant crimson-laced wrapping, mace.

A bit about the Spice Wars and a lot about nutmeg… To look at this tiny, globe-shaped (albeit fragrant) spice and read that almost an entire island-chain civilization was slain because of it truly boggles the mind, narcotic or not. In the Middle Ages, the wealthy and the royal in Europe knew about the medicinal properties of nutmeg. According to the Hippocratic-endorsed Greek medical theory of humours, which was still practised by European physicians of the day, nutmeg was a 'hot food'. It was believed that nutmeg could balance 'cold foods' like fish and vegetables and it was thought to cure the common cold. As the rumours spread of how nutmeg might prevent the deathly plague, for which there was no cure, the demand for nutmeg increased, and determined Portuguese traders plotted to wrench control from the Indian and Arab traders and profit from this nutmeg business at any cost. The diminutive nutmeg seed was worth its weight in gold. Portuguese and Bandans traded amicably for a century. However, another powerful country and company was in the race and was not going to play by the rules. By 1621, the Dutch East India Company had slaughtered nearly the entire Bandanese population and taken total control of the Banda Islands and the nutmeg trade, charging astonishingly over-inflated prices to deliver the precious nutmeg to Europe.

The British still occupied a little slice of the Bandanese Spice Islands when the Dutch seized control. Managing to escape with hundreds of nutmeg seedlings, the British took them to the Caribbean island of Grenada, then under British rule. The price of nutmeg and other precious tropical spices dived and so began the demise of the Dutch East India Company.

The nutmeg tree prefers living on the breezy oceans edge in rich volcanic soil. One male tree can pollinate up to 12 female trees, which will not begin bearing fruit for 10–15 years but will then continue fruiting for a further 30–40 years.

Sweetly scented nutmeg, in the US traditionally used extensively during winter holidays in eggnog, pumpkin pie and milk custards, is also included in an enormous array of savoury recipes. It pairs well with lamb, chicken and pork dishes, garam masala curry dishes, Northern European potato recipes and is always sprinkled on creamed spinach.

The active compound in nutmeg, myristicin, is a central nervous system stimulant, and on-going studies indicate that it increases sexual activity and eases anxiety and stress. Nutmeg is also considered stimulating to the brain and gives an energy boost to the body. An additional compound found in nutmeg could have benefit for anti-aging of the skin, as it appears to block the enzyme elastase, which breaks down the elastin protein strands that are a preventative for sagging skin.

'Nutmeg is the shelled, dried seed of the plant *Myristica fragrans*. Ground, it's an indispensable part of pumpkin-pie spice and also lends its distinct flavour to eggnog, béchamel sauce and the Moroccan spice mix ras-el-hanout.

Taken orally, it has been used to treat a variety of gastrointestinal symptoms, including diarrhea, nausea, abdominal pain and intestinal gas. Nutmeg is also thought to have antimicrobial properties. It has also been used for treating cancer, kidney disease, insomnia and inducing miscarriage, though scientific evidence is lacking for these uses. Nutmeg oil has been used as a topical anaesthetic, including for mouth sores, toothache and joint pain.

There are some safety concerns about using nutmeg medicinally. There have been case reports of both acute and chronic toxicity from nutmeg overuse. High doses, the equivalent of eating 5–20g of ground nutmeg or one to three whole seeds, might cause psychoactive effects including hallucinations. Long-term use of nutmeg in doses of 120mg or more daily has been linked to hallucinations and other mental side effects. Finally, nutmeg may interact with medications that are metabolized by cytochrome p450. However, all of these potential concerns occur at amounts far exceeding those that would be used in cooking and baking.'

Linda Shiue, MD

Tamarind *The Sweet-Tart Spice*

The huge evergreen tamarind tree, native to tropical Africa, is prized for its edible pod-like fruit. Drought resistant and tolerant of high winds because of its extensive root system, but sensitive to frost, the regal tamarind, whose name is derived from the Arabic for 'Date of India', grows in nearly all the tropical and subtropical regions of the world. Clusters of long-fingered brown pods accumulate on branches and, when fully ripened, are harvested. One 40–75m (131–246ft) tree can yield up to 200kg (440lb.) of pods per year. The pods are peeled open, revealing the seeds surrounded by the sour-prune-like pulp, which is compressed into square 2.5cm (1in.) thick 'bricks' and allowed to firm up before being wrapped in cellophane and shipped all over the world. Tamarind is also available as a concentrate and a powder.

Tamarind's tart dark-brown pulp is liquefied in water (four parts water to one part tamarind pulp) to make tamarind water or juice. Tamarind syrup is made from sugar dissolved in tamarind juice and is used in the popular agua de fresca tamarindo in Mexico and in sweet-tart, refreshing tropical cocktails. Appropriately titled the 'lemon of the East', tamarind is used in numerous dishes of Malaysian, Indian, Thai, Indonesian and Central and South American cuisines, including curries, chutneys, hot-and-sour soup and dips for samosas. For a delicious breakfast, drizzle a spoonful or two of tamarind juice or jam atop creamy yogurt and sprinkle with pistachios and a handful of blueberries. It is also added as the surprise tangy ingredient in Worcestershire and brown sauces, barbecue and steak sauces and Angostura bitters. Its tart caramel-like flavour is a delicious change to the usual lemon juice and its healthy nutrients and flavour will get those creative juices flowing!

Tamarind mellows and sweetens with age but keeps indefinitely due to its high acid content. However, be warned that if it sits on the shelf too long, it will become a hard brick.

Rich in tartaric acid, which gives it its super sour flavour, tamarind contains a wealth of B-vitamins, especially thiamine for energy and strength, bone-building minerals, energy-rich potassium and vitamin K and its phytonutrient, one-two antioxidant punch! Its traditional health benefits include relief for dry eye and other optical conditions as well as for digestive and gastric conditions, due to its high fibre content, and is also said to offer relief to those suffering from bile-duct issues.

https://biblio.ugent.be/input/download?func=downloadFile&recordOId=990834&fileOId=1017918

> Tamarind has a tradition of popularity for both its tangy yet sweet flavour profile and its properties as a digestive. Moreover, for centuries, people have found healthful uses for tamarind pulp to alleviate inflammation, sore throats and conjunctivitis. It contains a rich blend of minerals (potassium, calcium, magnesium, selenium, copper, iron and zinc) and vitamins (A, C, E, K, thiamin, riboflavin, niacin and folic acid).
>
> More recently, it has been celebrated for its dietary fibre, which features non-starch polysaccharides (NSP) that include natural gums, hemicelluloses, mucilage, pectin and tannins. The fibre also binds to toxins, which include cancer-promoting chemicals that may be in the food we eat. As a result, this reduces toxin exposure to the lining of the colon and its risk of causing cancer. In addition, tamarind fibre binds to bile salts and reduces their re-entry into the body via the colon. The significance of this is that bile salts are produced by cholesterol and thus their reduction in turn lowers LDL 'lousy' cholesterol, which can form plaques in blood vessels. Tamarind is rich in tartaric acid, which gives a sharply sour taste to food, in addition to its inherent activity as a powerful antioxidant.
>
> Malabar tamarind (*Garcinia gummi-gutta*) as dried fruit contains about 30 per cent hydroxycitric acid (HCA). Recent interest in HCA stems from its activity as a powerful inhibitor of fat formation in animal studies (it has not yet been studied effectively in humans). Also of interest is its demonstration in small-animal studies to reduce consumption of food. It is anticipated that more research will be focused on tamarind for healthy weight.
>
> (Safety note: Tamarind ought to be consumed in dietary amounts to avoid its laxative effect.)

Param Dedhia, MD

CRUSHED AVOCADO AND PINK PEPPERCORN TOAST

A quick fun starter, hors d'oeuvre or appetizer for lunch. Crushing a creamy avocado on top of naturally fermented sourdough instead of wholemeal bread makes this recipe not only more flavourful but also more easily digestible as fermented foods contain naturally occurring probiotics to boost digestive health. It's paired here with quick-pickled radish plus black pepper, which helps increase nutrient absorption.

SERVES 2

2 or 3 radishes, trimmed and cut into matchsticks
3 tbsp rice wine vinegar
1 tbsp minced parsley
large pinch salt
large pinch sugar
2 or 3 slices sourdough bread

60ml (¼ cup) extra virgin olive oil, for brushing bread, plus extra to drizzle on top
1 avocado
40g (1½oz.) crumbled feta
squeeze of lemon juice
½ tsp each pink and black peppercorns, crushed

Put the radishes into a small bowl with the vinegar, parsley, salt and sugar. Mix together and set aside.

Using a knife or cookie cutter, cut the bread into shapes. Brush with olive oil on one side and crisp in a hot pan, or put in a preheated oven set at 180°C (350°F/gas mark 5), until golden brown and toasted.

Peel the avocado, remove the stone, then cut into eight pieces. Place one piece on each piece of toast and crush with a fork. Top with the pickled radishes and feta and sprinkle over a squeeze of lemon juice and some crushed peppercorns.

CUCUMBER AND CORIANDER FIZZ

Not your usual juice squeeze, this delicious combination of spices and fibre-rich veggies topped with fresh blackberries is packed with antioxidants and boosted with peppercorn. Omit the blackberries and add to spicy tomato juice and vodka for a quick and delicious Bloody Mary!

SERVES 2

350g (12oz.) hothouse or Persian cucumber, skin on
½ tsp black peppercorns, toasted and ground
2 tsp coriander seeds, toasted and ground
10g (¼oz./3 tbsp) chopped fresh coriander (cilantro)
15g (½oz.) piece fresh ginger, peeled and grated into a paste or minced (about ¼ cup minced)

4 mint sprigs
2 tbsp lime juice, or to taste
2 tbsp agave syrup or honey, to taste
soda water, to top up
ice cubes, to serve
6 blackberries, to garnish

Blend all the ingredients except the soda water, ice cubes and berries.

Equally divide between two ice-filled glasses and top up with soda water. Garnish with the blackberries.

CORIANDER, PEPPERCORN

SEEDED LAVASH BREADSTICKS

Neither crackers, nor biscuits, these crispy breadsticks are not the usual pizza-dough type but are packed full of flavourful healthy spice. Arrange in tall (well-cleaned) flower vases for a dramatic presentation and serve with your favourite veggie dips, hummus or the Jerusalem Artichoke Dip on page 70.

MAKES ABOUT 36

4 tsp olive oil	4 tsp cumin seeds
1 tsp dry yeast	1 tbsp black cumin (onion or nigella) seeds
1 tbsp mild honey	½ tsp celery seeds
500g (1lb. 2oz./4 cups) bread flour	½ tsp dried rosemary, crumbled
1 tsp kosher salt	olive oil, for brushing
1 tbsp coriander seeds, toasted and ground	sea salt flakes, for finishing
2 tsp peppercorns, toasted and ground	

Pour 300ml (1¼ cups) of warm water (38–50°C/100–120°F) into a stand mixer, or use a large metal bowl with a wooden spoon, add the oil, yeast and honey and mix well using a wooden spoon. Gradually add about one third of the flour, stirring with a dough hook or spoon for 1 minute. Sprinkle in the salt, coriander and pepper, then gradually add the remaining flour and the cumin, black cumin and celery seeds and rosemary, stopping occasionally to scrape down the sides of the bowl with a spatula. Add additional flour as needed if the dough is too sticky.

Knead using the dough hook, or turn the dough out onto a lightly floured wooden board and knead by hand, for a further 10 minutes until smooth and elastic. Place in an oiled container, cover and chill overnight.

The following day, preheat the oven to 200°C fan (400°F/gas mark 6). Punch down the dough and leave it to rest for 30 minutes.

Divide the dough into six pieces, keeping each one covered with cling film (plastic wrap) or a damp clean cloth. Roll out one piece, cover and let it rest as you roll out the others. When the dough is thin and has rested for about 5 minutes, brush with oil. Cut into 30cm (12in.) long breadsticks and leave to rest for a further 5 minutes. Roll out again and sprinkle on the salt flakes. Carefully lift the breadsticks and place them 1cm (½in.) apart on silicone- or parchment-paper-lined baking trays and bake in the oven until golden brown and crisp, about 10–15 minutes.

Cool on wire racks and store in a tightly covered tin layered with parchment paper.

HOT SMOKED LEAF AND CORN SALMON

Peppercorn is good for you. Once worth its weight in gold, and the flashpoint of bloody battles at sea, peppercorn is now quite common, inexpensive and is front and centre on the spice stage. Its active compounds, especially piperine, are enhanced when it is paired with other spices such as turmeric, suggesting that a grind of fresh peppercorn on nearly everything we consume will help the absorption of nutrients in our food. You'll also need wood chips for this recipe – we used manuka and rosemary – soaked in water to avoid fire. The kawakawa leaves used in the seasoning are pepper leaves from a piperine-related bush that grows prolifically in New Zealand. If you are unable to get hold of them, they can be substituted with 6–8 small wild pepper leaves (bai cha plu), available from Thai or Asian grocers.

SERVES 16 AS A CANAPÉ OR 8 AS A STARTER

1kg (2lb. 4oz.) salmon fillet, skin on, deboned

For the brine:

300g (10½oz./1½ cups) brown sugar

175g (6oz./¾ cups) kosher salt

For the seasoning/topping:

1 tbsp manuka honey

1 tsp each of dried whole pink, green, white and black peppercorns

1 tsp toasted fennel seeds, lightly crushed

grated zest 1 lemon

3–4 kawakawa leaves, torn into small pieces (see recipe intro)

a few grinds mixed peppercorns

In a bowl, mix together the ingredients for the brine. Place the salmon fillet, skin side down, in a large roasting dish. Cover the fillet completely in the brine mix and refrigerate for 4–8 hours. The brine mix will draw moisture out of the fillet and turn to liquid.

Wash the brine mix from the fillet under cold water and thoroughly dry using kitchen paper. Let the fish sit in the fridge for a further 1–2 hours. Remove the salmon from the fridge about 30 minutes before you are ready to smoke it to let the fish come to room temperature.

Preheat a hooded barbecue to 200°C (400°F/gas mark 6), placing a small tin bowl of water and the soaked wood chips in a large shallow foil dish on the lower cooking surface. Close the lid.

While the barbecue is heating up, place the salmon skin-side down on an oiled baking rack and, using a pastry brush or your hands, coat with the manuka honey. In a bowl, mix together the remaining seasoning/topping ingredients and sprinkle over the fish.

When the temperature is reached and the wood chips have started smoking, place the baking tray with the salmon on the upper rack of the barbecue. Close the lid and reduce the temperature to 140° (280°F/gas mark 1). Gently smoke for about 2–3 hours, checking every now and then that the wood chips are not burning – you may need to add a few more.

The salmon is ready when creamy spots appear on the outer flesh of the fillet. (This is cooked protein.) Depending on your barbecue, these spots may take less, or more, time to appear. Turn the barbecue off and, leaving the lid up, leave the salmon to cool. Carefully remove from the baking rack and transfer to a serving platter or tightly wrap in cling film (plastic wrap) and chill until needed.

TURKEY, FETA, STUFFING AND CRANBERRY SALAD

What to do with all the winter-holiday, family-gathering leftovers? After a day or two of feasting on family favourites, this is an easy, fun and healthy way to make a little space in the fridge. Instead of making them from scratch (though they are very easy), you could add a hydrated stock cube and a little oil to a cup of leftover stuffing to make the thin croutons that top this light salad, which is finished with spoonfuls of Cranberry Compote and drizzled with a cranberry and coriander seed and (cilantro) leaf vinaigrette.

SERVES 4

300g (10½oz.) rocket or cress and butter lettuce, torn

500g (1lb. 2oz.) cooked turkey, torn into shreds

100g (3½oz.) feta, cut into small cubes

200g (7oz.) Cranberry Compote (see below)

For the stuffing croutons:

40g (1½oz./⅔ cup) breadcrumbs

I tsp poultry seasoning

½ tsp each of garlic and onion powder

pinch each salt, sugar and cayenne pepper

1 tsp ground coriander

3 egg whites

½ chicken or vegetable stock cube, dissolved in ½ tsp hot water

4 tsp vegetable oil

For the vinaigrette (makes 300ml/1¼ cups):

120ml (½ cup) red wine vinegar

3 tbsp cranberry juice

1 garlic clove, minced

1½ tsp lemon juice

1½ tsp toasted ground coriander

1 tbsp minced coriander (cilantro) leaves, plus extra whole leaves to serve

1 tsp roughly chopped tarragon

1 tsp roughly chopped parsley

30g (1oz./¼ cup) dried cranberries

120ml (½ cup) extra virgin olive oil

To make the stuffing croutons, preheat the oven to 190°C (375°F/gas mark 5). Mix the breadcrumbs and seasonings together in a small bowl. In another small bowl, beat the egg whites and dissolved stock cube. Whisk in the oil then gently mix the breadcrumbs into the egg whites. Adjust seasonings. Using a small metal spatula, spread the stuffing batter into little circles or square shapes directly onto a silicone- or parchment-lined baking tray. Sprinkle with flake salt and bake for 10–12 minutes until crisp. To make the vinaigrette, put all the ingredients except oil into a blender with a tight-fitting lid and blend well. With the machine running, slowly drizzle in the oil so it will emulsify together. Season with salt to taste. To assemble, scatter the salad leaves on the plates and top with turkey, feta and teaspoonfuls of Cranberry Compote. Top with croutons. Drizzle the dressing over the top and scatter on a few coriander (cilantro) leaves to finish.

CRANBERRY COMPOTE

MAKES 2¼ CUPS

350g (12oz./3½ cups) cranberries

1 cinnamon stick, charred

200g (7oz./1 cup) granulated sugar

2 allspice berries

1 tangerine, sliced into 4 horizontally

¼ tsp white pepper

large pinch salt

Put all the ingredients into a pan with 240ml (1 cup) of water and bring to a gentle simmer. Cook for about 8 minutes then remove from the heat. Strain out the fruit and spices and set aside. Simmer the liquid until reduced by half.

Return the fruit and spices to the pan and stir to combine. Cool, then cover and chill until needed.

COCOA BUTTER ROASTED VEGGIE SALAD
WITH COCOA NIB VINAIGRETTE

Rachel Pol

'The first time I went to a cocoa farm in my native Panama I fell deeper in love with chocolate. It also made me feel responsible for the Native Indian communities who have abandoned cocoa farming because a fair price is not being met. Since then, we have been working with small growers to improve consistency and fair trade their cocoa beans, encouraging the new generation back into cocoa farming. Besides making our own chocolate from bean to bar with only two ingredients, cocoa nibs and raw sugar, we are constantly finding different ways to use it. Cocoa butter is a high stable fat with a long shelf life, rich in antioxidants. The cocoa nibs are packed with powerful nutrients, antioxidants and mood lifters that add a lovely crunch, with subtle notes of chocolate and a mild nutty flavor. This recipe draws inspiration from the Panamanian Rainforest, where cocoa is grown and root vegetables are widely available.' RP

SERVES 4

1 sweet potato, cut into small wedges
10 baby carrots, halved
20 pearl onions, peeled
1 turnip, cut into small wedges
1 parsnip, sliced diagonally 1cm (½ in.) thick
1 large potato, cut into small wedges
1 butternut squash, peeled and cut into 2.5cm (1in.) cubes
1 fennel bulb, cut into small wedges
1 tsp fennel seeds
1 tsp coriander seeds
1 tsp cumin seeds

3 tbsp cocoa butter, melted
1 tsp salt
55g (2oz./2 cups) fresh rocket (arugula), to serve

For the cocoa nib vinaigrette:
2 tbsp cocoa butter
2 tbsp cocoa nibs
4 tbsp olive oil
2 tbsp rice wine vinegar
½ tsp sugar
1 tsp salt

Preheat the oven to 200°C (400°F/gas mark 6). Spread out all the vegetables on a foil-lined baking tray.

Put the fennel, coriander and cumin seeds in small pan and heat over medium heat for 2 minutes, shaking occasionally. Transfer to a spice grinder and grind to a coarse powder.

Add the melted cocoa butter, spice mixture and salt to the veggies and toss well to coat thoroughly. Roast in the oven for 45 minutes until the veggies are tender and caramelized.

Make the cocoa nib vinaigrette. In a small pan over medium–high heat, melt the cocoa butter, add the nibs and sizzle for 30–45 seconds. Add the olive oil, rice wine vinegar, sugar and salt and take off the heat.

Serve the roast veggies on bed of rocket, drizzled with the cocoa nib vinaigrette.

SWISS RAINBOW CHARD AND FENNEL GRATIN

This is not your typical gratin: the rainbow chard variety 'Bright Lights' is full of pinks, reds, oranges and yellows, which makes a colourful presentation and a moreish way to eat more vegetables. The comforting scent of freshly grated nutmeg in this gratin will bring a smile to your face: nutmeg is thought to combat depression and wrinkles!

SERVES 4

600g (1lb. 5oz.) rainbow chard stems (keep leaves for another use)

2 tbsp grapeseed or vegetable oil

3 large (300g/10½oz.) red onions, chopped

1 tbsp thyme leaves

475ml (2 cups) full-fat (whole) milk

1 large fennel bulb, cored and sliced vertically into thin pieces

½ tsp fennel seeds, lightly toasted and ground

2 bay leaves, cut in quarters

3 garlic cloves, peeled and thinly sliced

2 tsp freshly grated nutmeg

1 tsp ground mace

3 tbsp butter or oil

3 tbsp flour

1 tsp ground white pepper

200g (7oz.) Havarti cheese, grated

50g (1¾oz.) hard cheese, e.g. Pecorino, Parmesan or mature Cheddar, grated

85g (3oz./1¼ cup) panko or dry breadcrumbs, seasoned with a pinch each salt, pepper, thyme leaves and paprika

juice of ½ lemon

paprika, for sprinkling on top

Preheat the oven to 180°C (350°F/gas mark 4). Remove the strings from the outer edges of the chard stems and trim the stems to about 15cm (6in.) in length, depending on the size of your baking dish. Add the stems to a large pan of boiling salted water and blanch until fork tender. Drain and set aside.

Heat the oil in a cast-iron or heavy pan on low heat and sauté the onion and thyme leaves until soft.

While the onions cook, gently warm the milk in a small saucepan and add the fennel bulb and seeds, bay leaf, garlic, nutmeg and mace. Poach the fennel until fork tender, then take off the heat. When cooled, strain the milk into a jug and reserve the fennel.

Melt the butter or oil over medium–low heat in a 1-litre (1-quart) pan and sprinkle in the flour and pepper. Whisk until it becomes a thick paste, then pour in one third of the seasoned milk. Add the remaining milk in stages, continuing to whisk for 2–3 minutes until smooth; the sauce will thicken as it cooks. Take off the heat and set aside.

To assemble the gratin, sprinkle a layer of seasoned breadcrumbs on the bottom of an oiled 30cm (12in.) square casserole, baking dish or loaf pan. Next arrange half the chard, side by side like matchsticks, spread over a layer of sauce, then a layer of onion followed by one of fennel, a squeeze of lemon juice and salt and pepper to taste and a layer of Havarti cheese. Repeat these layers, topping the final layer with breadcrumbs then the Parmesan. Sprinkle a little paprika over the top and place the casserole on a foil-lined baking tray and, with your hands, press the gratin down to compact the layers. Bake for 45 minutes until golden brown and bubbly. Remove from the oven and leave to settle for 30 minutes. Serve just warmed.

GREEN CHILLI PRAWN CEVICHE
WITH PALM-SUGAR POPCORN
Christine Manfield

'Coriander seeds are one of the most useful spices to have in the kitchen: they balance other more pungent spices and are a wonderful partner to myriad aromatic flavours. The harmonious fusion of flavours and textures in this ceviche preparation takes its inspiration from South America. Rather than using fresh corn, I have spiced up popcorn with ground coriander seeds and salt tossed through a palm sugar caramel to give the popcorn a real flavour boost and complement the green chili, lime juice and ginger in the tiger's milk dressing. Avoid using tiger prawns (shrimp) as the flesh is too firm for this recipe.' CM

SERVES 6

400g (14oz.) raw sashimi-grade shelled and deveined banana (or king) prawns (shrimp), sliced on the diagonal

½ avocado, diced

½ green (unripe) mango, peeled and julienne sliced

6 pomelo or grapefruit segments, broken into small pieces

½ small cucumber, peeled, seeded and julienne sliced

6 yellow grape tomatoes, quartered

1 small red onion, finely diced

½ long green chili, seeded and finely sliced

handful watercress leaves, stems removed

handful roughly chopped coriander (cilantro) leaves

1 punnet green shiso cress, snipped

For the tiger's milk dressing:

4 small green chilies, chopped

½ small fennel bulb, chopped

2 tsp chopped coriander (cilantro) roots

2 tbsp coriander (cilantro) leaves

1 small green tomato, chopped

2 small garlic cloves, chopped

1 golden shallot, chopped

2 tbsp chopped fresh ginger

zest of 1 lime

zest of ½ orange (or mandarin)

60ml (¼ cup) lime juice

1 tbsp caster (superfine) sugar

50ml (scant ¼ cup) extra virgin olive oil

For the palm-sugar popcorn:

3 tbsp grapeseed or vegetable oil

115g (4oz./½ cup) popping corn

85g (3oz./scant ½ cup) palm sugar

1 tsp coriander seeds, toasted and ground

1 tsp sea salt flakes

First make the tiger's milk dressing: process everything together in a blender until smooth. Keep refrigerated until ready to serve.

To prepare the popcorn, pour enough oil into a small saucepan to just cover the base and heat over low–medium heat. When hot, add the popcorn and cover with a lid. Shake the saucepan regularly until the corn has finished popping. Remove from heat and pour onto a flat tray.

Heat the palm sugar with 1 tablespoon of water in a saucepan and cook until caramel colour. Pour over the popcorn and stir with a chopstick to evenly coat. Sprinkle over the coriander and salt.

Put the prawns into a bowl, pour over the dressing and leave to marinate for 5 minutes. Add all the salad ingredients and mix gently with your hands.

Arrange the ceviche onto serving plates, scatter the palm-sugar popcorn over the top and serve.

WHOLE ROASTED FISH
WITH COCOA BUTTER AND TOMATO-ONION RELISH
François Kwaku-Dongo

'Every country has a street food that is typical of its region. In Abidjan, where I grew up, on the Ivory Coast in West Africa, everyone will tell you about 'poisson braisé avec attiéké'. It's a favourite childhood food memory and is basically fish braised on charcoal served with hot sauce and cassava grain. Cocoa butter, a major ingredient in chocolate making, can also be used in savoury dishes. Here, I use cocoa butter instead of butter or oil to roast my fish, which gives it a nutty aroma.' FKD

SERVES 4

4 x 550g (1lb. 4oz.) whole fish such as sea bream, striped bass or tilapia, scaled and gutted

140g (5oz./⅔ cup) melted cocoa butter

1 tsp kosher salt

1 tsp ground black pepper

½ bunch parsley, including stems

For the tomato-onion relish:

1 medium (140g/5oz.) yellow onion, quartered and thinly sliced

1 small (140g/5oz.) vine-ripe tomato, peeled and thinly sliced

1 tsp kosher salt

½ tsp ground black pepper

½ tsp bird's-eye chili, seeded and minced

60ml (¼ cup) white vinegar

3 tbsp vegetable oil

100g (3½oz./½ cup) melted cocoa butter

1½ bunches curly parsley, chopped

For the cassava grain:

275g (9¾oz./1½ cup) cassava grain or couscous

100g (3½oz./½ cup) melted cocoa butter

40g (1½oz./2 heaped tbsp) minced garlic

40g (1½oz./2 heaped tbsp) minced fresh ginger

1 spring onion (scallion), finely chopped

½ bunch curly parsley, finely chopped

1 tsp kosher salt

½ tsp ground black pepper

Preheat the oven to 190C° (375°F/gas mark 5). Set the fish in a large, shallow roasting pan, brush all over with the melted cocoa butter and season generously inside and out with salt and pepper. Stuff the cavity with the parsley.

Roast the fish in the centre of the oven for about 20 minutes, occasionally spooning the pan juices over the fish. The fish is done when the flesh is white throughout and an instant-read thermometer inserted into the thickest part near the head registers 57°C (135°F). Let the fish stand for 10 minutes, then carefully transfer it to a large platter and remove the parsley.

While the fish is roasting, prepare the relish. Toss all the ingredients together in a mixing bowl.

Prepare the cassava grain. Set up a double boiler. Put the cassava in a medium-sized bowl and cover with cling film (plastic wrap). Set the bowl on top of the boiling water and steam until soft, about 5 minutes. Set aside. (If using couscous, follow package directions.)

Meanwhile, heat the cocoa butter in a saucepan, add the garlic and ginger and cook until soft. Add the cassava grain and stir well. Cook for 3 minutes then remove from the heat and transfer to a mixing bowl. Stir in the spring onion (scallion) and parsley and season with salt and pepper.

To serve, spoon the relish over the fish and serve the cassava grain at room temperature on the side.

TAMARIND AND TAHITIAN LIME ROASTED DUCK
WITH GINGER-ONION CONFIT AND CRACKLING

This duck dish was originally created in 2001 for Cuisines of the Sun, a food and wine event in Hawaii. It was judged by the late, brilliant and formidable chef Jean-Louis Palladin as his favourite dish of the night. Packed with sweet tamarind, fragrant tropical spices, thin-skinned tropical limes and topped with warming ginger-onion confit, the duck is served with Crispy Cardamom Polenta (see page 157) and earthy roasted baby beetroot.

SERVES 6

1.5kg (3lb. 5oz.) duck legs and thighs, bone in, skin on

4 tbsp olive oil, plus a little for roasting the beetroot

4 tbsp dry sherry

475ml (2 cups) roasted duck or chicken stock

2 fresh or 4 dried kaffir lime leaves, bruised

5cm (2in.) piece fresh ginger, peeled

250g (9oz.) tamarind paste

6 small red, yellow or candycane baby beetroot, trimmed

1 tsp ground allspice

juice and zest of 2 Tahitian, Mexican or Italian limes

4 tbsp sweet chili sauce

1 tbsp kecap manis (Indonesian sweet soy sauce)

1 tbsp soy sauce

Crispy Cardamom Polenta (see page 157), to serve

1 small handful watercress, to garnish

1 small bunch chives, chopped, to garnish

For the spice mix:

½ star anise

2 allspice berries

½ cinnamon stick

For the ginger-onion confit:

100g (3½oz./¾ stick + 1 tbsp) butter

4 large onions, halved and thinly sliced

5cm (2in.) piece fresh ginger, peeled and finely chopped

Preheat the oven to 180°C (350°F/gas mark 4).

First make the spice mix. Heat a small pan over medium heat and toast all the spices until fragrant. Set aside.

To prepare the duck, trim off any excess skin from the meat and set aside in the fridge to make crackling later. Heat the oil in a large ovenproof pan over medium heat and fry the duck on all sides until the skin is crisp and golden brown. Drain the duck on kitchen paper and set aside. Return the pan to the heat and add the sherry. Cook for 2 minutes to deglaze the pan then remove from the heat. Add the prepared spice mix to the pan along with the stock, lime leaves, ginger, tamarind paste and duck legs and thighs. Stir everything to combine, cover with a tight-fitting lid and transfer to the oven to cook for 1½ hours or until fork tender.

Cut the baby beetroot vertically in half and place in a small roasting pan with a little oil and a sprinkle of salt and roast in the oven until soft, about 25 minutes. Cool and then peel and cut in half. Keep warm.

To make the crackling, slice the reserved duck skin into 5mm (¼in) pieces and place on a baking tray. Sprinkle with the ground allspice and roast in the oven with the duck for 30 minutes, until crispy and the duck fat is a clear yellow colour. Remove from the oven and drain on kitchen paper. Keep warm.

To make the ginger-onion confit, melt the butter in a frying pan (skillet) over medium heat, then add the onions and ginger. Cook slowly, stirring occasionally, until the onions are soft and golden. Season to taste and set aside.

When the duck is cooked, remove from the oven and lift the duck pieces out of the pan onto a chopping board. Shred the meat, discarding the skin and bones. Transfer the meat to a medium pan. Strain the cooking liquid then pour the liquid over the duck meat and stir in the lime zest and juice, chili sauce, kecap manis and soy sauce. Bring to a gentle simmer, season to taste, cover and keep warm.

To assemble the dish, place the polenta pieces in the centre of six serving plates and spoon over the duck. Spoon the ginger-onion confit around the duck and top with the roasted beetroot and duck-skin crackling. Serve garnished with watercress and chives.

FLEMISH PEPPERCORN RIB EYE STEAK
WITH CHILI-DUSTED TOBACCO ONIONS

This steak and its alluring peppercorn sauce brings back memories of moving as a teen to Europe – my backpack full of ballet slippers and a tiny Berlitz dictionary – where I landed a job with the Royal Ballet of Flanders in Belgium, somewhere I didn't understand the local language, but made fast friends with a neighbouring family of gourmet cooks. The tobacco onions, also called angry onions, have the hot kick from a pepper-paprika blend and are simple to prepare and cook and even easier to eat.

SERVES 4

4 x 225g (8oz.) rib-eye (or Scotch fillet) steaks

For the peppercorn sauce:

240ml (1 cup) demi-glace, veal or beef stock

120ml (½ cup) double (heavy) cream

60ml (¼ cup) cognac or brandy

60ml (¼ cup) Syrah, Zinfandel or other peppery red wine

4 thyme sprigs

3 tbsp green peppercorns in brine, drained, liquid reserved

2 tbsp unsalted butter

pinch brown sugar to taste

For the chili-dusted tobacco onions:

1 litre (1 quart) peanut (groundnut) or vegetable oil

125g (4½oz./1 cup) self-raising flour

1 tbsp fine polenta (cornmeal)

1 tsp salt

1 tsp sweet Hungarian paprika

½ tsp ground black pepper

½ tsp cayenne

½ tsp smoked paprika or chipotle powder

½ tsp ground cardamom

3 large (350g/12oz. total weight) yellow or sweet onions, thinly sliced into 3mm (⅛ in.) rings

To make the sauce, whisk the demi-glace or stock, cream, cognac, wine and thyme together in a saucepan and bring to a simmer. Reduce by a third. Crush 1 tablespoon of the peppercorns, then add them all, with a little juice from the jar, to the pan. Whisk in the butter a little at a time using a wire whisk to thicken the sauce until it is smooth. Remove the thyme sprigs then season to taste with a pinch of brown sugar.

Make the chili-dusted tobacco onions. Heat the oven to 110°C (225°F/gas mark ¼). Line a baking tray with kitchen paper and set aside.

Heat the oil to 180° (350°F) on a food thermometer in a deep saucepan over medium heat. Whisk all the remaining ingredients except the onion rings in a medium-sized bowl. Add the onion rings and carefully toss to coat. Remove the onion from the flour mixture, shaking to remove excess, and spread out on a plate or tray. Fry the onions in the hot oil a few slices at a time for approximately 10 minutes or until crisp and golden brown, making sure you don't overcrowd the pan. Use a slotted spoon to remove the onions and drain immediately on kitchen paper. Repeat until all onions are fried. Keep them warm in the oven while you cook the steak.

Heat a barbecue or flattop grill to high or place a frying pan (skillet) over high heat until the pan is sizzling hot to sear the steaks. Pat the steaks dry, then brush them with oil on both sides and season with salt. Sear on the first side over high heat for about 3 minutes. Turn the steaks over and cook an additional 5–7 minutes for medium-rare. Remove the steaks from the grill, or the frying pan (skillet) from the heat, and leave to rest for 5 minutes.

To serve, spoon the peppercorn sauce over the steak (or on the side) and top with the onion rings. Serve with a luscious red wine or Belgian beer.

TOASTED PEPPER, LEMON AND STRAWBERRY SWIRL ICE CREAM

Black pepper is a surprising companion to sweet summer berries and here adds an addictively spicy base note to a creamy lemon- and strawberry-infused ice cream. Have fun with your guests when asking them to guess the flavour; they will be mystified when trying to settle on the secret ingredient but will be instantly converted to its aromatic charms.

SERVES 6

For the ice cream:	**For the strawberry compote:**
zest of 2 lemons	340g (12oz) strawberries
100g (3½oz/½ cup) caster (superfine) sugar	100g (3½oz./½ cup) caster (superfine) sugar
1½ tsp black peppercorns, toasted and ground	2 tsp limoncello
pinch salt	pinch salt
150ml (⅔ cup) freshly squeezed lemon juice	
480ml (2 cups) crème fraîche	

Put the lemon zest, sugar, peppercorns and salt into the bowl of a food processor or blender and process until the zest is fine and well combined. Add the lemon juice and blend until the sugar dissolves. With the motor running, add the crème fraîche. Cover and chill for 1–3 hours to allow the flavours to meld.

Wash, hull and slice the strawberries into a bowl. Add the sugar, limoncello and a pinch of salt and fold until the strawberries are coated. Lightly mash with a fork. Cover and let stand for an hour, stirring occasionally, then chill for 1–3 hours.

Freeze the lemon mixture in an ice-cream maker, following the manufacturer's instructions, or pour into a dish and freeze, stirring occasionally, until frozen.

Layer a third of the lemon ice cream into a freezer container, then add a third of the strawberry compote. Repeat these layers twice more, then cover and freeze.

PUMPKIN BREAD PUDDING

Nutmeg, and its webbed coral-red mace wrapper, has almost as strong an olfactory memory recall as the spice vanilla. It's also believed to help with memory, so go on, allow yourself another spoonful of this delicious dessert!

SERVES 6

375g (13oz./1½ cups) puréed roasted pumpkin or butternut squash
240ml (1 cup) double (heavy) cream
1 tsp sea salt
1 tbsp freshly grated ginger
1 tsp ground cinnamon
1 tsp freshly ground nutmeg
1 tsp ground mace
85g (3oz./¼ cup) molasses or treacle
210g (7½oz./⅔ cup) maple syrup

½ tbsp pure vanilla extract
1 tbsp brandy
4 large eggs
4 croissants, sliced horizontally and toasted
250g (9oz.) pitted prunes, cut into small dice
60g (2¼oz./scant ½ cup) crystallized ginger, chopped
300g (10½oz/scant 1 cup) Cranberry Compote (see page 108)
butter, for buttering the dish
nutmeg-dusted whipped cream or vanilla ice cream, to serve (optional)

In a large bowl, combine the puréed pumpkin, cream, salt, ginger, cinnamon, nutmeg, mace, molasses, maple syrup, vanilla, brandy and eggs and beat well.

Add the toasted croissant slices and gently turn over in the custard mixture until they are thoroughly coated. (You might want to wear gloves as it's really gooey!) Using your hands or a large spoon, layer the croissants into the prepared dish, sprinkling with the chopped prunes, crystallized ginger and Cranberry Compote (see page 106) between each layer and finishing with a layer of croissant. Tightly cover the dish with cling film (plastic wrap) then foil. Refrigerate and allow to soak for at least 1 hour or preferably overnight.

Preheat the oven to 160°C (325°F/gas mark 3). Butter a deep casserole dish.

Bake in the oven for about 1 hour (a knife inserted in the centre should come out clean). Remove the cling film (plastic wrap) and foil and bake for an additional 15 minutes to lightly brown the top. Remove from the oven and let cool to room temperature.

To serve, cut into slices, gently heat in the oven or microwave and serve with a spoonful of nutmeg-dusted whipped cream or vanilla ice cream.

COCOA NIB, SEED AND CHERRY BARS

Lovely, luxurious, crunchy cocoa nibs not only taste delicious but they're also good for the heart, thanks to the flavanols. These easy-to-make-and-take bars are full of them, as well as those 'happy-brain' cherry anthocyanins.

MAKES ABOUT 16 SQUARES

115g (4oz./1¼ cups) rolled oats, toasted (do not use quick-cooking oats)

100g (3½oz./¾ cup) Brazil nuts, roughly chopped

2 tbsp chia seeds

30g (1oz./¼ cup) sunflower seeds

3 tbsp cocoa nibs

90g (3¼oz./¾ cup) dried cherries or cranberries

55g (2oz./scant ⅓ cup) crystallized ginger

40g (1½oz./½ cup) unsweetened coconut flakes (chips)

6 tbsp (90ml/⅓ cup) runny honey or date syrup

125g (4½oz./½ cup) sunflower or nut butter (such as peanut or almond butter)

Preheat oven to 160°C (325°F/gas mark 3).

In a food processor, pulse the oats, Brazil nuts, chia and sunflower seeds, cocoa nibs, dried cherries or cranberries and ginger until finely chopped. Fold in the coconut flakes (chips) then add the honey and sunflower or nut butter, mixing to combine. Pour the mixture into a 23cm (9in.) square (or small rectangular) pan. Press to flatten and level the top and bake for 20 minutes. Cool and cut into bite-sized squares or bars.

SPICED COCOA NIB COFFEE

What better way to enjoy a bit of good-for-you cocoa? Teamed up with some more favourite spices, this is a warm comfortable way to get your daily dose of flavanols.

SERVES 2

115g (4oz./1 cup) cocoa nibs

⅛ tsp cardamom seeds

1 allspice berry

½ cinnamon stick, broken into chips

½ vanilla pod (bean), chopped

whole milk, coconut or almond milk and sweetener to serve (optional)

Put the cocoa nibs, cardamom, allspice and cinnamon in a sauté pan and toast over low heat for about 10 minutes, until fragrant, swirling the pan to prevent the spices burning.

Grind the toasted spices with the chopped vanilla in a spice grinder until the mixture resembles coffee grounds. This will make more than you need, so store tightly sealed in a jar or tin to save for another day.

Spoon 7 tablespoons of the cocoa blend into a French press. Pour in 475ml (2 cups) of filtered boiling water, cover with a cloth or cozy to keep warm and steep for 7–10 minutes. Press the plunger down and pour into two cups or mugs. Serve with your favourite kind of warmed milk and sweetener if you wish.

VALENCIA SMOOTHIE

The winning combination of orange, cocoa powder and cold-brew coffee is a natural low-sugar pick-me-up.

SERVES 1

3 tbsp oats	juice and zest of ½ orange
35g (1¼oz./¼ cup) raw cashew nuts	1 banana, sliced
1 tbsp cocoa powder	2 pitted dates, chopped
pinch kosher salt	120ml (½ cup) cold-brew coffee
generous pinch cardamom	4 cracked ice cubes
¼ tsp cinnamon	

Soak the oats and cashew nuts in 60ml (¼ cup) water overnight.

Drain the oats and cashew nuts and put in a single-serve juicer-blender with all the remaining ingredients and blend until smooth.

Pour into a tall glass and serve immediately.

TAMARIND, NUTMEG, STAR ANISE

TAMARIND SMOOTHIE

Tamarind looks like a dusty brown flavourless legume, but the pod hides a wealth of rich flavours, ancient remedies and promising and unusual talents, from alleviating dry-eye syndrome to counteracting kidney stones. The tamarind spice purée can be made two days ahead of time and can be doubled easily.

SERVES 1

1 heaped tbsp tamarind paste	1 tsp lemon juice
¼ tsp ground cinnamon	sprinkle of lemon zest
¼ star anise (⅛ tsp ground)	240ml (1 cup) coconut milk
½ vanilla pod (bean) or ¼ tsp ground vanilla powder or pure vanilla extract	ice cubes, to finish (optional)
	freshly grated nutmeg, to serve
1 tbsp coconut sugar, or to taste	
1 medium-sized apple, cored and sliced into quarters	

Put the tamarind paste into a pan with 175ml (¾ cup) of water and boil until smooth. Strain the juice back into the pan and discard the tamarind seed.

Bring the juice back to the boil, add the cinnamon, star anise, vanilla and coconut sugar. Remove from the heat and leave to cool. Once cool, remove the vanilla pod (bean) and star anise, or leave the star anise to blend into the smoothie.

Put the tamarind juice into a blender and add the apple and lemon juice and zest. Blend in the coconut milk, adding ice cubes to thicken. (For a thicker smoothie, freeze the coconut milk into cubes.) Dust with freshly grated nutmeg and serve.

Warming spice

When there's a chill in the air, these spices will provide warmth to body and soul, leaving you with a healthy glow from their alleged ability to increase circulation, open pores and sinuses and stimulate the body's defence mechanisms to stave off chills, aches, pains and disease.

Warming Spice Health Heroes
Chili Pepper ★ Ginger ★ Mustard Seed ★ Horseradish ★ Wasabi

An infusion of warming spices ground and blended together – spicy, sweet, brain-fog-clearing ginger; tangy, sharp, pulmonary-clearing cardamom; tummy-soothing, maple-scented fenugreek; a grating of digestive-easing nutmeg; and the toasty bio-enabler peppercorn – is a recipe that will warm your insides with phytonutrients and power-packed vitamins. But whether you include them in a spice-infused tisane; a toddy of cold-fighting garlic, honey, lemon and ginger; or a rich, spice-rubbed roast dinner, the comforting, healing aromas and flavours of these spices will provide a rush of health-protective and feel-good endorphins that will push away the winter blues.

Chili peppers cause our pain sensors to rapidly release fight-or-flight endorphins that flood the taste buds and the brain then rush to the circulatory and digestive systems with warming-to-the-bone capsaicin. Horseradish is a circulatory-system star, a super antiseptic and a strong decongestant that helps open blocked respiratory passages. Ginger is said to improve circulation and is recognized as a spice with a talent for warming the body. It has been used for hundreds of years in traditional medicine as a diaphoretic to open the pores and induce sweating, increasing circulation and heat. Mustard seed may support the circulatory system with its large number of minerals, including iron, manganese and copper, which team together with active isothiocyanates (disease-preventing compounds) to warm and strengthen the body. Wasabi has similar attributes to horseradish and also contains warming isothiocyanate compounds and circulation-boosting properties.

Other warming spice heroes

Garlic This super-warming and stimulating antioxidant and antimicrobial hero of ancient Greek and Chinese medicine was fed to Egyptian slaves to give them good health and long-lasting strength. Its heating and stimulating effects have been recognized for thousands of years and it has been used as a remedy to treat everything from the common cold to contagious diseases.

Cardamom A fragrant pungent and warming spice used in chai tea, cardamom helps to lower blood pressure. Its most active oil, cineole, impressively both antibacterial and an antioxidant, has been recently trialled as an aid for asthma and other respiratory ailments, showing great promise.

Cumin The divine aroma of cumin seeds roasting in a pan will stimulate your taste buds, which is the first step towards good digestion. Cumin is considered a warming spice as it boosts blood circulation, improves the flow of oxygen through your cells, aids digestion and staves off the effects of food poisoning in the digestive system with its antibacterial power. It also helps to loosen phlegm and is a powerful expectorant. Black cumin, or nigella, has appetite-stimulating characteristics and is a natural thermogenic (heat-producer).

Black Peppercorn These pungent balls act as a warming bio-enabler, increasing blood flow and maximizing absorption and benefit of other nutrients. They are also good for easing discomfort in the digestive tract, reducing gas while increasing hydrochloric acid in the stomach, which helps to reduce stomach distress and fight bacterial growth in the intestines.

Fenugreek One of the earliest plants known to have been used medicinally, fenugreek may improve liver function and reduces pain with its warming, diaphoretic (perspiration-inducing) attributes. The raw seeds, softened by soaking in warm water, have traditionally been used to treat sluggish digestion. Fenugreek also relieves muscle and joint pain by increasing blood flow and reducing inflammation.

Nutmeg Said to help eliminate toxins in the body through supporting liver and gallbladder functions, nutmeg is thought to be especially beneficial to those suffering from liver disease. Nutmeg oil can warm and ease stomachaches by removing the excess gas from your intestines and is also thought to increase appetite.

Chili Pepper *The Endorphin Spice*

Known and grown around the world, chili peppers are native to the Americas, where they have been consumed since 6000BC. The Mayans had a great idea: I'm hooked on lattes boosted with a spoonful of raw cocoa powder, toasted Ceylon cinnamon and just a dash of hot chili powder (though the authentic version is a little extreme on the Scoville heat scale for me)!

Christopher Columbus is credited for having 'discovered' capsicums (family members include the heatless green bell pepper, the scorchingly hot scotch bonnet and some 3,000 other relatives) while searching, unsuccessfully, for black pepper. Soon thereafter, chili seeds travelled aboard Spanish and Portuguese galleons and were soon scattered into the far reaches of India, China, Indonesia, Africa and Europe.

Several studies have demonstrated the antioxidant properties in chili and its ability to scavenge free radicals, reduce antioxidative stress and promote cellular integrity. It turns out that chili-consuming countries generally have lower rates of cardiovascular disease than populations that eat a bland diet.

The hotter the chili pepper, the more capsaicin it contains, the highest levels of this alkaloid being found in the chili seeds and inner 'rib' membrane, accounting for the hot spicy sensation one experiences and that 'chili heads' crave to distraction. When you eat a capsaicin-laden chili, your body's pain receptors react immediately: Ouch! That's really hot! Then the body releases endorphins, natural morphine-like compounds that flood the body in immediate response to pain and are thought to be one of the strongest drugs produced in the body. There may be an instant welling of tears, but soon after, you get an exultant whoosh, a runner's high – a chili rush of pain, then chili pleasure. Incidentally, chili is considered an aphrodisiac for that very reason. It has also been credited with inducing a euphoric sense of wellbeing and enhancing mood, alertness and improved physical coordination.

Another good reason to eat chilies is, of course, their flavour: they simply make food taste better, from South African piri piri chicken, to Mexican Pork Chile Verde (see Anne Conness's version on page 40) and from Chinese kung pao chicken to India's vegetarian vindaloo curries. Mexican culture has two names for nearly every one of the country's 150 varieties of chili: a fresh green jalapeño, for instance, becomes a rich dark-red chipotle when dried. Dried chilies have a concentrated, complex and sweeter flavour, lasting an indeterminate amount of time as long as kept covered and dry. Fresh chilies come in shades of green, yellow, orange, red, purple and black and have a freshness and hydrating bite of heat, perfect for fresh salsas, sauces, gazpacho (see pages 144–5) and vegetarian dishes.

When buying fresh chilies, feel for firmness and look for ones that have shiny dry skin and are heavy for their size. Stored loosely and dry in the fridge, they will keep for about two weeks. They will also freeze well if tightly wrapped.

> It's the capsaicin in chilies (concentrated most of all in the seed pod, then the ribs, then the seeds and a modest amount, comparatively, in the flesh) that makes your nose run and your palate tingle. That tingle, a jangling of the seventh cranial nerve and not one of the five or six flavours, depending on who you believe, is good for you: it has helped people with cluster headaches, diabetic neuropathic pain and irritable bowel syndrome. Capsaicin has been commercialized: it's in patches, capsules, creams and nasal sprays, and available over the pharmacy counter.
>
> Capsaicin works by depleting the body's nerve fibres of substance P, a neurotransmitter the body employs to transmit pain from one place to another. Capsaicin also desensitizes the GI tract to pain in those who already have pain. Hotter chilies seem to have more benefits, including an improved ability to clear insulin from the bloodstream. By the way, a chili's excessive heat can be turned down by rinsing your mouth with something cold (5 degrees C) – it does not have to be milk or something sugary, though both of those cold solutions work. Sadly, beer does not work better than water. **"**

John La Puma, MD

http://www.ncbi.nlm.nih.gov/pubmed/7708405 cluster ha; http://www.ncbi.nlm.nih.gov/pubmed/21573941 IBD; http://www.ncbi.nlm.nih.govpubmed/24867591 IBD-more; http://www.ncbi.nlm.nih.gov/pubmed/2385629

Ginger *The Balancing Spice*

My partner, mother and siblings are all comfortable and relaxed gliding along in a sailing boat. I love the gentle ocean breezes, monitoring the anchor, making simple meals in the galley and working the winches for the sails to securely hold the wind, but when the sea surface becomes like the inside of a washing machine, it's time to reach for that bit of ginger in hope that my queasy tummy will subside as my ballet brain fights for equilibrium to balance that salty sea foundation.

Ginger, a rhizome that most likely originated in Southern China or Northern India, has been grown since ancient times and used ever since to ease digestion and nausea. The pungent spicy-hot taste of fresh ginger is due to gingerols, the dominant compound, which is converted to a gentler sweeter essence, zingerone, when cooked. Dry ground ginger is more pungent than fresh because gingerol converts to the concentrated form, shogaol. Candied or crystallized ginger is made by simmering fresh ginger pieces in sugar syrup, dredging in granulated sugar and drying them. Pink sushi ginger or nori, which is used as a sushi garnish, is thinly sliced ginger, pickled with sugar, rice wine vinegar and salt. Ginger is also bottled and fermented to make ginger beer and made into ginger oil to flavour food and drink or use as medicine.

Ginger (*Zingiber officinale*) is also a potential brain tonic and super food: a large test-study of middle-aged and elderly women showed that ginger can improve brain function in such tasks as singular focused thinking, cognitive skills and memory and can protect against age-related damage to the brain, with no obvious side effects. Ginger's antibacterial chemistry is also effective against gum disease such as gingivitis and periodontitis.

Current pharmacological research indicates the urgent need for the development of new, safe and efficacious drugs to help reduce the global burden of tuberculosis, on which current-day antibiotics have little effect and are impossibly difficult to logistically distribute to the millions of people in need, the majority of whom live in remote villages. Natural products, especially those from the phytogenetic (plant-based) environment have been less intensively researched, even though they are known to contain structurally diverse active compounds and have been used as traditional cures for centuries. A medical research team has been investigating Ghanaian medicinal plants that include *Zingiber officinale* for their antituberculosis activity. Traditionally used by Ghanaian communities to treat coughs and other disease conditions with symptoms of tuberculosis, this handful of plant life is being studied as a possible channel towards prevention or cure of this most infectious and deadly disease.

Galangal (the word is derived from the Chinese for ginger) is likewise a rhizome. Used in Thai, Malay and Indonesian cuisine, galangal has a thinner, lighter pinkish skin and a hotter but more delicate taste and is grown almost exclusively in India and Eastern and Southeastern countries. Lesser galangal is the type most used for traditional medicinal purposes. Rich in iron, sodium and vitamins A and C, it is used in similar traditional cures to ginger.

www.ncbi.nlm.nih.gov/pmc/articles/PMC4801013/

'The underground stem or rhizome of *Zingiber officinale*, edible yellow ginger is a super spice. Fresh ginger juice is used for treating burns, and the essential oils have been used to relieve pain. Ginger can slow inflammation in the body, protect DNA, quell nausea (especially in pregnancy), treat motion sickness and indigestion and even migraine. Migraine? Barely an eighth of a teaspoon (540mg) of powdered ginger, dissolved in water, was tested against sumatriptan, a potent, approved, injectable migraine drug, and found to be equivalent when given at the very start of the headache: similar pain relief within two hours. How might ginger work to help headaches? It may stop the production of chemicals called prostaglandins, which mediate inflammation in the body and cause muscle contractions. I like to have people use food instead of extracts when they can... and ginger comes crystalized, in lollipops and syrups.

Note: there is mixed data about an interaction between ginger and the anticoagulant medication Coumadin, so if you are taking the latter, talk to your doctor about both.'

John La Puma, MD

http://www.ncbi.nlm.nih.gov/pubmed/23657930; http://www.ncbi.nlm.nih.gov/pubmed/26488162

Mustard Seed *The Prevention Spice*

The tiny mustard seed, a member of the brassica genus (which includes broccoli, Brussels sprouts and kale), is full of goodness and promising disease-prevention properties. These little seeds initially have no aroma, but when activated with the addition of liquid, such as water or vinegar, they release enzymes that create an intensely strong nose-running flavour, full of minerals and vitamins, including selenium, magnesium, B-complex vitamins and antioxidants A, C and K. Mustard seed will keep indefinitely.

Mustard may improve immunity and contains a large number of minerals that support the circulatory system (iron, manganese and copper), which team up with the warming properties of active isothiocyanates (sulphur phytochemicals, disease-preventative compounds that also gives cruciferous vegetables their memorable taste) to strengthen the body.

There are many species of mustard, but the most commonly used for food and food medicines are the oily mustard seeds, called condiment mustard. Mustard has always been of importance in Europe as it is one of the few spices that grows locally and quite prolifically so is inexpensive to acquire. The common white or yellow mustard, *Sinapas alba* is often 'prepared' with the addition of vinegar, turmeric, salt and 'secret seasonings', usually sold in squeezy bottles and extensively used in the US to top hamburgers and hot dogs. In Britain, water is added to dried yellow mustard powder and served as a nose-tingling addition to hot and cold roasts, or cooked with vegetables and vinegar to make the bright yellow condiment piccalilli. The sweet-and-spicy Italian version, mostarda di frutta, is traditionally made with powdered mustard, quince and fresh fruits. Both are favourites with cheese boards or served alongside cooked cold chicken and meats.

Brown (also called Chinese) mustard, *Brassica juncea*, was traditionally made with grape must 'mustard' or wine plus vinegar, salt and honey (see Vanilla Honey Mustard, page 164) and both whole-grain and ground prepared mustard is popular all over Europe. In France, three main types of mustard are treasured: Bordeaux mustard, mild and brown, contains vinegar, sugar and often tarragon or other soft herbs; Dijon is creamy yellow and strongly flavoured; moutarde à l'ancienne, made of crushed mustard seeds, has a mild taste. Germany has its own mustard, similar to the Bordeaux style, sometimes including beer, which is served with its world-famous sausages. Mustard is also an important ingredient in traditional sauerkraut and other naturally fermented vegetables.

The tiny black mustard seed (*Brassica nigra*) contains considerably more heat and is used almost exclusively in Indian and Eastern cuisine. The seeds are fried in hot oil to tame the pungent heat and impart a nutty flavour.

Mustard oil is made from brown mustard seed and other mustard species. It is used in Eastern cuisine and has strong preserving qualities so is added to pickles and chutneys. Mustard oil is also used, surprisingly, as a traditional topical treatment to stimulate hair growth.

❝ The seeds of the cruciferous mustard plant, which come in yellow, brown and black varieties, have been used both medicinally and in cuisine since ancient times. In fact, Hippocrates, the father of Western medicine, used mustard seed in his practice. Crushing or exposing the seeds to water activates enzymes, which give mustard its characteristic sharp, hot taste as well as releases its medical properties.

Medicinally, mustard has been used traditionally in a topical form, for body aches and as a poultice to ease respiratory congestion. It has also been used as both a laxative and an emetic [to cause vomiting].

Like other members of the brassica genus, mustard seeds contain antioxidants, including isothiocyanates. The isothiocyanates in mustard seed (and other brassicas) have been repeatedly studied for their anticancer effects. In animal studies – and particularly in studies involving the gastrointestinal tract and colorectal cancer – intake of isothiocyanates has been shown to inhibit formation of cancer cells and growth of existing cancer. Finally, mustard seeds are good sources of selenium and magnesium, two minerals that have multiple health benefits, including in moderating blood pressure, managing migraines and menopause. (Note: using mustard topically can cause skin irritation, including burns and ulcers, with prolonged use.) ❞

Linda Shiue, MD

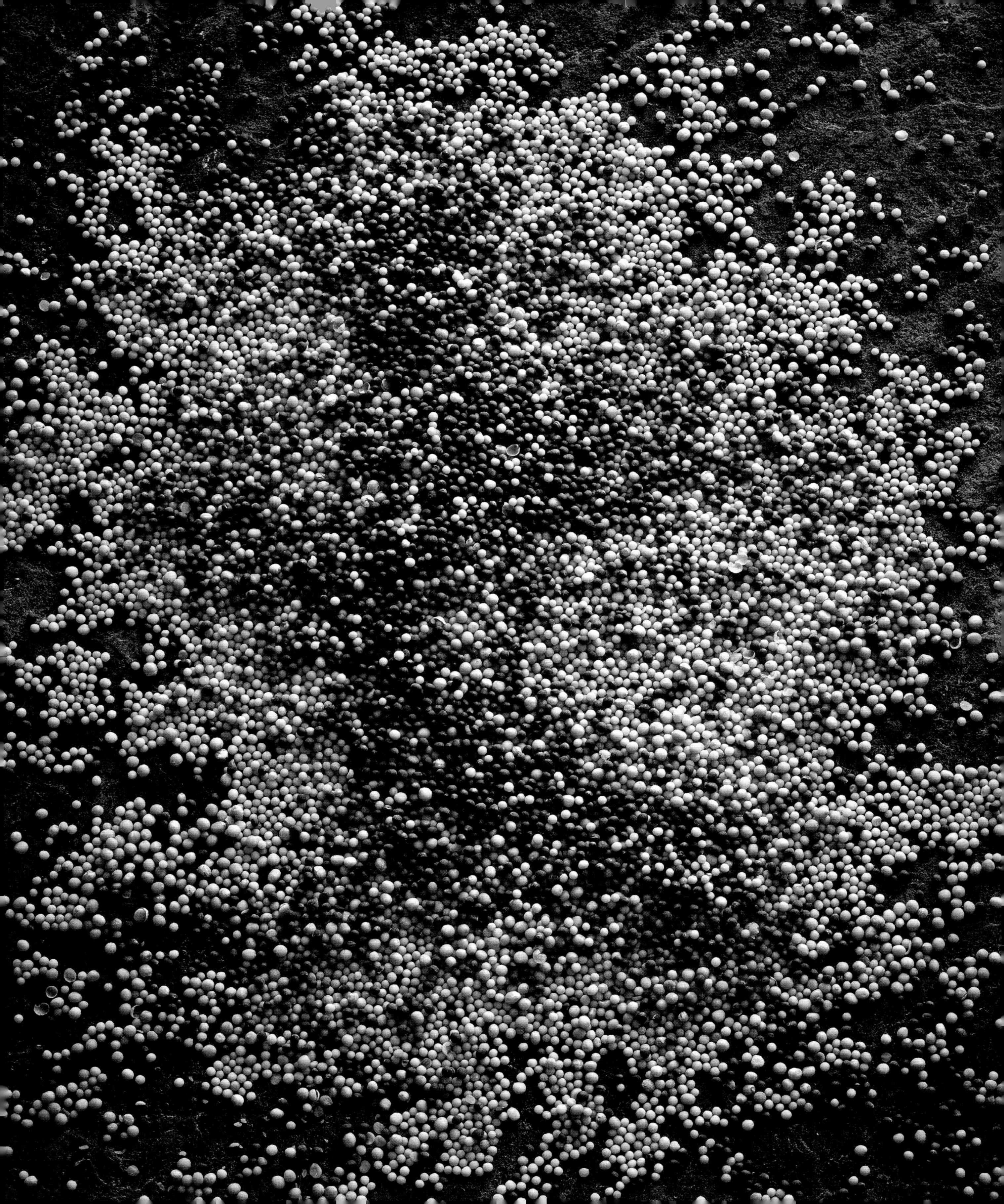

Horseradish *The Antibiotic Spice*

This relative of mustard and cabbage has been growing in English fields since the 15th century. In fact, it has nothing to do with either horses or radishes (it looks more like a gangly white carrot to me), but a lot to do with food and medicine. Unlike chili pepper, which is hot on the tongue, the tingling heat from crucifers, such as mustard, wasabi and horseradish, is inhaled – a much faster delivery system!

This perennial cruciferous root with taupe-coloured skin and white flesh has no scent when picked or purchased, but once the skin is broken, the volatile oil sinigrin breaks down into an enzyme called allyl isothiocyanate, which has a scent similar to mustard oil. This enzyme is a natural and powerful antibiotic. Loaded with healing phytochemicals, horseradish contains an abundance of energetic compounds that are actively being tested to aid the lungs, digestion, joints, muscles and the immune system. Indeed, there is on-going anticancer research on these horseradish compounds.

Horseradish has been popular for centuries all over Europe. In the US in the 1800s, a young entrepreneur named Henry John Heinz made horseradish in vinegar and sold it in little jars: America's first convenience food. The H. J. Heinz Company, commonly known simply as Heinz, later paired bottled horseradish with tomato ketchup to invent cocktail sauce to spoon atop boiled shrimp and seafood with a lemon-wedge garnish. Horseradish is also popular infused in vodka in a Bloody Mary, mixed with sour cream for a jacket potato and served with a slice of prime rib, or with poached salmon, blended with mustard, cream and a squeeze of lemon and fresh dill.

Germany takes top honours not only for its medical research into horseradish but also for its horseradish-focused sauces, often serving this pungent nose-opening condiment simply peeled and grated with meals.

Note that grated and peeled horseradish needs to be used immediately, or preserved in vinegar, as it loses its flavour and oxidizes once prepared. Most horseradish preparations require little or no heat but when cooked become milder, so I recommend adding horseradish at the end to taste. If you are preparing horseradish at home, make sure your kitchen is well ventilated and all ingredients are at hand.

❛ Horseradish, a member of the brassica or cruciferous vegetable genus, is a long root native to the Mediterranean. It has an easily recognizable sharp taste when grated, which complements beef as well as smoked fish.

The sharpness characteristic of horseradish comes from the release of volatile compounds. Medicinally, these volatile compounds have long been used to ease respiratory congestion, and also to treat sinusitis and bronchitis. Their efficacy in treating these ailments is due to the fact that horseradish is a great source of vitamin C, higher than in oranges and lemons. In addition, the volatile compounds in horseradish have antimicrobial activity. Traditionally, people have considered horseradish to have diuretic properties and have used it to treat urinary tract infections, kidney stones and fluid retention. It has also been used to treat joint pain, gallbladder disorders, sciatic nerve pain, gout, colic and intestinal worms in children, though scientific data are lacking for these.

There is a potential concern that eating large amounts of horseradish or other cruciferous vegetables can decrease thyroid function, however this has only been shown in animal studies and would not be a concern at normal levels of consumption of these nutritious vegetables. ❜

Linda Shiue, MD

Wasabi *The Mountain Brook Spice*

Most sashimi aficionados have never seen true wasabi: in fact, there is very little real wasabi on the world market as most is made from horseradish – commonly referred to as 'wasabi Japanese horseradish'. Most powdered wasabi is bitter, and often not made from true wasabi rhizomes, and, most surprisingly, the wasabi horseradish most consumed by Americans is in a pill capsule, not on sushi. The powder used in sushi bars is 99 per cent horseradish. This is not to say, of course, that horseradish is inferior: as we've seen, it has a plethora of exciting uses for food and health. But where's the real wasabi and how does it differ?

Initially known as 'wild ginger', wasabi has similar attributes to ginger and a flavour palette similar to horseradish, to which it is only distantly related. Horseradish and wasabi also share the brain-clearing heat rush of a similar type of enzyme. But wasabi can thrive only in restrictive conditions and it takes many years for the crucifers to mature. Most of the world's true wasabi (*Eutrema wasabi* or *Wasabia japonica*) is native to Japan, where it is grown from a total of 17 wasabi cultivars, forms an integral component of the national cuisine and has been recognized since the 10th century for its medicinal properties. It is now successfully grown in other countries, too, including Canada, Brazil, Israel, the US state of Oregon and the pristine mountain regions of New Zealand. In Japan, this perennial pale-green-fleshed rhizome has been cultivated on the banks of bubbling mountain brooks for over 1,000 years. Commercial wasabi growing is based on two growing methods: the upland or soil-grown wasabi and the 'flooded-field' or water-stream-grown wasabi. The latter yields a superior rhizome-to-leaf ratio and, as the rhizome is the part of wasabi most popularly consumed, this is the most profitable method.

Nutritionally and for wellbeing, what sets wasabi apart from mustard and horseradish is its promising anticancer properties. There is evidence that its active isothiocyanate (ITC) compounds may have a chemopreventive effect on cancer, including of the lung, breast, liver, oesophagus, bladder, pancreas, colon and prostate. Promising studies continue.

Agriculturally, there is on-going research to develop a natural fungicide using natural phytogenetic wasabi extracts to prevent fungal damage to oilseed, rapeseed and canola crops.

If using a tin of 'wasabi' powder, check the ingredients to ensure it contains wasabi rather than horseradish, mustard and green food colouring. Add just enough water to hydrate and enjoy with your sushi. You can also add it to salad dressings, mashed potatoes, a seafood sauce or even ice cream!

Also known as Japanese horseradish, wasabi (*Wasabia japonica*) is a distinct herb from horseradish, native to Japan. Its stem is freshly ground to produce a condiment that accompanies raw fish, though in Western sushi restaurants, the bright green paste that comes alongside your sushi is more likely to be food-colouring-enhanced horseradish combined with mustard.

Wasabi is thought to have many health benefits, including antimicrobial, potential anticancer (being rich in antioxidants), anti-inflammatory and also blood-thinning properties (specifically, decreasing platelet aggregation). Japanese manuscripts dating as far back as the eighth century mention wasabi, when it was used more as a medicinal herb than as food.

Wasabi is a source of fibre, protein and many micronutrients, including vitamins A, C and many B vitamins. It is a good source of many minerals, including calcium, iron, magnesium, phosphorus, potassium, sodium and zinc. Wasabi also has high levels of antioxidants, the isothiocyanates. In a recent study of the antibacterial properties of various foods, wasabi ranked as the most potent antibacterial against *E. coli* and *Staphylococcus aureus*. This means that the wasabi you eat with your raw fish may not only enhance the flavour, but may also help prevent food poisoning. It has also been shown to be effective against respiratory pathogens, and may also help prevent sinusitis by acting as a decongestant, which diners will notice immediately when eating too much wasabi at once.

Linda Shiue, MD

CHILI, PEPPERCORN, CUMIN

HERB AND HARISSA GAZPACHO
WITH CRISPY CHICKPEAS

This traditional Spanish late-summer chilled tomato soup gets an international twist with a protein-rich, gluten-free, spicy, harissa-crusted chickpea topping in place of toasted bread croutons. Use soft, over-handled, 'well-loved' tomatoes for this, but make sure that they are still fresh and not mouldy or fermented.

SERVES 4

1.3kg (3lb.) fresh soft 'well-loved' tomatoes

7 celery sticks, strings peeled

2–3 cucumbers (550g/1lb. 4oz.), peeled and seeded

½ onion or 2 shallots

handful (10g/¼oz.) chopped soft fresh herbs, e.g. basil and parsley

1 tbsp Gazpacho Harissa Paste (see opposite)

juice of 3 lemons

1 litre (4¼ cups) low-sodium vegetable juice

3 tbsp olive oil, plus extra for drizzling

1–2 tsp fine sea salt

1 firm ripe avocado

Crispy Chickpeas (see opposite), to serve

Bring about 10cm (4in.) of water to the boil in a large pan. While the water is heating, turn each tomato upside down and make a small 'X' at the base just to pierce the skin. Have a medium bowl half filled with ice and water and a slotted spoon at the ready. Add the tomatoes to the boiling water, leave for a couple of minutes, then remove and plunge them into the iced water. Peel off the skins and cut out the core. Pour out the water and use the bowl to build your gazpacho.

Roughly chop the tomatoes, celery, cucumbers and onion and add to the bowl. Add the herbs, harissa paste, lemon juice, vegetable juice and olive oil.

Use a stick (or bar) blender to mix the soup, leaving some small chunks. Season with salt and additional harissa to taste. Chill until icy cold.

Peel and stone the avocado and cut the flesh into small pieces. Ladle the gazpacho into chilled soup bowls, top with a spoonful of avocado and garnish with a drizzle of olive oil, then scatter over the crispy chickpeas.

GAZPACHO HARISSA PASTE

MAKES ABOUT ⅔ CUP

2 tsp black peppercorns

2 tsp coriander seeds

1 tsp cumin seeds

1 tsp fennel seeds

2 tsp chopped garlic (or to taste)

½ green chili, seeded and minced

zest of ½ lemon

1 tbsp olive oil

1 tbsp ground chipotle powder or smoked paprika powder

½ tsp ground cayenne

2 tbsp ground sweet Hungarian paprika

Toast then finely grind the peppercorns and the coriander, cumin and fennel seeds.

Using a mortar and pestle, grind the garlic, chili and lemon zest. Add the toasted ground spices and the olive oil. Add the remaining spices and grind into a paste, using more oil if needed.

Stored tightly sealed and chilled, the paste will keep for several months.

CRISPY CHICKPEAS

MAKES ABOUT 3 CUPS

200g (7oz./1 cup) dried chickpeas (or 3 cups canned, drained and air-dried)

1 tsp baking soda

250ml (1 cup) grapeseed or vegetable oil

1 tbsp Gazpacho Harissa Paste (see above)

¼ tsp garlic powder

Put the dried chickpeas and baking soda in a 1-litre (1-quart) pan and pour over enough water to cover. Cover the pan and leave to soak for 8 hours.

Strain, rinse and return the chickpeas to the pan. Cover with water and bring to the boil, then reduce to a simmer and cook for 2 hours, or until fork tender. Cool on a large baking tray to let the chickpeas dry.

Mix the harissa blend and garlic powder in a medium-sized bowl and set aside.

Heat the oil in a large frying pan (skillet) to about 180°C (350°F). Test a chickpea: if the oil bubbles around it, it is ready to fry. Cook the chickpeas in batches, making sure the pan does not become overcrowded, for about 3–4 minutes, until crispy.

Drain on kitchen paper, then quickly toss in the bowl of spices.

Sprinkle on top of the gazpacho.

Illustrated on pages 142–3

HORSERADISH, GARLIC, NUTMEG

COUNTRY ONION MUSHROOM SOUP

This is a quick and simple, thick, potage-style soup that I created as executive chef of Bridge Street restaurant in Bigfork, Montana, owned by the award-winning Chateau Montelena Winery in Napa, California. The restaurant was surrounded by a lovely herb and veggie garden, where I grew the horseradish used in this dish. When the time came to make it, the entire kitchen crew would back away as this fresh spice is odourless when uprooted, but once you break the skin, the smell is pungent! The volatile oil it contains is a powerful natural antibiotic but it can make you swoon and your eyes fill with tears!

SERVES 2–4

1 head garlic	50ml (scant ¼ cup) port
1 tbsp olive oil	475ml (2 cups) vegetable stock
1 tbsp grapeseed oil	200g (7oz./1 cup) mashed potato
250g (9oz.) mushrooms	1–2 tsp lemon juice
⅛ tsp (large pinch) nutmeg	2 tsp pure horseradish, fresh or from a jar, to taste
1 tbsp fresh thyme leaves	⅛ tsp freshly grated nutmeg, to garnish
125g (4½oz./½ cup) Turmeric Melted Onions (see below)	garlic bread, to serve (optional)

Preheat the oven to 180°C (350°F/gas mark 4). Cut the top off the garlic head to expose the cloves, then peel away just the outer layers of the garlic-bulb skin, leaving the skins of the individual cloves. Wrap loosely in foil and drizzle a tablespoon of oil over the garlic. Close the foil at the top, place on a baking tray and roast in the oven for about 30–35 minutes until soft and golden brown.

While the garlic is roasting, make the Turmeric Melted Onions (see below.)

Heat the grapeseed oil and sauté the mushrooms with the nutmeg and thyme leaves in a 2-litre (2-quart) pot until almost dry over medium heat, about 5 minutes.

Reduce the heat to low, add the Turmeric Melted Onions and half the roasted garlic (keep the other half for other use; it will keep for about 2 weeks refrigerated) and mix well. Add the port and reduce for 2 minutes or so. Add the stock and simmer for 3–5 minutes.

Stir in the mashed potato, lemon juice and horseradish and season to taste with salt and pepper.

Serve warmed in big bowls, topped with a sprinkle of freshly grated nutmeg, accompanied by your favourite garlic bread, if wished.

TURMERIC MELTED ONIONS

MAKES 2 CUPS

50g (1¾oz./½ stick) butter	4 medium brown onions (450g/1lb.), halved and thinly sliced
60ml (¼ cup) grapeseed or vegetable oil	10 grinds black pepper (optional)
1 tsp ground turmeric	

Heat the oil and melt the butter in a pan over medium–high heat, stir in the turmeric and cook for 1 minute. (Adding turmeric to the sizzling oil intensifies the flavour and nutrients; the pepper adds even more goodness.)

Add the onions and when they begin to let off steam, turn the heat down to medium–low and cook for 20–30 minutes, stirring occasionally, until translucent, melted and light-yellow-brown in colour.

Add the pepper and stir for a few minutes.

Remove from heat, cool, then cover and chill until needed.

CHILI, GINGER, CUMIN

KULI KULI PEANUT CAKES
WITH QUICK CHILI-PICKLED ONIONS AND TOASTED BLACK CUMIN SEEDS

Inspired by the age-old Nigerian snack, kuli kuli is packed full of protein and this version has an added chili kick, layered with the subtle sweetness of cinnamon. It is good for the circulation and makes a great gluten- and dairy-free vegan two-bite hors d'oeuvre.

MAKES 24 (4cm/1½ in.) CAKES

200g (7oz./2 cups) blanched lightly oven-toasted peanuts (groundnuts)

4 tsp freshly grated ginger

12 drops hot chili sauce (Tabasco), or to taste

2 tsp soft brown sugar

1 tsp cinnamon, ground

¼ tsp flaked salt, or to taste

peanut (groundnut) oil, for frying

½ cinnamon stick (optional)

chervil or parsley leaves, to garnish

For the chili-pickled onions:

1 small red onion (about 100g/3½oz.), halved and thinly sliced

½ fresh hot red chili, e.g. jalapeño, Anaheim or Serrano, sliced into thin rings

zest of 1 lime and juice of ½

60ml (¼ cup) rice wine vinegar

1 tsp minced parsley

1 tbsp black cumin seeds (nigella or onion seeds), plus extra for garnishing

First make the chili-pickled onions. Mix all the ingredients together in a small bowl, cover and chill until ready to use.

Using a food processor, or by hand with a mortar and pestle, grind the peanuts (groundnuts) and ginger together until sesame-seed size. Add a little peanut oil if the nuts are too dry but don't allow it to turn into peanut butter.

Blitz in the hot chili sauce, sugar, cinnamon and salt. Tightly squeeze a bit in your hand to make sure the kuli kuli isn't too oily or it won't be crispy when you cook it. Use up to 4 teaspoons of water to help the mixture hold together. Shape into 4cm (1½in.) sized cakes (about 15g/½oz.) and place on a tray.

Pour peanut (groundnut) oil into a frying pan (skillet) to a depth of 4cm (1½in.), add the half cinnamon stick (if using) and heat to 165°C (325°F).

Fry the cakes in batches until golden brown, about 2 minutes each side. Drain on kitchen paper. If your kuli kuli turn out soft rather than crispy, pop them into a low oven (110°C/225°F/gas mark ¼) to dry out and harden without burning.

To serve, mound a large pinch of chili-pickled onions on top of the kuli kuli and garnish with a chervil or parsley leaf and a sprinkle of black cumin seeds.

CHILI, GARLIC

TURKISH EGGS

Peter Gordon

'These are known as çılbır in Turkey, (pronounced chil-bir) and they always have raw garlic mixed into the yogurt. At The Providores, where they are our biggest-selling brunch dish, and also very popular on the all-day menu, we don't add the garlic as our customers find it too confronting. Like Turkish cooks, I use a generous amount of a mild and seedless but truly tasty chili flake called kirmizi biber, which is also known as Aleppo chili. I have also made it using Korean chili flakes, which likewise give the buttery oil a delicious red hue. We always serve this with toasted sourdough.' PG

SERVES 4 (ALLOW 2 EGGS PER PERSON)

300g (10½oz./1¼ cups) thick plain yogurt

1 garlic clove, finely crushed

½ tsp flaky salt

50ml (scant ¼ cup) extra virgin olive oil

50g (1¾oz./½ stick) unsalted butter

1 tsp dried chili flakes (more or less to taste)

1 tbsp snipped dill or flat parsley

8 eggs

100ml (scant ½ cup) white vinegar (this may seem excessive, but it isn't!)

Whisk the yogurt, garlic and salt with half the olive oil for 15 seconds then put to one side (it's best served at room temperature).

In a small pan, cook the butter until pale nut brown (beurre noisette). Remove from the heat and add the chili flakes, then swirl the pan gently to allow them to sizzle for 20 seconds. Add the remaining olive oil and dill and put the mixture to one side, keeping it warm.

Add the vinegar to 1½ litres (1½ quarts) of simmering water in a medium-sized, deep pan and poach the eggs. Never add salt to the water when poaching eggs as it causes them to break up.

To serve, divide three quarters of the yogurt among four warmed bowls. Place two drained poached eggs in each bowl then spoon on the remaining yogurt. Drizzle the chili butter on top and eat straight away.

WILD RICE SALAD
WITH ASIAN ORANGE VINAIGRETTE

The most commonly eaten food in the world, rice is paired with hundreds of ingredients and here is one of my favourites: a rice salad with wasabi and orange. From the brassica genus (like broccoli and Brussels sprouts), wasabi has an undeniable heat and, as well as quickly clearing the sinuses, is being studied for its possible anticancer benefits.

SERVES 4 AS A MAIN OR 6 AS A STARTER

175g (6oz./1 cup) brown rice	**For the Asian orange vinaigrette:**
175g (6oz./1 cup) white rice	240ml (1 cup) seasoned rice vinegar
175g (6oz./1 cup) wild rice	240ml (1 cup) grapeseed or canola oil
120ml (½ cup) orange juice	2 tbsp toasted sesame oil
200g (7oz./2 cups) dried apricots, sliced	2 tbsp soy sauce
70g (2½oz./½ cup) crystallized ginger, minced	juice of 1 or 2 limes plus zest of 1
225g (8oz.) fresh water chestnuts (or 1 small can, drained)	120ml (½ cup) orange juice (from poached apricots, see above)
160g (5¾oz./1½ cups) toasted pecans, roughly chopped, ½ bunch chives, snipped	2 tsp freshly grated wasabi, or 1 tbsp wasabi mustard powder, mixed with water to make a thick paste

Cook the different types of rice according to package directions. Drain and chill.

Heat the orange juice, add the apricots and ginger and simmer for 10 minutes. Remove from heat and leave to cool. Drain and reserve the juice for the vinaigrette.

To make the vinaigrette, combine all the ingredients in a bowl and mix well.

Toss the rice, water chestnuts, pecans and chives in a large bowl. Add the drained apricots and ginger. Pour over the dressing and mix well.

Chill, covered in the fridge, for at least 2 hours and up to a day.

GALANGAL, CARDAMOM

BANANA-LEAF-WRAPPED SNAPPER
WITH BANANA CORIANDER SALSA AND CREAMY CARDAMOM POLENTA

This Thai-tropics-inspired dish is perfect to cook and share out of doors on a summer's day. Galangal, which is similar to ginger and has a smooth pungent flavour when cooked, was used in ancient Indonesia – and indeed is still used today in traditional Indonesian medicine – to help joint pain and inflammation. Its warming qualities provide a perfect balance to this warm, sunny dish.

SERVES 4

1 large banana leaf

4 x 175g (6oz.) boneless snapper fillets

115g (4oz.) fresh galangal (or ginger), grated

1 large red (bell) pepper, thinly sliced

1 large green (bell) pepper, thinly sliced

1 large yellow (bell) pepper, thinly sliced

8 fresh kaffir lime leaves, half chopped

3 shallots, sliced in rings

3 tbsp butter, softened

2 tbsp rice wine vinegar

¼ tsp salt

fresh ground pepper, to taste

1 tbsp grapeseed or vegetable oil, for brushing

For the banana coriander (cilantro) salsa:

1 green-tipped banana

2–3 tbsp coconut milk

zest and juice of 2 limes

2 tsp sweet chili sauce

dash fish sauce

2 tsp grated fresh galangal (or ginger)

¼ tsp ground cardamom

55g (2oz.) palm hearts or bamboo shoots, diced

30g (1oz./3 tbsp) diced red onion

⅓ bunch coriander (cilantro), or to taste

¼ bunch Thai basil, or to taste

Make the Creamy Cardamom Polenta and Crispy Shallots (see opposite).

Preheat the oven to 180°C (350°C/gas mark 4) or heat a barbecue.

Wave the banana leaf over a gas flame, or use a blowtorch or candle, for a few seconds until the leaf is shiny and supple. Cut into four hearts about 5cm (2in.) longer and wider than the fish. (If you can't get hold of bamboo leaf, simply use parchment paper.) Rinse the fish fillets and gently pat dry.

Combine the galangal or ginger, (bell) peppers, chopped kaffir lime leaves and a third of the shallots in a saucepan with 1 tablespoon of the butter and sweat until soft.

Brush one side of each banana leaf heart with oil and scatter over the (bell) pepper-onion mixture, then place one fillet on top of each. Top each with 1 kaffir lime leaf. Fold over the banana leaf like an envelope and secure with kitchen twine or toothpicks. Cook on a stovetop grill plate or on the barbecue for about 15 minutes, turning once halfway through.

Make the sauce while the fish cooks. Melt 1 tablespoon of the butter in a small saucepan with the remaining shallot. Stir for 2 minutes then add the vinegar and 2 tablespoons of water. Simmer until reduced by a quarter. Slowly whisk in the remaining butter until it begins to emulsify/thicken. Set aside until ready to serve.

Make the banana coriander (cilantro) salsa. Peel and cut the banana into small dice and set aside. Whisk together the coconut milk, lime juice and zest, chili sauce, fish sauce, galangal or ginger and cardamom. Add the palm hearts, onion, Thai basil and coriander (cilantro). Season to taste.

To serve, cut the twine or remove the toothpicks and open the banana leaf. Carefully arrange the fish on the polenta. Scatter the peppers around the fish. Spoon the sauce over the fish and top with crispy shallots. Serve with the banana coriander (cilantro) salsa.

CREAMY CARDAMOM POLENTA

Coconut milk adds a tropical healthy richness to polenta. Stirring it as suggested makes a creamy texture infused with the alluring taste of cardamom. This also makes a nourishing breakfast bowl topped with fresh fruit and sprinkled with coconut sugar.

SERVES 4

500ml (2 cups + 2 tbsp) coconut milk and 500ml (2 cups + 2 tbsp) water

1 tbsp brown sugar

1 tsp salt

140g (5oz./1 cup) polenta (not quick cooking) or fine yellow cornmeal

85g (3oz./⅓ cup) Greek-style or coconut yogurt, to finish

1 tsp black (or green) cardamom seeds, toasted and ground

Bring the coconut milk and water to a boil with the sugar and salt in a heavy 2-litre (2-quart) pan. Add the polenta in a thin stream, stirring constantly with a wooden spoon. Cook over moderate heat, stirring constantly, for 3 minutes.

Reduce the heat to low and simmer the polenta, covered, stirring for 1 minute after every 10 minutes of cooking, for about 30–35 minutes in total.

Remove from the heat and stir in the yogurt until combined. Spoon onto plates or into a serving bowl and sprinkle a pinch of cardamom on top.

The polenta can be made 30 minutes ahead and kept covered at room temperature (do not let it stand longer or it will solidify). Just before you serve, reheat it over low heat – you may need to add a bit more warmed liquid if it's too thick – then stir in the yogurt until thoroughly blended.

VARIATION: CRISPY CARDAMOM POLENTA

If making polenta for the duck recipe on page 118, reduce the liquid of your choice to 700ml (3 cups) and add 2 tablespoons of butter or oil. Cook as directed above, then pour the polenta into an oiled baking tray and smooth the top. Cool and cut into shapes. Fry in a pan over medium heat with a little butter or oil on both sides until golden brown and crispy.

CRISPY SHALLOTS

3 shallots, cut and separated into thin rings

rice flour, to coat

oil, for deep frying

flake salt

Toss the shallot rings in rice flour.

Pour the oil into a small pan to a depth of about 2.5cm (1in.) and heat to 180°C (350°F).

Shake the flour from the shallot rings and fry in batches, until golden and crispy. Drain on kitchen paper then sprinkle with flake salt.

Illustrated on pages 154–5

★

MUSTARD, GINGER, GARLIC, CARDAMOM

TONGA CHILI-LIME CHICKEN

Created at a Tongan vanilla plantation using ingredients available on the plantation, including passion fruit, freshly juiced limes, fresh ginger and vanilla, which I made into a mustard, this dish easily adapts for parties by substituting the thighs and drumsticks with the same amount of chicken wings.

SERVES 6

750g (1lb. 10oz.) chicken thighs and/or drumsticks, bone in, skin on

1 small handful coriander (cilantro) leaves, for garnishing

For the marinade:

2 garlic cloves, chopped

1 tbsp freshly grated ginger

1 tsp coriander seeds, toasted

½ tsp cardamom seeds, toasted

240ml (1 cup) grapeseed or vegetable oil

60ml (¼ cup) lime juice

½ medium onion (100g/3½oz.), chopped

120ml (½ cup) passion fruit juice (or fresh pineapple juice), or 4 passion fruit, pulped and seeded

1 tbsp coconut or brown sugar

¼ tsp salt

120ml (½ cup) seasoned rice wine vinegar

2 tsp Dijon mustard, or Vanilla Honey Mustard (see page 164)

large pinch nutmeg

30g (1oz./½ cup) fresh coriander (cilantro) leaves, chopped

2 fresh red chilies, thinly sliced

Cut any excess fat off the chicken pieces and discard, then transfer the chicken to a medium-sized bowl or casserole dish. Using a mortar and pestle, grind the garlic, ginger and coriander and cardamom seeds to make a paste. Transfer this paste to a food processor (or use a stick blender), add all the remaining marinade ingredients except the chilies, and whizz until smooth. Stir in the sliced chilies then pour the marinade over the chicken to coat. Cover the dish, or put everything into a zip-sealing bag, and chill for 2–8 hours.

Preheat the oven to 180°C (350°F/gas mark 4).

Drain the chicken from the marinade and set aside. Bake the chicken pieces for 25 minutes, or until juices run clear. Remove from the oven, transfer onto a serving plate, cover and let rest for 10 minutes.

To serve, reduce the leftover marinade and drizzle it over the chicken, then scatter the coriander (cilantro) leaves, and the chilies from the reduced marinade over all and serve immediately.

HORSERADISH, GARLIC

'THE THATCHED COTTAGE' COTTAGE PIE

I first sampled this classic British comfort food at The Thatched Cottage far from the London lights. The Thatched Cottage version has a secret nose-running spice in the minced beef with mashed potato topping. I watched as fresh horseradish root was pulled from an old wooden barrel planter, then brushed, peeled, chopped, quickly blanched (to retain the bright white colour) and the pieces tossed in a blender with warmed white vinegar. We all held our breaths as the lid was removed and the coarse pungent root was quickly packed into a glass jar and the lid hastily sealed in place. Horseradish makes the perfect counterpoint to creamy soothing potato mash, and current German studies indicate that it contains enormous amounts of natural antibiotic, helping to counteract respiratory infections and diseases such as bronchitis, pneumonia and strep throat.

SERVES 4

2 tbsp oil

500g (1lb. 2oz.) minced (ground) beef

2 onions, chopped

2 carrots, peeled and chopped

2 garlic cloves, minced

1 tbsp dried mixed herbs

1 tbsp Worcestershire sauce

1 beef stock cube

240ml (1 cup) dry white wine

10g (¼oz./¼ cup) parsley leaves, chopped

3 tbsp HP sauce

2 tbsp tamarind paste

Worcestershire sauce and extra horseradish, to serve

For the horseradish mash:

1 kg (2lbs. 4oz.) floury baking potatoes (e.g. Maris Piper, King, Russet), peeled and cut in half

½ tsp sea salt, or to taste

120ml (½ cup) milk

55g (2oz./½ stick) salted butter

2 tbsp fresh or jarred pure horseradish (not creamed)

Preheat the oven to 180°C (350°F/gas mark 4).

Heat a large frying pan (skillet) and add the oil. Sauté the beef over low heat, stirring with a wooden spoon to break up any lumps. Add the onion, carrot, garlic and dried mixed herbs, stirring well. Add the Worcestershire sauce, stock cube and 500ml (2 cups) of water. Cover and simmer for 10 minutes.

Add the wine, parsley, HP sauce and tamarind paste, then simmer and reduce to thicken. Season to taste.

For the mash, put the potatoes in a pan with the salt and pour in enough water to cover. Bring to the boil then turn down the heat to a simmer and cook until the potatoes are fork tender.

Drain and mash using a ricer or potato masher. Mash in the milk, butter and horseradish, adjusting seasoning to taste, until smooth.

Spoon the beef into four individual ovenproof dishes or one large baking or casserole dish. Spoon or pipe the mashed potatoes on top, covering the beef filling completely, and using the back of a fork, make a decorative pattern on top. Place the dish or dishes on a foil-lined baking tray and bake until bubbly, about 20 minutes for individual dishes or 30 minutes for a large one. If you wish, you can place it under the grill (broiler) for an additional 10 minutes to brown the top.

Serve with Worcestershire sauce and extra horseradish.

CHILI, GINGER, GARLIC, CUMIN

SAZON RUB BEEF ROAST
WITH CHIMICHURRI ARGENTINA

A popular cut of beef known in South America as 'cuadril' and elsewhere as rump roast or tri-tip, this is a shoulder of beef with the fat cap intact. This spice crust is inspired by the hugely popular South American dry spice blend sazon. This blend is packed full of fresh oregano, garlic and spices. You can apply the rub to the beef up to two days ahead and the sauce, too, can be made a day in advance. Chimichurri Argentina is a parsley- and oregano-packed, pesto-type sauce, bright with vinegar and hot with chilies.

SERVES 4–6

1kg (2lb. 4oz.) piece of beef rump cap (aged 3 months is ideal)

For the sazon rub:

1 tbsp grapeseed oil, plus extra for brushing

1 tbsp lime juice

1 tbsp coriander seeds, crushed

1 tbsp cumin seeds

1 tbsp salt

2 tsp fresh oregano

2 tsp chipotle powder

1 tsp freshly grated ginger

1 tsp black peppercorns

1 tsp chili flakes

1 tsp dried mint

½ tsp ground turmeric

For the chimichurri Argentina:

2 bunches (60g/2¼oz.) fresh parsley

1 bunch (25g/1oz.) fresh oregano

4 garlic cloves, peeled

120ml (½ cup) apple cider (or juice)

½ apple, peeled, cored and chopped

1 tbsp apple cider vinegar

1 whole fresh red jalapeño or other chili pepper, seeded and chopped

120ml (½ cup) extra virgin olive oil

Combine the rub ingredients together in a small bowl.

Pat the beef dry using kitchen paper. Score the fat, making incisions about 1cm (½in.) deep 5mm (¼in.) apart. Brush with oil to coat. Pack the rub into the fat on top of the beef, then cover and chill for 2 hours. Remove the beef from the fridge at least an hour before cooking to let it come to room temperature.

Make the chimichurri Argentina. Put all the ingredients except the oil in a food processor, or small blender, and pulse until coarsely chopped. Slowly drizzle in the oil until combined, adding more if you wish. Spoon into a serving bowl, cover and chill until needed.

Turn on the extractor fan, then heat a stovetop grill pan/plate or barbecue to medium–high, place the beef on it, fat-side up, and cook for about 6 minutes, then carefully turn it over and cook fat-side down for an additional 6–8 minutes. Test for doneness with a thermometer if you like (it should have reached 55°C /130°F for rare/medium–rare).

Remove from heat and transfer to a carving board. Loosely cover with foil and let rest for 15–20 minutes. Thinly slice the beef across the grain and serve with the chimichurri Argentina.

BREAD AND BUTTER PERSIAN PICKLES

This tangy but slightly sweet pickle is delicious and is made with Persian (also known as Lebanese) cucumbers, which have a slightly thicker skin than hothouse ones, and few if any seeds.

MAKES 3 MEDIUM-SIZED JARS

900g (2lb.) Persian cucumbers, thinly sliced	1 tbsp turmeric
450g (1lb.) white onions, thinly sliced into half moons	2 tsp black peppercorns, toasted
2 large (bell) peppers (red and yellow), seeded and cut into thin strips	1 tsp each yellow and black mustard seeds
2 tbsp sea salt	1 tsp each celery, fennel and ajwain seeds, toasted
140g (5oz./1 cup unpacked) brown sugar	¼ tsp whole cloves
140g (5oz./¾ cup) granulated sugar	1 litre (4¼ cups) white vinegar

Layer the vegetables into a strainer and gently toss with the salt. Cover with a clean cloth and leave for 3 hours.

Drain the vegetables, rinse thoroughly and drain again.

Put the sugars, spices and vinegar in a large stainless-steel or enamel pan (remember that turmeric stains!) and bring to the boil. Add the vegetables and return to the boil for 1 minute. Turn off the heat and spoon the vegetables into sterilized jars, then pour the liquid over all. Seal the jars, rinse under running water and cool on the work surface.

Store in a dark pantry and keep refrigerated once opened.

VANILLA HONEY MUSTARD

I originally created this for my first book, Vanilla Table, *but kept it aside as I was interested in researching and creating a line of condiments, preserves and fermented vegetables. As vanilla and mustard are actually both naturally bitter, pairing them together with a dash of honey and vinegar and a bit of horseradish heat makes for a sweet, hot and aromatic combination that is just the thing for adding a bit of chutzpah to a plain-tasting dish.*

MAKES ABOUT 500ml (2 CUPS)

115g (4oz./¾ cup) yellow mustard seeds	½ tsp dried tarragon
55g (2oz./6 tbsp) black mustard seeds	1 tbsp sea salt
325ml (1⅓ cups) white wine vinegar, plus more if needed	I vanilla pod (bean) split, scraped and cut into 6 pieces, or 1 tsp vanilla paste
2½ tbsp mild-flavoured runny honey	
1 tsp grated horseradish, fresh or from a jar	

Grind the yellow mustard seeds in a spice grinder or mortar and pestle to the desired texture, but leave the black seeds whole. Mix together in a bowl and stir in half the vinegar. Let stand for 15 minutes, then add the remaining ingredients, combining well and adding additional vinegar if too dry. Cover with a clean cloth and leave to stand overnight.

Spoon the mustard into sterilized jars and seal. It will be ready to use in 4 weeks and will keep, stored in a cool dark place, for up to 12 months.

PEAR AND BARLEY TART
WITH GINGER MILK SHERBET
Sarah Johnson

'This dessert is truly a sum of all its parts. The nuttiness of the barley adds depth to the subtle, floral notes of the pear. And while warm crumble and ice cream are a classic match, the clean coolness of the sherbet gives way to the heat of the ginger, calling you back for another bite. It is worth seeking out ripe pears for this dish. When selecting the pears, press the bottom of the fruit gently with your thumb. The flesh should give ever so slightly. Avoid overly soft pears that will fall apart when cooked and put aside under-ripe fruits that have yet to develop flavour. Ginger has become one of my favourite ingredients to cook with. In this milk sherbet, I enjoy the lighter texture over more traditional ice creams as I find it brings out the fresh lemony flavours of the ginger that would otherwise be lost in the richness of an ice cream. While this dessert has an autumnal feel, the sherbet pairs well with fruits from other seasons, too. Try this tart with rhubarb and strawberries in spring, or blackberries and peaches in summer. In winter, serve the ginger ice milk in a bowl with clementines and kumquats and a scattering of the toasted barley crumble over the top.' SJ

SERVES 6–8

For the ginger milk sherbet:

500ml (2 cups + 2 tbsp) whole milk

70g (2½oz.) fresh ginger, peeled and sliced into thin disks

1 small egg white

55g (2oz./¼ cup) sugar

1 tsp freshly grated ginger

For the barley crisp topping:

85g (3oz./generous ½ cup) barley flour

40g (1½oz./⅓ cup) plain (all-purpose) flour

3 tbsp demerara sugar

2 tbsp granulated sugar

pinch salt

85g (3oz./¾ stick) unsalted butter, at room temperature, diced

10g (¼oz./1½ tbsp) barley flakes

For the barley shortcrust pastry:

175g (6oz./1½ sticks) butter, at room temperature

115g (4oz./generous ½ cup) caster (superfine) sugar

45g (1½oz./⅓ cup) icing (confectioner's) sugar

2 egg yolks

85g (3oz./generous ½ cup) barley flour

160g (5¾oz./1¼ cups) plain (all-purpose) flour

For the pear filling:

about 1kg (2lb. 4oz./about 5 or 6) ripe pears, cored but not peeled, cut into bite-sized pieces

100g (3½oz./½ cup) sugar, plus more to taste

juice and zest of ½ lemon

½ tsp freshly grated ginger

To make the ginger milk sherbet, put the milk and sliced ginger in a pan and bring to the boil. Immediately remove from the heat and cool to room temperature. Cover and chill. (This part can be done a day in advance and stored overnight.)

When cooled, strain the milk through a fine mesh sieve, discarding the ginger. Using an electric mixer, or by hand, whisk the egg white until light and frothy. Slowly add the sugar while continuing to whisk your meringue until soft peaks form. Add the freshly grated ginger to the milk, then gently fold in the meringue. Don't worry about incorporating the meringue entirely; the mixture will look separated, but will come together once it is churned. Churn immediately in an ice-cream maker according to the manufacturer's instructions. Transfer the milk sherbet to the freezer and continue to chill. This sherbet is best enjoyed the same day but will keep for several days.

To make the crispy topping, combine the flours, sugars and salt into a large bowl. Add the chilled butter and toss to coat. Rub the butter between your fingers into the dry ingredients until it resembles coarse breadcrumbs.

Add the barley flakes and mix until the mixture holds together when squeezed in your hands. Take care not to overwork the flour or the mixture will lose the crumbly tender texture when baked. Cover and place in the fridge until you are ready to use. (The topping can be prepared up to a week in advance.)

To make the pastry, in a mixer with a paddle, beat the butter until smooth. Stop, scrape down the side of the bowl, then add both sugars, mixing on medium speed until incorporated. Stop, scrape down the side of the bowl, then, with the mixer running, add the eggs one at a time, ensuring each egg is emulsified, scraping after each egg. Add the flours and salt, pulsing until just combined.

Turn the pastry dough out onto a work surface and gently bring together to a ball (you should not have to knead.) Wrap in cling film (plastic wrap), rest and chill in the fridge for at least 30 minutes. Preheat the oven to 160°C (325°F/gas mark 3).

Remove the pastry from the fridge and allow to come to room temperature. While the dough is softening, butter a 28cm (10in.) tart tin and line the base with parchment paper.

Roll the dough out onto a piece of parchment paper, using the rolling pin to transfer the dough to the tart tin. Trim off the excess to the edge of tin. Leave to rest in the fridge for another 30 minutes.

Remove the pastry from the fridge, prick the bottom of the tart shell with a fork and bake for 15–20 minutes until slightly golden. Remove from the oven and cool completely before filling the tart.

Put the pears into a bowl and sprinkle with the sugar, lemon zest, juice and ginger. Gently toss to coat. Let sit for at least 10 minutes. Taste the fruit and add more sugar if desired. Spoon the pears into the prebaked pastry case, adding any leftover sugar or juice clinging to the bowl. Sprinkle over the crisp topping, carefully pressing it into the fruit. Bake for 25–35 minutes, until golden and bubbly.

Remove from the oven and leave to rest for 20–30 minutes. Serve warm with a generous scoop of the ginger milk sherbet.

Illustrated on pages 166–7

GREAT GRANDMA TUPPER'S TRADITIONAL MOLASSES COOKIES

Molasses and ginger are a great mineral boost combination and what better way to enjoy them than in these soft and chewy moreish treats, full of mineral-rich iron, calcium, magnesium and copper. The recipe for them dates back to the 1930s; while I have added a bit more ginger than Grandma Tupper, the dusting of granulated sugar on top, and tasting the sugar crunch when biting into this sweet but healthy treat, is timeless.

MAKES ABOUT 20

225g (8oz./1 cup) granulated sugar, plus extra for sprinkling

1 tsp salt

2½ tsp ground ginger

2 tsp ground cinnamon

¼ tsp ground cloves

325g (11½oz./1 cup) molasses or treacle

1½ tsp baking soda

2 large eggs, beaten

225g (8oz./2 sticks) vegetable shortening or unsalted butter

2 tsp freshly grated ginger

550g (1lb. 4oz./4½ cups) plain (all-purpose) flour, plus extra for flouring the board

150g (5½oz./1 cup) raisins

35g (1¼oz./¼ cup) crystallized ginger, chopped

Stir the sugar, salt and spices together in a large bowl.

In a separate bowl, beat the molasses and soda.

Add the beaten eggs, shortening or butter and grated ginger to the sugar and spice mixture and beat well, then beat in the molasses.

Sift in the flour, add the raisins and crystallized ginger and mix well. The dough should be soft and sticky; if it is a humid day, you may need to add a little more flour. Divide the dough into three, shaping into discs, and wrap each piece in cling film (plastic wrap) and chill for 1–2 hours.

Preheat the oven to 160° (325°F/gas mark 3). Flour a board well and pat out the dough about 5mm (¼in.) thick and cut into shapes using a floured knife or a round cookie cutter.

Sprinkle the tops with granulated sugar, transfer to a baking tray and bake for 15 minutes.

Leave to cool for a few minutes on the baking tray then transfer to a wire rack and cool completely.

Stored sealed in a tin or jar, the cookies will keep for 3 weeks – if they last that long!

Restorative spice

When you are challenged with an overabundance of decisions to make and more on your to-do list than there are minutes in the day, a restorative spice in a smoothie, dinner dish or a simple cuppa will help your body reboot, restoring health, radiance, strength and balance.

Restorative Spice Health Heroes
Garlic ★ Cardamom ★ Pomegranate ★ Fenugreek ★ Thyme

The potent and abundant active compounds contained in these spices show promise in restoring health and rebalancing the body by assisting our automatic natural functions to heal and reset with renewed strength, vitality and balance to better enable the body to regulate itself.

Garlic, with its long-standing reputation as a heroic natural antibiotic and its ability to reduce nitrosamines (chemical carcinogens), has many talents and works its curative, restorative magic to repel colds, flus and inflammatory diseases. Cardamom's active cineole healing compounds, contained in its tiny pungent seeds, are packed full of antibacterial, antioxidant and antiseptic power. Fenugreek restores and rebalances blood sugar with its active bio-identical compound diosgenin, which helps to restore insulin and triglyceride levels. It also contains high amounts of fibre to aid in restoring proper digestion. Thyme helps restore healthy respiration and balanced pulmonary function. Rich in volatile compounds, including thymol, thyme's many talents include disabling bacterial infection and contagious diseases and lessening the effects of damage from over-indulgence in alcoholic beverages. Pomegranate, and its active polyphenol compound, ellagic acid, shows promising results as a restorative for its anti-wrinkle effects: it is used as a treatment to fight the collagen degradation that causes skin aging. Pomegranate may also help in fast-tracking immediate strength recovery after vigorous exercise and may benefit the restoration of sperm quality and quantity and the increase in testertone levels in men.

Other restorative spice heroes

Lemongrass A cup of soothing lemongrass tea will help restore your body and mind thanks to its powerful antioxidant citral, which activates key detoxifying enzymes that can defend cells from damage by free radicals. It is being tested as a treatment for oral thrush and vaginal yeast infections. Lemongrass shows great promise in anticancer activity: citral is thought to help protect, restore and rebuild damaged cells.

Bay Leaf Laurel bay oil, cineole, is known as a strong antioxidant. More powerful than other plant-derived phyto-chemicals such as vitamin C, the antioxidant compounds in bay leaves are released in cooking as the scent of bay infuses your food. Encouraging studies indicate that consuming bay leaf may help combat diabetes 2 by restoring blood sugar and LDL-cholesterol to healthy and balanced levels.

Hibiscus Helping to rebalance digestion and liver function, the active acid in hibiscus (hydroxycitric acid) inhibits the production of amylase, an enzyme produced by the salivary glands and the pancreas to help the body digest carbohydrates. Hibiscus contains very high levels of vitamin C and is considered to restore digestive health with its gentle laxative properties.

Cocoa A decadent and frequently craved spice packed full of an abundance of phenolic antioxidants, cocoa also contains the feel-good amino-acid tryptophan, used by the brain to make the neurotransmitter serotonin, which helps restore a sense of life balance and give pause to the frenetic pace that occasionally overwhelms our lives with stress.

Basil Familiarly fragrant basil relieves stress, supports the adrenal glands, helps to restore and rebalance levels of cortisol and is being studied for its promising antiaging benefit. Basil's powerful antioxidant phytonutrients orientin and vicenin and the volatile oils eugenol and apigemen can aid in the rebalancing of stress hormones.

Saffron This beautiful bright-yellow stamen hides powerful properties in its most important phytochemical, crocetin. Studies have shown positive results that saffron in tea may help rebalance high-blood-pressure levels. This active phytonutrient compound in saffron may also help improve eye and vision health brought on by the onset of cataracts. Crocetin is also a strong anti-inflammatory that can help to restore lung function in those suffering from asthma by reducing inflammation in the lungs.

Garlic *The Russian Penicillin Spice*

'Garlic! Garlic! The secret of staying young!' So goes the opening line of a song dedicated entirely to garlic in the '90s Broadway musical *Dance of the Vampires*. The thousands of years of history, myths, beliefs and medical science surrounding garlic are mind-boggling. Chinese records dating from 2700BC indicate that garlic was used as a remedy for its heating and stimulating effects; Egyptian slaves building the great pyramids were fed garlic for strength; Ancient Greeks gave garlic to their soldiers and Olympic athletes were prescribed garlic tonics or simply chewed garlic as a remedy for any number of ills, from the common cold to deadly viruses and contagious diseases. Garlic was so revered that it was offered up at temples to the Greek gods. In the Middle Ages, Arabian physicians lauded garlic for its magical and astonishing curative power, while in Western Europe it was believed that the 'stink rose' smell of garlic would repel vampires! During World War II, it was called Russian penicillin because, after running out of penicillin, the Russian government issued its soldiers with cloves of garlic to keep them strong and healthy.

Garlic (*Allium sativum*) contains active organosulfur compounds, which are responsible for its health-giving properties (see below). Although the odour of fresh garlic causes some to avoid it, the overwhelming amount of positive health data should encourage you to include this superhero spice in your daily diet.

www.ncbi.nlm.nih.gov/pmc/articles/PMC3249897/

Garlic is used in kitchens all around the world: it is added to the classic dishes of Italy, France, Greece, Mexico, China and India, to name but a few. Choose garlic heads – they vary in size and can contain up to two dozen cloves – that are firm with no soft cloves, and store in an open container in a cool dry place rather than in the fridge, to prevent the garlic growing mould and passing its odour to the rest of the fridge contents! Properly stored, garlic will keep for up to three months. If it begins sprouting, simply cut away the green growth, which will be bitter. If you are using many cloves in a recipe, plunge whole cloves of unpeeled fresh garlic into boiling water for one minute, use a slotted spoon to scoop out, then immediately plunge into iced water until cool. The paper skin will then be soft enough to peel off easily. Garlic also comes in granulated or powdered form, which will keep for about a year.

Large mild-tasting cloves of elephant garlic are not in fact true garlic but a type of onion related to leeks. However, beautiful garlic scapes, sold in daffodil-like bunches, are the flowering stems of the garlic plant produced before the garlic bulbs mature. In season from early summer, scapes look like curling spring onions and are best eaten lightly sautéed and added to an omelette, or chopped and sprinkled over salads. You can also use them to make a scape and basil pesto.

> Garlic owes its taste and odour to organosulfur compounds, which have been shown to have anticancer properties. When garlic is chopped or crushed, the enzyme allinase is released, which activates its anticancer, anti-inflammatory effect. It is therefore important to leave it for at least ten minutes after chopping before you cook it. Laboratory research and studies in humans have shown garlic's ability to reduce the formation of nitrosamines, which are chemical carcinogens. It is also possible that the reduction in nitrosamine formation is a result of garlic's antimicrobial properties. Research has shown that garlic modifies the metabolism of hormones, such as oestrogen and progesterone, through induction of cytochrome P450 enzymes. This could be extremely important in the regulation of hormone-dependent cancers such as prostate and breast cancer. Garlic and its various compounds seem to be able to block the carcinogenic action of various chemicals that target different tissues in the body. It is therefore logical to assume that it exerts its carcinogenic action through more than one mechanism. Allyl sulfur compounds present in garlic have anti-inflammatory effects and reduce the risk of cardiovascular and cerebrovascular diseases.
>
> There is still much more to discover through research.

Eleni Tsiompanou, MD, PGDip, MSc Nutritional Medicine

Cardamom *The Spice Bomb*

The third most expensive spice in the world, cardamom, hailed the 'Queen of Spices', seduced emperors and adventurers for centuries with its sweet-tangy scent as a flavouring and as a medicine. A distant relative of the ginger family, it has been used as a traditional remedy for thousands of years for digestive problems from bad breath to stomach upsets. Its many volatile oils are also thought to help with lowering blood pressure, and its most active oil, cineole – impressively both antibacterial and antioxidant – has been recently trialled as an aid for asthma and other respiratory ailments.

This spice bomb is believed to have been discovered in the Cardamom Hills of Southern India. The tall cardamom bushes grow prolifically and are harvested commercially today primarily in India and Guatemala, the pods being picked from the base of each bush.

Cardamom's alluring aroma includes scents of citrus, evergreen, clove, camphor and black pepper. Hailed by many chefs as the most versatile spice in the cabinet, it is included – as whole pods, seeds or ground – in Indian and Chinese spice blends, slow-cooked stews, modern Asian fusion dishes and traditional Scandinavian breads and desserts, and it blends seamlessly with both sweet and savoury spices, including anise, cinnamon, clove, cumin, caraway, chili pepper, ginger, paprika, saffron and vanilla. Fifteenth-century writings tell of cardamom in rice dishes and 'sherbets' and it is still used today to give steamed rice a rich mysterious flavour. The majority of cardamom grown today is consumed in traditional coffee drinks in the Middle East and India, creating an unforgettable hot drink with a bright and lingering flavour. The wandering Bedouins of the Arabian Peninsula carry with them a special coffee pot with a tiny secret chamber to hold a cardamom pod. The white cardamom often favoured by British, European and Scandinavian countries is the green pod gently bleached to soften the camphor-like scent, which is thought to add additional sweetness.

Ideally, buy and use whole pods and choose smooth, smaller pods with an even greenish hue. They will last for years kept in an airtight container away from sunlight. Split open the pods to reveal the pungent seeds and grind a little at a time as the volatile oils quickly lose their punch and pungency. If you purchase ground cardamom, use it within six months.

Black cardamom, a closely related species, has a completely different flavour profile. When the pods are picked and dried, they exude a smoky flavour with peppery overtones that works well with slow-cooked meats, vegetables and stewed fruits.

❛ Cardamom offers much beyond its sweet aromatic allure. Its essential oils have been credited over the centuries for serving as an antiseptic (dental and oral health), antispasmodic (digestive, soothing and regularity), diuretic (urinary health), expectorant (pulmonary health) and stimulant (sense of wellbeing).

As a reservoir of antioxidants, cardamom promotes the body's protection against stress and common sicknesses. Animal studies have demonstrated its ability to increase glutathione, a key antioxidant enzyme native to our bodies. Above and beyond being a rich source of minerals (potassium, calcium, magnesium, manganese, copper and iron) and vitamins (riboflavin, niacin and vitamin C), it is now garnering interest to defend against cancers promoted by hormones. Cardamom contains key compounds indole-3-carbinol (I3C), which reduces oestrogen activity by disrupting activity at the oestrogen receptor, and di-indolyl-methane (DIM), which induces apoptosis, promoting an antiproliferative effect on cancer cells. These phytonutrients are commonly celebrated in the cruciferous vegetables such as broccoli, Brussels sprouts, cabbage, cauliflower and kale. I3C and DIM are being studied to reduce the risk of breast cancer, ovarian cancer and prostate cancer.

In the realm of cardiovascular health, cardamom showed efficacy in reducing blood pressure when studied in a small number of participants who consumed cardamom daily for three months. Research suggests that its action is similar to commonly prescribed antihypertensive medicines called calcium channel blockers.

(Safety note: cardamom pods should be used in small amounts since large quantities of this spice can irritate the gastrointestinal lining and promote stomach ulcers.) ❜

Param Dedhia, MD

Pomegranate *The Hippocratic Spice*

This jewelled 'fruit of paradise' originated in Persia and the Persian word is aptly translated. 'May food be your medicine and medicine be your food': so says the famous quotation attributed to Hippocrates, the father of modern medicine, who allegedly favoured this spice. He is said to have used pomegranate-seed extracts for numerous ailments, including skin and eye inflammation, as well as to aid digestion and cleanse the blood. In many ancient cultures, the pomegranate has been a symbol of health, luck, fertility and immortality.

The power of pomegranate comes from its active and extensive range of antioxidant polyphenols. Most parts of the pomegranate – including the flower, fruit rind, leaf, dried seed (anardana) and fresh seed, root and trunk bark, fresh fruit and juice – have been utilized medicinally worldwide in almost every traditional medicine discipline. Today, every bit of the pomegranate is under vigorous research and study to analyze the possible anticancer benefit of this remarkable fruit not only to help balance levels of the prostate-specific antigen marker (PSA) but also to enter non-toxic battle with, and possibly even reverse, prostate cancer (second only to lung cancer as the most deadly cancer for men). And pomegranate, deliciously packed with a medicine-cabinet's worth of natural remedies in its ruby-red sphere, has no side effects.

Pomegranate seeds have been used for medicinal purposes for thousands of years and today it is thought that the juice pressed and strained from the seeds may also be effective against heart disease, high blood pressure, inflammation as well as some cancers. The antioxidant oil shows promising high antiaging benefit when used on face and hands and is being studied for its preventative skin-cancer benefits. It also offers speedy recovery after a good run with thirst-quenching relief to rehydrate and refresh the body.

A single pomegranate contains about 500 seeds and yields one cup of seeds or half a cup of juice, with a sweet, tart, almost dry but refreshing taste from the nutrient-rich polyphenols.

Fresh whole pomegranate is available from autumn all through the winter and will keep for up to a month if refrigerated. Fresh seeds can be frozen for up to six months. Bottles of unopened juice, dried seeds, powder and molasses are all long-shelf-life staples, enabling you to enjoy and benefit from pomegranate every day. Try pomegranate molasses (made by reducing the juice to a thick molasses-like syrup) added to meat marinades, as a glaze for salmon, or simply drizzled over labneh with muesli and fresh berries. Or finish a healthy squash soup with a handful of fresh pomegranate and toasted pumpkin seeds and a squeeze of lime.

❛ Pomegranate is one of the most ancient fruits, considered sacred by many religions. It is symbolic of life, regeneration, birth, fertility, prosperity and a bright future. Pomegranate is rich in vitamin C, potassium and antioxidants as well as other chemicals. There is growing interest in its benefits in reducing the risk of prostate cancer, lymphoma, diabetes, high blood pressure and cardiovascular disease. Several laboratory and animal studies have shown that pomegranate has an effect on cell growth and tumour size. Human studies have also shown promising results on the reduction of PSA, the prostate cancer marker after surgery for prostate cancer, slowing tumour growth and therefore increasing survival and improving quality of life. It is also been shown to have antiviral and antibacterial properties against dental plaque. There are no side effects. ❜

Eleni Tsiompanou, MD, PGDip, MSc Nutritional Medicine

Fenugreek *The Fascinating Spice*

What do New York nights and the spice fenugreek have in common? On humid nights when the wind was blowing moderately from West to East across the Hudson River that separates Manhattan from New Jersey, complaints would pour in to the 311 hotline about a mysterious odour. After many phone calls to and from the mayor and a bit of sleuthing, investigators discovered that the smell was coming from a factory in North Bergen, New Jersey, that processes fenugreek seeds! Even if you've never heard of fenugreek, it's likely you've tasted it in something: the fenugreek being processed by the New Jersey plant was probably destined as a flavouring ingredient in vanilla, maple syrup or butterscotch-flavoured syrups.

Like cinnamon, fenugreek exudes a sweet scent and is also being studied as a possible aid to reduce blood sugar, a vital concern for those with diabetes. Raw seeds soaked in water soften and expand and have been traditionally used to normalize digestion. Fenugreek is also considered in many cultures to increase libido in men, breast size in women and act as a powerful aphrodisiac. This makes complete sense as one of the active components in fenugreek has similar bio-identical properties to the hormone oestrogen. Sure beats rhino horn!

Fenugreek is one of the oldest cultivated medicinal plants: it is praised in Egyptian papyrus writings dating back to around 1500BC. Native to Southern Europe and Asia, it also grows in North and South America, North Africa and the Middle East.

A versatile annual plant that grows to about 60cm (2ft) tall, fenugreek produces light-green leaves similar to clover and small white flowers that can be used fresh as salad greens and, when dried, added to soups, stews and pastes. The long, slender, flat pods extending from the branches each contain 10–20 small, hard, golden-brown fenugreek seeds. The fresh seeds have a pungent aroma and a fairly bitter taste, which has been described as similar to burnt celery, but when lightly toasted, they smell of maple syrup. Toast the seeds carefully; if toasted too long, they'll become so intensely bitter they'll be inedible. Traditionally used in sauces, chutneys, pickles, long-cooking stews, naan bread and numerous grain recipes, fenugreek is also

celebrated in this book with a sweet dish: Fenugreek Poached Pear with Dessert Dukkah (see page 206).

Look for fenugreek, which sometimes goes by the name 'menthi', at Middle Eastern grocers, specialty shops or online. Store whole seeds in an airtight glass container in a cool, dark place, where they should stay fresh for several months. Powdered or paste-form fenugreek should be kept in air-sealed packets in the fridge.

www.ncbi.nlm.nih.gov/pubmed/26098483

❝ Fenugreek shows itself to be a most interesting seed as it is bitter in taste in the raw form yet flavour-rich and aromatic if lightly roasted. This herb has honoured healthy living and wellness over the ages. Historically, it has been used to promote digestive wellness with its rich fibre content (non-starch polysaccharide) and to assist nursing mothers to release breast milk. It has been found to be a rich source of vitamins – A, C, K and B (the B vitamins include thiamine, riboflavin, niacin and pyridoxine) – and to supply key minerals – potassium, calcium, magnesium, manganese, copper, iron, zinc and selenium. Fenugreek has also been shown to reduce cholesterol and balance blood sugar.

The non-starch polysaccharides (NSPs) of fenugreek include saponins, pectin, tannins, hemicellulose and mucilage. In addition to aiding digestion, these NSPs, especially saponins, reduce the production of "bad" LDL-cholesterol by reducing the reabsorption of bile salts in the colon. Furthermore, they may reduce the risk of colonic cancers by binding toxins increasingly found in our food.

Fenugreek may help both type I and type II diabetes by two unique properties: its amino acid, 4-hydroxy isoleucine, which helps release insulin, and its natural fibre, galactomannan, which slows the rate at which sugar is absorbed into the bloodstream. Together these smooth the release and availability of sugar in our bloodstream.

As cardiovascular risk in men and women continues to increase, it is time to revisit traditional spices to balance cholesterol and sugar.

(Safety note: excess intake of fenugreek seeds by pregnant mothers can increase the risk of premature childbirth.) ❞

Param Dedhia, MD

Thyme *The Breath of Life Spice*

Native to the Mediterranean and Southern Europe, common thyme (*Thymus vulgaris*) is part of the mint family and related to oregano. Hundreds of different species, cultivars and varieties of thyme are now grown, picked and savoured worldwide, including Variegated Lemon, Caraway, tangerine-scented Azores, Silver Queen, Goldstream and Bressingham Pink. Thyme prefers sunny, stony locations and its mid-summer flowers attract bees, which produce enchanting thyme-scented honey, and also help repel whiteflies.

Culinary thyme, hedge thyme, wild thyme and all the other thymes contain a great amount of the phytonutrient thymol, also found to a lesser degree in oregano and mint. Thymol is believed to help the lungs ward off a host of pulmonary symptoms and diseases. One sniff of fresh thyme makes you want to breathe in deeply and relax. The Greek word for thyme roughly translates as 'to fumigate' and the ancient Greeks and Romans burned branches of aromatic thyme as incense to purify their temples and homes while inhaling the smoke to invoke a sense of courage and strength.

From Hippocratic Greece until the 1930s, oil of thyme was used on surgical dressings and burned in hospital wards to fend off contagious diseases. The fresh and dried leaves, and the steam-extracted essential oil, are medicinally potent and thyme is one of the most versatile plants in traditional medicine. Thymol's commanding antibacterial talents are being analyzed in the search to discover new solutions in the war on MSRA (Methicillin-resistant *Staphylococcus aureus*) and other resistant bacterial strains. Thyme may also protect the body and brain from an alcohol-infused cocktail or pub-crawl-weekend hangover with its detoxifying properties, and its dominant active compound is added to mouthwashes and topical analgesic ointments. Ingesting large amounts of fresh or dried thyme has no adverse effect, but oil of thyme in extreme doses can be toxic. Consult with your doctor first.

Thyme leaves are a standard component of the classic bouquet-garni blend of thyme sprigs, bay leaf, parsley and rosemary that is used to infuse flavour into soups, stocks and many classic French dishes. Fresh and dried thyme are constant companions to recipes of many cuisines worldwide, but French, Greek and Italian dishes create a particular magic when thyme is added. One of the most used spices in your cupboard, thyme has a powerful scent with a gentle flavour and can be easily used in a cornucopia of ways. Try Lidia Bastianich's Pan-Roasted Monkfish with Thyme-Oil-roasted Tiny Tomatoes, Toasted Barley and Leeks (see page 196) or Courgette and Red Pepper Parcels (see page 24). Dark chocolate desserts or biscuits are scrumptious with a little thyme added and this herb also pairs well, in both savoury and sweet dishes, with citrus.

Fresh thyme stores best wrapped in damp paper and chilled. Six average sprigs will yield about a tablespoon of thyme leaves.

❝ Thyme, whose distinct fragrance is used widely in French cooking, is a spice whose flowers, leaves and oil are used as medicine.

Thyme leaves are administered orally to treat respiratory conditions, including bronchitis and coughs, and there is some evidence to support this use. It has also been used traditionally to treat gastrointestinal symptoms and as a diuretic. Thyme may have both anticoagulant and antiplatelet effects, so people taking "blood thinners" may want to avoid ingesting large quantities of thyme.

Thyme oil, rich in volatile compounds including thymol, is used as an antimicrobial in mouthwashes and liniments. Commercially, thymol has been combined with the antiseptic chlorhexidine as a dental varnish to prevent tooth decay. Thyme oil has also been used traditionally as a topical application: applied to the scalp to treat baldness and to the ears to fight bacterial and fungal infections. ❞

Linda Shiue, MD

SEEDED ANZAC THINS

Light and delicate, these crunchy, seeded, spice wafers are both surprisingly sweet and savoury. The maple-scented fenugreek works harmoniously with the other spices and, although you use only a small measure, it is one powerful spice! Traditionally added to curry, fenugreek is being studied as a therapeutic aid in weight loss and balancing cholesterol.

MAKES 24

125g (4½oz./1 cup) plain (all-purpose) flour

40g (1½oz./½ cup) desiccated unsweetened coconut

55g (2oz./⅔ cup) rolled oats, lightly toasted (don't use quick-cooking oats)

40g (1½oz./3½ tbsp) coconut or caster (superfine) sugar

1 tbsp sesame seeds

1 tbsp poppy seeds

1 tbsp fresh thyme leaves

1 tsp anise seeds

⅛ tsp ground fenugreek

1 tsp orange zest

1 tsp baking powder

¼ tsp salt

90–120ml (6–8 tbsp) extra virgin olive oil

1 egg white, for glazing

raw sugar and sea salt flakes, for glazing

Preheat the oven to 200°C (400°F/gas mark 6).

In the bowl of an electric mixer fitted with the paddle attachment, or in a large bowl using a spoon, mix the flour, coconut, rolled oats, sugar, sesame and poppy seeds, thyme leaves, anise seeds, fenugreek, zest, baking powder and salt until just combined.

In a small bowl, whisk the olive oil with 80ml (⅓ cup) of iced water. Add this to the dry mixture and mix until combined, scraping down the sides of the bowl as needed.

Shape a tablespoon of dough into a ball. Place four balls at a time on a piece of parchment paper, about 10cm (4in.) apart and cover with another piece of parchment or with cling film (plastic wrap). Roll out into very thin ovals, about 20cm (8in.) long. Transfer the dough and parchment to a baking tray. Lift off the top piece of parchment.

Whisk the egg white with 1 teaspoon of water, a pinch of salt and sugar until foamy. Brush the ovals with this glaze and sprinkle with a pinch of raw sugar and flake salt.

Bake, rotating the baking sheets halfway through, until the wafers are brown around the edges and in spots on top, about 8 minutes. (Check the wafers are cooking evenly and turn trays as needed; don't walk away and leave them as they can burn in moments!)

Transfer the wafers to a wire rack to cool, then store them stacked between layers of parchment paper in an airtight container.

SOUR CHERRY, THYME AND CHEDDAR SCONES

Originally created for Sausal El Segundo in Los Angeles, these scones are not too sweet and full of goodness, with grains, purported antiaging thyme leaves and high-anthocyanin brain-food cherries. The pepper is thought to increase the benefits of these active compounds as well as adding inviting toasty pepper aromas.

MAKES ABOUT 9 LARGE OR 15 SMALL SCONES

250g (9oz./2 cups) plain (all-purpose) flour

25g (1oz./3 tbsp) rolled oats (don't use quick-cooking oats)

2 packed tbsp soft brown sugar

1½ tsp chopped fresh thyme leaves, or ¾ tsp dried thyme

zest of ½ lemon

1 tbsp ground flax seeds

1½ tsp baking powder

½ tsp toasted ground black pepper, plus extra for sprinkling on top

¼ tsp kosher or sea salt

¼ tsp toasted ground star anise

55g (2oz./½ stick) butter, chilled, cut into 1cm (½in.) cubes

1 large egg, beaten

90ml (6 tbsp) sour cream, chilled

55g (2oz./½ cup) grated mature Cheddar, or Parmesan

1 egg beaten, for glazing

2 tbsp rolled oats, for sprinkling on top

185g (6½oz./²⁄₃ cup) low-sugar cherry jam or compote

In a large bowl, whisk together the flour, rolled oats, brown sugar, thyme, lemon zest, flax seeds, baking powder, pepper, salt and star anise. Chop in the chilled butter with two forks or a pastry blender until the mixture resembles coarse cornmeal.

Add the beaten egg and cream and stir quickly and lightly with a fork until incorporated, being careful not to overwork the dough.

Turn the dough out onto a lightly floured surface and pat out or gently roll into a 1cm (½in.) deep rectangle, using additional flour sparingly. Sprinkle all but 3 tablespoons of the grated cheese on top.

Fold into thirds, seal sides gently and roll out again into a rectangle. Cut with a knife into 8cm (3in.) squares (or 15 smaller two-bite squares) and place on a parchment- or silicone-lined baking tray. Make a large thumbprint in the centre of each scone. Cover and chill for 30 minutes or until you are ready to bake, or wrap tightly and freeze for up to a month.

Just before baking, preheat the oven to 190°C fan (375°F/gas mark 5). Brush each scone with egg wash and sprinkle with the oats, remaining cheese and a few grinds of black pepper, then fill each thumbprint with about 2 teaspoons of cherry jam.

Bake for 15–17 minutes (12–14 minutes for smaller squares) until the tops are golden brown. Transfer to a wire rack to cool.

GRILLED AUBERGINE PATE
(BAINGAN BHURTA)
Raghavan Iyer

'Traditionally in Northern Indian villages and in restaurants there, cooks drop aubergine (eggplant) directly onto hot coals in a bell-shaped, clay-lined oven (tandoor) that often generates intense heat (up to 370°C/700°F). It's easy to duplicate the same technique with a charcoal or gas grill. The smoky aubergine (eggplant) flavour offers an excellent backdrop to the subtle aromas of cloves and cinnamon in the garam masala. I often serve the pâté with naan, pita, or even slices of crusty crostini as a great starter to a meal.' RI

SERVES 6

2 small (about 450g/1lb. each) aubergine (eggplants)

2 tsp coriander seeds, ground

1 tsp cumin seeds, ground

1 tsp coarse sea or kosher salt

1 tsp garam masala

½ tsp ground cayenne pepper

¼ tsp ground turmeric

1 small red onion, finely chopped

115g (4oz./½ cup) passata (tomato sauce)

juice of ½ medium lime (1 tbsp)

1 tbsp freshly grated ginger

2 medium garlic cloves, finely chopped

25g (1oz./½ cup) finely chopped fresh coriander (cilantro) leaves and tender stems

2 tbsp ghee (clarified butter) or vegetable oil

1 tsp cumin seeds

1 large lime, cut into 8 wedges

Heat an oven grill (broiler) or heat coals or a gas grill for direct heat.

Pierce the aubergine (eggplants) with a fork in five or six places.

To grill (broil): grill (broil) the aubergine (eggplants) 5–8cm (2–3in.) away from the heat, turning them occasionally to ensure even cooking, until the skin is completely blackened and blistered, 20–25 minutes.

For cooking on the barbecue or grill: place the aubergine (eggplants) on the grill or directly onto hot coals, turning them occasionally to ensure even cooking, until the skin is completely blackened and blistered, 20–25 minutes. Transfer the aubergine (eggplants) to a large bowl, cover with cling film (plastic wrap) and set aside for about 30 minutes. The steam that rises from within will sweat the aubergine (eggplants) and help loosen the skin for easy peeling.

Peel and discard the skin and stem. Put the pulp in a bowl and mash using a potato masher, or with your hands, to a smooth consistency. Keep the juices and any liquid that pools at the bottom of the bowl.

Add the ground coriander and cumin, salt, garam masala, cayenne, turmeric, half the onion, the tomato sauce, lime juice, ginger, garlic and half the chopped coriander (cilantro); mix well.

Heat the ghee in a wok or deep 30cm (12in.) frying pan (skillet) over medium–high heat. Add the cumin seeds and allow them to sizzle and turn reddish brown, about 15 seconds. Immediately add the remaining onion and stir-fry until light brown around the edges, 2–3 minutes.

Add the aubergine (eggplant) mixture and stir-fry until almost all the liquid evaporates, 15–20 minutes.

Transfer to serving bowl and garnish with the remaining coriander (cilantro) and the lime wedges.

POMEGRANATE SEED TABOULI

Nutty and nutritious, with those little bursts of the sweet–tart intoxicating flavour of healthy pomegranate, this is great as a side dish or packed into your lunchbox.

SERVES 4-6

200g (7oz./1 cup) kasha (toasted buckwheat) or farro

1–2 large shallots, chopped

120ml (½ cup) extra virgin olive oil

60ml (¼ cup) fresh lemon juice

1 tbsp pomegranate molasses

2 tsp cumin seeds, toasted and ground

3 bunches (175g/6oz.) finely chopped flat-leaf parsley

25g (1oz./1 cup) chopped fresh mint

zest of 1 lemon

4 tbsp pomegranate seeds

Put the kasha or farro in a small saucepan with 500ml (2 cups + 2 tablespoons) of water, cover and bring to the boil. Reduce the heat and simmer until tender, about 15–20 minutes. Cool.

Whisk together the shallots with the olive oil, lemon juice, pomegranate molasses and cumin. Season with salt and pepper.

In a large bowl, mix the cooled kasha or farro with the chopped parsley, mint and lemon zest, then fold in the whisked dressing and the pomegranate seeds. Serve cold.

RAW BEETROOT, FENNEL AND APPLE CRUNCH SALAD

This super nutrient-packed recipe makes an easy midday salad full of healthy spice heroes! Sprinkled with mint, pomegranate and toasted quinoa, this crunch salad will keep you going through the afternoon energy dips.

SERVES 4 AS A SIDE

115g (4oz.) fennel, thinly sliced, a few fronds reserved for garnish

½–1 small garlic clove, chopped

1 tbsp apple cider vinegar

1 tbsp grassy extra virgin olive oil

¼ tsp salt

115g (4oz./½ medium) red beetroot, finely grated

70g (2½oz./½ small) Granny Smith apple, cored and diced

20g (¾oz./3 tbsp) roughly chopped toasted walnuts, reserve a spoonful for garnish

10g (¼oz.) finely sliced spring onion (white part only)

15g (½oz./small handful) mint leaves, shredded thickly

1 tbsp chopped parsley

zest and juice of ½ lime

zest of ½ orange, juice of 1 small orange

2 tbsp grassy extra virgin olive oil

1 tsp ground cumin seeds, toasted and ground

½ tsp fennel seeds, toasted and ground

½ tsp cardamom seeds, toasted and ground

½ tsp smoked paprika

½ tsp pomegranate molasses

¼ tsp salt

10 grinds black pepper

1 tbsp toasted quinoa

Marinate the fennel and garlic in the vinegar, oil and salt and chill until softened, at least 30 minutes or overnight.

Mix together with all the remaining ingredients except the quinoa.

Garnish with the toasted quinoa and the reserved walnuts and fennel fronds.

VEGETABLE PAELLA
(PAELLA DE VERDURAS)
José Andrés

'Paella is the quintessential rice dish of Spain. This recipe features saffron, which provides a distinctive flavour, as well as garlic — several special garlic varieties grow in Spain's countryside. The beauty of this recipe is its flexibility with the seasons. I love to shop at my local farmers' market with my daughters to select the vegetables for the weekend's paella. Ask about what's fresh at the markets near you.' JA

SERVES 4–6

60ml (¼ cup) Spanish extra virgin olive oil
1 bunch spring onions (scallions), thinly sliced
100g (3½oz./1 cup) button mushrooms, halved if larger
85g (3oz./½ cup) diced red (bell) pepper
70g (2½oz./½ cup) diced courgette (zucchini)
70g (2½oz./½ cup) diced carrots
1 tsp minced garlic
55g (2oz./¼ cup) sofrito (see below)
240ml (1 cup) dry white wine
pinch saffron
1.2 litres (5 cups) mushroom or vegetable stock
200g (7oz./1 cup) Spanish Bomba rice (if using Valencia rice, use only 1 litre/4¼ cups stock)
40g (1½oz./¼ cup) fresh green peas
alioli, for serving (see below)

For the sofrito (makes about 3 cups):

10 ripe plum tomatoes, sliced in half
350ml (1½ cups) Spanish extra virgin olive oil
4 small Spanish onions, finely chopped
1 tsp sugar
1 tsp salt
1 tsp pimentón, or Spanish smoked paprika
3 bay leaves

For the alioli (makes 1 cup):

1 small egg
240ml (1 cup) Spanish extra virgin olive oil
1 garlic clove
1 tsp sherry vinegar or fresh lemon juice
sea salt, to taste

First make the sofrito. Place a grater over a mixing bowl and grate the open side of the tomatoes down to their skins. Discard the skins. Heat the oil in a pan over medium–low heat. Add the onions, sugar and salt. Cook, stirring occasionally, until soft and caramelized, about 45 minutes. Stir in the grated tomatoes, pimentón and bay leaves and cook over medium heat until the tomatoes have broken down and the oil has separated from the sauce, about 20 minutes. Discard the bay leaves and store the sauce in the refrigerator, covered, until ready to use.

To make the alioli, put the egg, 2 tablespoons of the olive oil, the garlic and the vinegar or lemon juice into the bowl of a food processor fitted with a steel blade. Process the ingredients at high speed until the garlic is fully puréed and the mixture becomes a loose paste. While processing, slowly begin to add the remaining olive oil drop by drop. If the mixture appears too thick, add a teaspoon of water to loosen the sauce. Continue adding the oil until the sauce becomes rich and creamy and light yellow in colour. Season with sea salt to taste.

To make the paella, heat the olive oil in a 33cm (13in.) paella pan over medium–high heat. Add the onions and sauté until soft and lightly browned, about 3 minutes. Add the mushrooms, red (bell) pepper, courgettes (zucchini), carrots and garlic and cook for 2 minutes more. Stir in the sofrito and cook for 1 minute. Pour in the white wine and let it reduce by half, about 2 minutes.

Crumble the saffron into the pan and pour in the stock. Increase the heat to high and bring to the boil. Let boil for 2–3 minutes, then add the rice and peas and stir until well combined. Reduce the heat to medium–high, season with sea salt to taste and cook for 4 minutes. Do not stir the rice again as this can cause it to cook unevenly.

Reduce the heat to low and cook for another 7 minutes. Remove the paella from the heat, cover with a clean cloth and let rest for 5 minutes. Serve with the alioli.

Photo credit: Christopher Banks

'SPAGHETTI AND MEATBALLS'
WITH THYME OIL AND GARLIC

A healthier take on the classic comfort food, the 'pasta' here is made from spaghetti squash. If unavailable, use courgettes, peeled into ribbons and steamed or pan-simmered. The 'meatballs' are vegan but the texture and taste are so much like beef you may consider surprising friends and family with this super-healthy vegan variation!

SERVES 4

For the 'meatballs':

150g (5½oz./¾ cup) dried brown lentils, rinsed and picked over

3 garlic cloves, sliced

10 thyme sprigs, plus extra to garnish

3 tbsp Thyme Oil (see below)

100g (3½oz./1 small) onion, roughly chopped

350g (12oz./3½ cups) white mushrooms, roughly chopped

3 tbsp low-salt tomato purée (paste)

1½ tbsp Dijon mustard, or to taste

85g (3oz./1 cup) rolled oats, toasted and roughly ground

1½ tsp dried thyme

240ml (1 cup) vegetable stock

additional oil or oil spray for baking

For the 'spaghetti':

1kg (2lb. 4oz.) spaghetti squash (yields about 750g/1lb. 10oz./4 cups)

2 tbsp thyme oil (see below)

a few saffron strands (optional)

Preheat the oven to 180°C (350°F/gas mark 4). Put the lentils, garlic and thyme sprigs in a small saucepan with 350ml (1½ cups) water. Bring to a boil, then simmer over low heat for 10 minutes – the lentils will be crunchy. Remove from heat, drain and cool slightly, discarding the thyme sprigs. Set aside.

Add the thyme oil to a sauté pan and cook the onions over medium heat until translucent, about 4 minutes. Add the mushrooms and cook for an additional 4–5 minutes, until the mushrooms release their liquid.

Transfer to a food processor, add the lentil mixture and pulse until puréed but with a few chunky bits.

Put the tomato purée (paste) into the pan and cook for 2 minutes to caramelize, then add the lentil mixture, mustard, oats, dried thyme and vegetable stock. Stir and cook until the liquid is absorbed and the mixture is fragrant. Season with salt and pepper and set aside to cool.

When cool to touch, shape into about 20 balls (each about 25g/1oz.) and place on a lined, oiled baking tray.

To make the 'spaghetti', split the spaghetti squash in half and scrape out the seeds for another use or discard. Add the thyme oil, a few saffron strands (if using) and 60ml (¼ cup) of water. Place the squash cut side down on an oiled baking tray and bake for 30–40 minutes, or until fork tender. Ten minutes through baking the squash, add the 'meatballs' to the oven to bake until browned, about 20–25 minutes.

Remove the squash from the oven and turn cut side up to cool for about 10 minutes. Using a fork, scrape the squash with a fork to make the 'spaghetti'. Drizzle with thyme oil, a few thyme sprigs and season to taste.

Arrange the 'spaghetti' on four plates and add five 'meatballs' to each. Serve with your favourite pasta sauce or a tin of warmed chopped tomatoes.

THYME OIL

MAKES 350ml (1½ CUPS)

350ml (1½ cups) extra virgin olive oil   about 15 fresh thyme sprigs

Insert the thyme sprigs in a bottle that will hold them upright. Using a funnel, slowly pour the oil into the bottle until it is completely covering the thyme. Press the sprigs deeper into the bottle so they remain submerged.

Seal the bottle and store in a dark cool pantry. The oil will be ready to use in a week and will keep, tightly sealed, for a month in a cool pantry or for 2 months in the fridge.

PAN-ROASTED MONKFISH
WITH THYME-OIL-ROASTED TINY TOMATOES, TOASTED BARLEY AND LEEKS
Lidia Bastianich

I worked with Lidia several years ago at a beachfront resort that hosted the then top food and wine event in the world, 'Cuisines Of the Sun', on Big Island, Hawaii. Lidia inspired me with her passionate discipline of Italian classic cooking techniques, her endless spirit and her infectious joy of food and life. She created simply flavourful fish-centric tastes seasoned with the plentiful produce available. This dish, adapted from a recipe in her cookbook Lidia's Italian Table *(William and Morrow, 1998) captures her simple, unfussy and mouth-watering cuisine.*

SERVES 6

300g (10½oz.) baby cherry tomatoes on the vine (or regular-sized cherry tomatoes, halved)

4 garlic cloves, unpeeled

9 long thyme sprigs

5 tbsp Thyme Oil (see page 194)

200g (7oz./1 cup) barley or fregola

450g (1lb./about 3 medium) leeks, cut into small rounds

1kg (2lbs. 4oz.) monkfish fillets

175ml (¾ cup) extra virgin olive oil

50g (1¾oz./generous ⅓ cup) plain (all-purpose) flour

3 garlic cloves, sliced finely

240ml (1 cup) dry white wine

120ml (½ cup) fish or vegetable stock

45g (1½oz./3 tbsp) unsalted butter

2 tbsp chopped fresh Italian parsley

¼ preserved lemon, thinly shredded

a few thyme leaves, to garnish

Preheat the oven to 120°C (250°F/gas mark ½). Spread the tomatoes and garlic cloves on a lined baking tray scattered with five thyme sprigs. Drizzle with 3 tablespoons of the Thyme Oil and season with salt and pepper. Bake for 35 minutes or until roasted and lightly caramelized. Set aside until ready to plate the fish.

Put the barley into a large pan and pour over 600ml (2½ cups) of water. Cover with a lid and bring to a rolling boil then lower the temperature to a simmer. Gently simmer, covered, for about 45–55 minutes until just tender and the water has been absorbed. Transfer to a baking tray, spread out and leave to cool.

Blanch the leeks in a medium pan of boiling salted water for 3 minutes. Drain thoroughly then leave to cool.

Using a paring knife, remove the outer mottled grey membranes and any dark-red portions from the fish fillets. Slice the fish on a slight angle into 1cm (½in.) thick medallions. Place the medallions a few at a time between two sheets of cling film (plastic wrap) and pound them lightly with the flat side of a meat mallet or the bottom of a small heavy saucepan to flatten them slightly.

In a large frying pan (skillet), heat 3 tablespoons of olive oil over medium–high heat. Add the blanched leeks and barley. Season with salt and pepper and cook, turning often, until nicely golden brown, about 12 minutes. Remove the pan from the heat and cover to keep warm.

Meanwhile, sprinkle the monkfish with salt and lightly dust with flour, tapping off any excess. In a large pan, heat the remaining olive oil and the sliced garlic over medium heat. Add as many of the monkfish slices as will fit in a single layer and cook turning once, until golden brown on both sides, about 5–7 minutes. Remove the monkfish to a plate and keep warm; repeat with the remaining monkfish.

Drain the remaining oil from the pan. Add the wine and bring to a boil, scraping the sides and bottom of the pan. Add the fish stock, butter and remaining four thyme sprigs and season lightly with salt and pepper to taste. Simmer until the sauce is reduced by about half and lightly thickened, about 7 minutes. Strain the sauce through a sieve and check the final seasoning.

To serve, stir the parsley into the barley and leek mixture, then spread over the base of a warmed serving dish. Drizzle with the remaining Thyme Oil. Top with the monkfish slices, spoon the sauce over the fish, then sprinkle with thyme leaves and preserved lemon and scatter the roasted tomatoes and garlic around the plate.

★

GARLIC, FENUGREEK, CARDAMOM

SPICY SPAZCHOOK
WITH BAHARAT HASSELBACK PARSNIPS

Created for a long summer's day barbecue in New Zealand with a fresh organic chicken from the local butcher, then raiding my spice shelves and garden pots full of herbs, I came up with what is now fondly referred to as Spicy Spazchook. Splitting the backbone open so the bird lays flat as it cooks is called spatchcocked. Chickens being called chooks in the southern hemisphere had a ten-year-old guest shouting 'good spazchook'! Try your own herb and spice blends in either hemisphere: it will be a hit whether oven-grilled (broiled) or cooked on the barbecue. The parsnip side dish is a riff on the classic hasselback 'slinky' potato dish; here parsnips are roasted with a baharat spice oil.

SERVES 4

1 whole large chicken, cleaned and split at backbone

2 large onions

For the marinade:

2 tbsp dry mustard powder

2 tbsp sweet pimentón, powder

½ tsp cracked cardamom pods

3 or 4 garlic cloves, minced (1 tbsp minced)

2 tbsp lemon juice

1 large handful fresh mixed herbs (parsley, basil, thyme, oregano, rosemary, sage)

20 grinds black pepper

1 tsp sea salt

2 tbsp brown sugar

240ml (1 cup) grapeseed or vegetable oil

For the fenugreek baharat spice oil:

120ml (½ cup) olive oil

2 tsp maple syrup or honey

1 tbsp toasted ground black peppercorns

1 tbsp paprika

2½ tsp ground cinnamon

2½ tsp coriander seeds, toasted and ground

2½ tsp ground cloves

2 tsp fennel seeds, toasted and ground

1 tsp ground nutmeg

¾ tsp cumin seeds, toasted and ground

½ tsp ground fenugreek

¼ tsp cardamom seeds, toasted and ground

For the baharat hasselback parsnips:

8 x 2.5–4cm (1–1½in.) thick parsnips, scrubbed then trimmed so each parsnip is the same length for even cooking

fenugreek baharat spice oil (see above)

120ml (½ cup) hot vegetable stock or water

12 fenugreek leaves, fresh or dried

knob (small piece) butter

Mix all the marinade ingredients in a small bowl and smear on the chicken. Place the 'spazchook' in a sealable plastic bag and marinate for 3 hours or overnight.

Mix all the ingredients for the fenugreek baharat spice oil together in a bowl.

Preheat the oven to 200°C (400°F/gas mark 6). Remove the chicken from the fridge.

Peel the parsnips on one side to make a flat surface to prevent rolling. Tuck a chopstick either side of the parsnip and gently 'saw' the vegetable in 3mm (⅛in.) slices. (The chopsticks will prevent the knife from cutting all the way through.) Use the tip of the knife to wiggle open the cuts. Drizzle the spice oil into the openings and lay the parsnips in a casserole dish. Pour in hot stock or water to a depth of 5mm (¼in.), add the fenugreek leaves and drizzle additional spice oil on top. Season with salt. Cover with foil and cook for 30–40 minutes until tender.

If oven grilling (broiling) the chicken, preheat the grill (broiler) to 180°C (350°F/gas mark 4). Slice unpeeled onions into five or six thick disks and arrange in an oiled roasting tin. Place the chicken breast-side down on top. Grill (broil) for 20 minutes, turn over and cook a further 20–25 minutes until juices run clear. Remove from oven, cover and let rest for 15–20 minutes. While the chicken rests, return the parsnips to the oven, uncovered, and cook for an additional 15 minutes to brown. To barbecue the chicken, grill off direct heat. Allow about the same cooking and resting times as above. Carefully remove the parsnips from the casserole dish and serve with the Spazchook Chicken. If there is any liquid left in the pan, whisk in a knob (small piece) of butter to thicken and spoon over the parsnips.

GARLIC

KIMCHI
Judy Joo

'Korean food is known for its gutsy and vibrant flavours and much of that comes from punchy ingredients such as ginger, garlic and chilies. Kimchi is a classic dish that showcases Koreans' love for spice. It is Korea's national dish and is eaten every day with every meal. My mum used to make huge quantities of this fermented cabbage dish once a year and store it in clay pots underneath our porch outside. It definitely smells a bit funky, so do wrap it well. You can eat it freshly made, put it in stews, stir-fries and use the 'juice' to kick up any recipe nicely. After one taste, you'll see why kimchi is popping up on menus around the world.' JJ

MAKES 1 LARGE JAR

2.5kg (5½lb./about 1½ –2) heads Korean cabbage (napa or Chinese cabbage)

325g (11½oz.) Korean coarse salt

150g (5½oz.) spring onions (scallions), cut into 5cm (2in.) pieces

200g (7oz.) carrots, cut into matchsticks using a julienne peeler

200g (7oz.) daikon (or Korean radish), cut into matchsticks using a julienne peeler

For the dashima stock:

7 medium dried anchovies, guts and heads removed

6 dried shitake mushrooms

5cm (2in) square of seaweed/kelp dashima

3 spring onions (scallions) (55g/2oz.), roughly chopped

1 small onion (115g/4oz.), roughly chopped

3 large garlic cloves (13g/½oz.), crushed

For the spice paste:

80g (3oz.) garlic (about 18 cloves)

40g (1½oz.) fresh ginger, grated

100g (3½oz.) seojutt (Korean salted shrimp)

20g (¾oz./5 tsp) granulated sugar

130g (4½oz.) gochugaru (Korean chili flakes)

100g (3½oz./scant ½ cup) Korean anchovy sauce

First brine the cabbage. Wash the cabbage well and split into quarters by cutting the bottom roots and pulling the tops apart. Dissolve half of the salt in 60ml (¼ cup) of water. Spread the remaining salt over and in between the leaves of the cabbage. Immerse the cabbage, cut side up, in the salted water (add more water if necessary) and weigh down with a plate so it is completely immersed. Leave overnight in the fridge.

The next day, rinse the cabbage well under running cold water two or three times and drain very well. Gently squeeze out any excess water and leave in a colander to drain further.

Make the dashima stock. Soak the anchovies, mushrooms and kelp for 20 minutes in 500 ml (2 cups plus 2 tablespoons) of cold water, then place in a pot over high heat. Add the spring onion (scallion), onion and garlic and bring to the boil, then lower to a simmer and cook for 20 minutes. Remove and strain. Allow to cool completely.

Make the spice paste. Combine the garlic, ginger, seojutt, sugar, gochugaru and anchovy sauce in a food processor and blend until smooth. Add just enough of the cooled dashima stock to make a smooth paste, about 200–250ml (about 1 cup) should be adequate. Stir in the spring onions, carrots and daikon.

Rub the spice paste all over the cabbage and in between each leaf. Place in a large container with a tight-fitting lid and store in a cool place (at around 2°C/35°F) to ferment for 2–3 weeks, then store in the fridge, where it will keep for at least a year – if it lasts that long!

POMEGRANATE PISTACHIO PARFAIT

With chia seeds full of protein and seductive ruby-red pomegranate juice packed with anthocyanins and prostate-healthy antioxidants, this light and easy-to-make pudding sweetened with honey is a dairy-free delight – refreshing, romantic and healthy!

SERVES 4

For the chia cream:
3 tbsp chia seeds
240ml (1 cup) almond milk
⅛ tsp almond extract
pinch salt flakes
2 tbsp honey
¼ tsp ground cardamom

For the pomegranate gelatin:
475ml (2 cups) pure pomegranate juice
1 tbsp honey
4 gold gelatin leaves (see page 46, or 3¼ tsp powdered gelatin)

For the vanilla labneh:
¼ tsp vanilla extract
¼ tsp granulated sugar, or to taste
pinch ground cardamom
85g (3oz./⅓ cup) labneh

To serve:
25g (1oz./3 tbsp) pistachios, chopped
2 fresh figs, quartered or torn, or dried figs, roughly chopped
a few drops rose water

To make the chia cream, mix together all the ingredients in a bowl, cover and chill for 3 hours or overnight.

Cover the gelatin leaves in ice-cold water and leave until soft. In a small saucepan, warm the pomegranate juice with the honey to dissolve. Drain and squeeze excess water from the gelatin then stir it into the juice. Divide the liquid among four dessert glasses. Chill until firm.

Whisk the vanilla, sugar and ground cardamom into the labneh.

Spoon the chia cream layer on top of the pomegranate gelatin layer then top with vanilla labneh. Sprinkle over some chopped pistachios and garnish with figs. Sprinkle over a few drops of rose water.

CARDAMOM CARAMEL ORANGE ICE CREAM

A bit of spiced decadence, this recipe is nevertheless a leaner style of ice cream containing no egg yolks and only half the amount of double (heavy)/whipping cream.

MAKES 1 LITRE (1 QUART)

For the caramel:	For the ice cream:
5 black cardamom pods, cracked	240ml (1 cup) coconut cream
1 tsp (about 8–10) green cardamom pods, cracked	240ml (1 cup) whipping cream
120ml (½ cup) fresh orange juice, strained	100g (3½oz./½ cup) granulated sugar
1 tbsp lemon juice	large pinch salt
zest of ½ orange	1 tbsp white rum (optional)
300g (10½oz./1½ cups) granulated sugar	2 egg whites, at room temperature
1 vanilla pod (bean), split and cut into 8 pieces	
120ml (½ cup) double (heavy) cream	
1 tbsp coconut oil	

Dry-toast the cardamom in a small pan then roughly grind the pods and seeds in a mortar and pestle.

For the caramel, in a small pan, heat the orange and lemon juice, orange zest, sugar, cardamom, half the vanilla pod (bean) pieces (reserve the remainder for the ice cream) and a pinch of salt to a simmer, taking care it doesn't bubble over. Stir occasionally and cook until the sauce is as thick as honey. Whisk in the cream and coconut oil until well blended. Let it stand for 10 minutes off the heat, then strain out the larger pieces of cardamom and cool completely. Cover and chill until needed.

To make the ice cream, in a medium pan, heat the coconut cream and whipping cream with three quarters of the sugar, the reserved half vanilla pod (bean) pieces and a large pinch of salt until steamy and the sugar has dissolved. Turn off the heat, whisk to help cool and add the rum if using. Cover and chill until cold.

Beat the egg whites in a bowl with a whisk or electric mixer until frothy. Stream in the remaining sugar and continue to whip until the whites form shiny stiff peaks.

Fold the cream into the meringue in stages until incorporated.

Freeze in an ice-cream maker according to manufacturer's instructions. Scoop one third of the ice cream into a container then spoon the caramel on top. Repeat the layers. Cover with cling film (plastic wrap) and freeze until firm.

FENUGREEK-POACHED PEAR
WITH DESSERT DUKKAH

As a 14-year-old budding dancer, I was obsessed with making steamed pears with Cool Whip topping sprinkled with cinnamon sugar. A tad more sophisticated in flavour, texture and colour, these Fenugreek-poached Pears are sublime sitting on a bed of Dessert Dukkah. The toasty maple characteristics of the fenugreek swirl on the tongue, but be mindful not to overtoast or you may have to start again.

SERVES 4

350g (12oz./1¾ cups) granulated sugar

2 tbsp lemon juice

½ cinnamon stick, toasted

2 allspice berries, toasted

½ tsp fenugreek seeds, toasted

3 fenugreek leaves

4 pears such as Bosc or Concorde, with stems

60ml (¼ cup) dessert wine, e.g. Sauternes, Botrytis Semillon or Riesling

2 strips lemon peel

Dessert Dukkah (see below), to serve

labneh or softly whipped cream, to serve (optional)

Put the sugar, lemon juice, cinnamon, allspice berries and fenugreek seeds into a 2-litre (2-quart) heavy metal pan and add 120ml (½ cup) of water. Bring to a simmer on medium–high heat, gently swirling the liquid occasionally, and reduce until syrupy and amber in colour. Carefully add a further 350ml (1½ cups) of water (be careful as it will bubble up). Stir to dissolve the caramel, then add the fenugreek leaves, pears, wine and lemon peel. Place a piece of damp muslin (cheesecloth) or a circle of parchment paper with a small cut in the middle over the pears inside the pan to keep them gently submerged. Poach until tender but still firm, about 18 minutes.

Remove the pears from the liquid, then chill the poaching caramel in an ice bath. Return the pears to the liquid caramel and cover and chill until needed. Make the Dessert Dukkah (see below).

To serve, arrange 1 heaped tablespoon of dukkah on each of four plates. Using a sharp knife, level the bottom of the pears so they stand flat. Arrange each pear in the middle of the dukkah and serve with the pear-poaching caramel sauce and labneh or softly whipped cream if wished.

DESSERT DUKKAH

MAKES 140g (5oz./1 CUP)

⅛ tsp fenugreek seeds

½ cinnamon stick, broken into chips

1 tbsp flax seeds

2 tsp coriander seeds

1 tsp cumin seeds

½ tsp caraway seeds

25g (1oz./¼ cup) pecans, toasted and cooled

25g (1oz./¼ cup) sliced almonds, toasted and cooled

40g (1½oz./⅓ cup) pumpkin seeds, toasted and cooled

2 tsp date or raw sugar

1 tsp salt flakes

¾ tsp vanilla powder (optional)

In a small pan over low heat toast the fenugreek seeds very lightly for just a few minutes and remove to the spice grinder to cool. Turn the temperature to medium then toast the cinnamon chips. Cool and finely grind together and transfer to a small bowl. Toast the flax, coriander, cumin and caraway seeds together over medium heat until you can smell the spices. Cool then grind finely.

Using a mortar and pestle, pound the pecans, almonds and pumpkin seeds together until roughly ground. Add to the small bowl with the spices, sugar, salt and vanilla powder (if using) and mix well.

Stored tightly covered in a cool place, the dukkah will keep for up to 3 weeks, or freeze it for up to 2 months.

CARDAMOM CHAI TISANE

This warming drink is spicy, aromatic and does not contain any caffeine or dairy. The spices are simmered slowly to allow them to infuse all of their delicate, health-boosting flavour into the drink. Perfect for the colder months, this will help to fend off sniffles and is also a good appetite suppressant to fend off late-afternoon growling tummies. The addition of warm and frothy coconut or almond milk makes this the perfect caffeine-free alternative to your usual afternoon latte.

SERVES 2

1 star anise

6 green cardamom pods, lightly crushed

2 cloves

2 black peppercorns, cracked

1 tbsp chopped fresh ginger

5cm (2in) piece of vanilla pod (bean), split, or ½ tsp vanilla paste

160ml (⅔ cup) coconut or almond milk (optional)

½ tsp honey or agave nectar

Pour 450ml (2 cups) of filtered water into a pan and bring to a gentle simmer over a low heat. Add the star anise, cardamom pods, cloves, peppercorns, ginger and vanilla pod or paste, cover the pan and leave to simmer for 30 minutes, stirring occasionally.

Meanwhile, warm the coconut or almond milk in a small pan until small bubbles start to appear on the surface. Remove from the heat and stir in the honey. Keep warm.

Pour the tisane through a colander and into a jug to strain out the spices. Divide the strained liquid between two cups.

Transfer the warm milk to a screw-top jam jar and seal the lid. Shake the milk until frothy and then pour over the tisane. Serve immediately.

Calming spice

In the chaos and busyness of today's world, which so often switches on our reactive fight-or-flight hormone cortisol, we need a pocket of peace to reorganize our thoughts and rebalance our life. These spices contain an abundance of phytonutrients that may help to soothe the body and calm the mind.

Calming Spice Health Heroes

Sage ★ Basil ★ Saffron ★ Mint ★ Lemongrass

Like sipping a comforting cuppa in your Nana's favourite teacup, these calming spices provide a soothing support with their inherent active phytonutritive natural soothing compounds. Many of these spices are rich in natural calming antidepressants while others help to relax and relieve body systems. Take five minutes of meditative peace and serenity then rejoin the day with clearer vision, purpose and focus. Not long ago people used to alleviate stress by taking a break to have a cigarette, but now you can nurture yourself by replacing unhealthy stress-reducing habits with a calming spice infusion, or make a recipe from the calming recipes in this book.

Basil, the eugenol-scented plant, supports the heart and adrenal-gland health with its multi-antioxidant phytophenols that may calm and reverse the levels of reactive, corrosive fight-or-flight cortisol hormones that are released when you're in stressful situations. The subtle yet powerful crocetin – the natural drug carotenoid chemical compound found in saffron flowers – has been used for centuries as a natural antidepressant. Lovely lemongrass can calm the nerves and refocus scattered thoughts and worries. The smoke of burning sage is revered for its negative-energy-clearing talents amongst Native American tribes, and sage is being studied for its mind-calming, meditative and thought-focussing properties. Mint is not only a frequently recommended carminative (relieving gas) for digestion but can also offer relief for nerve pain, quiet the mind and calm anxiety, and studies show positive results for on-going stress management.

Other calming spice heroes

Nutmeg This precious spice offers relief and support for a large number of complaints, including anxiety and depression as well as memory loss and low libido. The active compound found in nutmeg, myristicin, is a powerful natural narcotic, however, so care should be taken not to over-use it medicinally.

Oregano The classic Italian spice balances the acid–alkali scales in the digestive system, fending off free radicals that can wreak havoc with their corrosive effect, speeding up body-system aging. It offers a calming effect to the stomach and intestines, relieving pain and discomfort in the digestive system with its active compounds carovol and thymol.

Rosemary Studies have shown that rosemary can help relieve depression-like symptoms in animals as effectively as fluoxetine, a prescription antidepressant of the selective serotonin reuptake inhibitor (SSRI) class, with its concentrated and multiple antioxidant essential oils rosmarinic acid, carnosic acid and carnosol. According to the *International Journal of Medical Science*, human studies indicate that rosemary can improve memory, while in traditional medicine, it is used as a calming nerve tonic.

Ginger The calming gingerol compounds in ginger soothe and calm the symptoms of nausea brought on by migraines, seasickness, morning sickness and the after-effects of necessary prescription medications, such as chemotherapy. Ginger also acts as a carminative, soothing the digestive system and relieving it of gas.

Citrus Zest More effective than the scent of lavender, the smell and taste of citrus peel has a calming and lifting effect and may also reduce stress and anxiety. Lemon, orange and especially grapefruit peel can aid in refocusing the mind to help you work better on challenging analytical tasks.

Turmeric Among its plethora of talents, turmeric is lauded not only for its potential pain relief from joint inflammation, but also for being naturally soothing. Turmeric's active compound, curcumin, is a natural sedative: it calms and quiets nerves, settles those pre-performance jitters and, in a cup of turmeric milk tea, can help you sleep. A recent test study showed that taking 1000mg a day of curcumin may have the same results as taking an antidepressant and can also offer relief to those suffering from insomnia.

Sage *The Meditation Spice*

Sage has been culturally and religiously significant to many cultures for millennia: the ancient Greeks and the druids of Ireland used it to invoke clear, calm and meditative serenity while Native American tribes burnt it as incense to ward off negative or evil energy, increase clarity and purify the home.

Of nearly a thousand types of sage, a plant native to the Mediterranean and naturalized throughout Europe and North America, only a handful are edible. These include garden sage, true sage, sweet clary, purple sage and the fruity pineapple sage from Mexico. Hardy and drought tolerant, this sacred spice of Native Americans is often made into a tea to clear and calm the mind and to relieve sore throats and colds. Clary sage, a mild and sweet variety, has long been used as an eye treatment in many traditions. In Chinese traditional medicine, the root rather than the leaves of Chinese sage, also called red sage, is infused into a tonic called danshen that is prescribed primarily for its soothing and healing qualities and is also used to treat cardiovascular disease. Food production and processing use the volatile oil in sage to improve the stability and shelf life of cooking oils.

The familiar evergreen perennial shrub thrives in full sun and well-drained lean soil and has long, light-green leaf stalks that grow tender but strong oval-shaped leaves. The veined leaves have a velvet texture with soft tiny-toothed edges and some types can grow the size of salad leaves (up to 5cm/2in. in length). Generally green-grey on the top, sometimes bearing purple-tinged edges with a lighter shade of grey on the underside, the sage plant exudes a strong pungent, piney and aromatic scent. Sage blossoms, attractive to honey bees, bloom in mid-summer with small white, blue or purple flowers.

Sage is popularly used in rich, hearty Italian, German and Greek main courses, including the classic Roman dish Saltimbocca alla Romana, a sage-infused veal and prosciutto dish. Fresh sage also figures prominently in British cheeses and is an integral ingredient in the classic Sunday roast side dish hastily assembled from sage and onion stuffing mix.

The bitter-tasting fresh leaves are best used in cooked dishes or quickly blanched to soften the bitterness. A fun way to enjoy freshly picked sage, and a great topping for soups, salads and main courses, is to flash-fry sage leaves until crispy (see page 230). Sage is sold fresh and dried. Rubbed sage is the finest type of dried sage and I recommend it, as it is minimally ground and delivers a full flavour and aroma, but remember to use dried sage sparingly as it is far stronger than fresh: 1 teaspoon of dried rubbed sage is the equivalent to about 1 tablespoon of fresh sage.

' This herb has been used in the Mediterranean for literally thousands of years: it's often found carved into the beautiful statues of Roman figures, who treated it as a sacred, ceremonial plant. From a medicinal standpoint, sage has one of the longest histories of use of any medicinal herb.

The many terpene [strong-smelling organic compound] antioxidants found in sage are why it was so often used as a preservative for meat before the days of refrigeration.

Interestingly, it also has some significant potential to help with memory and prevent Alzheimer's disease. A placebo-controlled, double-blind, crossover trial on sage involving 44 participants showed significantly improved, immediate and several-hours-later measures of word and cognitive recall. The results represented evidence that sage is capable of acutely modifying cognition in healthy young adults.

The polyphenolic constituents, which are the antioxidant powerhouses, can provide substantial neuroprotection, which might decrease the likelihood of developing the amyloid plaques found in Alzheimer's disease. '

Geeta Maker-Clark, MD

http://www.ncbi.nlm.nih.gov/pubmed/12895685; Adv Exp Med Biol. 2015;863:95-116. doi: 10.1007/978-3-319-18365-7_5.

Basil *The Reverence Spice*

The name basil is derived from Medieval Latin and early French languages from the Greek word 'basilikos', meaning royal. Another relative of the mint family, basil relieves stress, supports the adrenal glands, normalizes levels of cortisol and is being studied for its promising antiaging benefit. Basil is full of free-radical activity in its antioxidant phytonutrients orientin and vicenin and the volatile oils eugenol and apigemen, which can aid the rebalancing of stress hormones. Currently under study, basil shows promise in reducing levels of the flight-or-flight hormone cortisol and the overwhelmed stress-out enzyme creatine (both of which are corrosive when called upon in excess).

The numerous varieties of basil include Thai, lemon, sweet, purple (or opal) and holy basil (tulsi). All can be grown from seed and thrive in warm conditions with full sun, well-watered roots and protected from strong breezes until established. Pick leaves frequently to encourage growth.

Basil is best used fresh or preserved in oil: when dried, it loses the aroma of fresh leaf although it still contains all the active health benefits in a concentrated form and is the best choice to season long-cooked dishes. When purchasing fresh basil, buy only what you will need for a few days as the leaves will blacken and bruise easily once picked and refrigerated.

All types of basil work readily in numerous cuisines and recipes. Nothing could be simpler than the three-ingredient Italian salad of buffalo mozzarella, tomato and basil drizzled with olive oil and balsamic vinegar; or handfuls of basil, garlic, pine nuts and olive oil whizzed together to make a heavenly pesto ready to fold into cooked fresh pasta. Thai basil is a perfect finish to stir-fries, seafood dishes and salads. The agrodolce on page 228 celebrates sweet basil folded into red onion and sour-cherry-glazed sweet potatoes to serve as a side or main, while Mindy Segal's addictive Cinnamon Basil Ice Cream (see page 248) is a perfectly decadent spice pairing.

Holy (or tulsi) basil has smaller leaves but is heartier so stands up to curries, poultry and meat dishes and is used primarily to season Malaysian, Indian and Indonesian cuisine. Native to, primarily grown in and revered in India, holy basil, or tulsi, is a popular tea blend worldwide and often includes fragrant and soothing rose petals. Holy basil got its name from its use in Indian ceremonial religious gatherings. Its clove-like aroma is due to its higher content of eugenol oil, the active phytonutrient compound found in clove and allspice (see page 18). It is also available in dried form and as a nutritional supplement.

❝ Basil, a very fragrant herb whose many varieties are used widely in Mediterranean and Asian cuisine, has volatile chemicals similar to those in thyme. These volatile chemicals possess antimicrobial and antioxidant properties. Basil is also rich in nutrients and contains many vitamins and minerals that are cardio-protective, including vitamin A, magnesium, beta-carotene, vitamin C and vitamin K, as well as calcium, iron, folate and omega-3 fatty acids.

Holy Basil is a different species from sweet or Thai basil, which are more commonly used in cooking Italian and Thai foods, respectively. Holy basil is native to India, where it is known as tulsi, and has been used for thousands of years in Ayurvedic medicine. Medicine is made from the leaves, stems and seeds. In Ayurvedic medicine, holy basil is considered an "adaptogen" – a substance that helps people manage life stress and anxiety. In addition to these uses, holy basil has been used for treating the common cold, influenza, asthma, bronchitis, diabetes, heart disease, malaria and tuberculosis. It has also been used as a mosquito repellent and to counteract snake and scorpion bites. Topically, holy basil is applied to the skin for ringworm. There has been recent interest in using holy basil seed oil for cancer, though there are only preliminary animal studies.

Note: holy basil may interact with blood-thinning medications. ❞

Linda Shiue, MD

Saffron *The Seductive Spice*

The most expensive spice in the world is the dried bright-yellow stigma from a small purple crocus. Each flower creates only three long, delicate stigmas and it takes about 250,000 of these threads to make 1kg (2lb. 4oz.) of pure saffron – that's over 4,000m² (about an acre) of flowers! This seductive, costly spice is intensely aromatic when released into food or drink, so thankfully a little goes a long way.

Saffron has been used since ancient times to treat a variety of ills, including depression, anxiety and hormonal imbalances and disorders in both men and women. Saffron's most important active phytochemical is crocin, a carotenoid phytonutrient that possesses free-radical-fighting activity and antitumor qualities. Saffron protects the body from the ravages of oxidant-induced stress and bacterial infection. Saffron has been vigorously tested and there is evidence that it exerts a significant chemopreventive effect against liver cancer. Bountiful in minerals and vitamins, especially potassium and vitamin C, saffron is also considered helpful in lowering blood pressure, calming the heartbeat and easing digestion.

Some of the first mentions of saffron in Ancient Greek times date back to the eighth century. During the Middle Ages, despite its high cost, people were crazy about saffron and it was added for flavour, colour and health to a range of dishes like 'pottage' a thin, porridge-like meat and grain stew, and the popular blancmange, often sweetened with honey and with or without meat.

Saffron's golden allure crosses cultures and cuisines – it truly is an international spice and can be found growing from Spain, Greece, Italy, Turkey and Iran to India and even Tasmania and New Zealand. Saffron is used to flavour dishes from most cultures: think of Mexican arroz con pollo, Italian risotto milanese, Spanish paella, the French peasant fish stew bouillabaisse with rouille, Indian biryranis, Scandinavia's traditional lussekatter and England's Cornish saffron bread (see the Cornish Saffron Popovers on page 222 for an inspired take on this).

Buy whole saffron threads in their purest form: the darker the yellow-orange colour the more active crocin and fragrance it contains. To make sure your saffron is authentic, drop a few stigmas in a small bowl of warm water. True saffron will dissolve, turning the water a yellow-orange colour, ready to add to your recipe; turmeric and other imposters won't. Saffron will keep up to three years tightly packaged away from air, light and moisture, so foil-wrap the clear glass vial or plastic box it often comes in. The finest way I've found to prepare saffron for a dish is described by Chef Todiwala on page 36.

❛ Saffron is one of the most ancient spices and certainly the most expensive. Aiani in Northern Greece, Iran and Spain are major exporters of this precious spice, which takes its name from the Arab word 'asfar' or 'za'faran', meaning yellow, due to the golden-yellow colour it gives to foods. One shouldn't confuse saffron with turmeric, the golden and much less expensive spice from India. Saffron has been found to have numerous effects, including antitumour, antidepressive, anti-inflammatory and antioxidant activity, which are currently being researched. Used in conjunction with modern medicine, it can assist in health preservation and recovery from many diseases. But remember, as with any substance that has pharmacological effects in the body, if you take too much, it can be toxic. The quantities that are used in food will not harm anyone. You can find high-quality saffron in Persian or Middle Eastern shops, where it is often cheaper than in high-street supermarkets. ❜

Eleni Tsiompanou, MD, PGDip, MSc Nutritional Medicine

Mint *The Chill-out Spice*

A versatile multi-climate plant that thrives easily in fields, marshes, mountains and your windowbox, mint grows year round. True mint is of the genus *Mentha*, of which there are estimated to be between 12 and 25 species, but there are also many hundreds of hybrids, cultivars and varieties of mint, and their names are a delight: there's lemon and orange, bergamot, apple and pineapple, plus slender, wrinkled-leaf and even chocolate mint. Commercially, the two most commonly grown, known and used are spearmint (*M. spicata*), and peppermint (*M. piperita* – a true mint pairing of *M. spicata* and water mint, *M. aquatica*).

Spearmint is differentiated by its lack of leaf stock and by its toothy-edged leaves with mosaic-textured tops. In plant mythology, it is considered to convey wisdom. This white-blossomed creeper prefers semi-shade and moist conditions and should be ringed or potted if you don't want mint wandering all through your garden. Spearmint's distinctive flavour is milder than that of peppermint as its aromatic primary compound is the volatile oil carvone. Spearmint also contains the flavonoid thymonin, caffeic acid derivatives, rosmarinic acid and limonene.

Spearmint is a safe remedy for children with its milder minty flavour and gentler active compounds. For childhood fevers, make a tea of spearmint and white horehound (related to mint), which will help relieve minor aches, pains and chills. In Japan in 2001, a group of medical researchers reported that essential oil of spearmint showed significant bactericidal activity against such disease agents as *Staphylococcus aureus*, *E. coli* and *Helicobacter pylori*.

Menthol, the main active ingredient of peppermint (*M. piperita*), is found in the leaves and flowering tops of the plant. It provides the cool sensation of the herb and these are often dried and used as a culinary spice or for beneficial heath use. Peppermint is primarily cultivated for its oil, which is extracted from the leaves of the flowering plant by steam distillation. The content of menthol determines the quality of its essential oil, which is used as a carminative (relieving gas) and stimulant, for its derivative menthol and for flavouring, especially chewing gum, breath mints and to mask the taste of what would be an unpalatable pill to swallow.

The medicinal parts of peppermint are derived from the whole plant and include a volatile oil, flavonoids, phenolic acids and triterpenes (precursors to steroids). The essential volatile oils, in addition to menthol, are arementhone and menthyl acetate. Menthyl acetate is what gives peppermint its 'minty' flavour.

Peppermint tea can stimulate the immune system and ease congestion of colds, fevery flus and upper respiratory infections. The German Commission E (see page 94) has officially recognized peppermint's ability to reduce inflammation of nasal passages. When menthol vapours are inhaled, nasal passageways are opened to provide temporary relief of nasal and sinus congestion. A plant with potent antiviral properties, peppermint can also help fight viruses that cause ailments such as the flu, herpes, yeast infections and mumps. Peppermint has also been used traditionally as an earache remedy, to dissolve gallstones, ease muscle tightness, relieve stress and anxiety and ease menstrual cramps.

Mint is also used in a myriad of ways in food and drink, from mint sauce, minted pea soup and salads to chocolate bonbons, ice cream and cocktails.

‘ The mint family includes many different plants, including the well-known spearmint and peppermint. Mint oil has a lovely refreshing taste that has been used to flavour everything from mouthwash to candy, and is used as a mouth refresher for the very reason that it is an antibacterial.

I use peppermint oil often in my practice for people with digestive issues, particularly irritable bowel syndrome. Some excellent studies have shown that peppermint can reduce the symptoms of abdominal pain and gastrointestinal upset that accompany such a diagnosis. These need to be taken in enteric-coated capsules, however, as the pure oil is far too strong to be taken internally.

A simple peppermint tea can achieve some digestive relief, though it can worsen heartburn!

As an antibacterial, antifungal, digestive and analgesic, the entire mint family is an easy-to-grow and well-regarded medicinal plant. ’

Geeta Maker-Clark, MD

http://www.ncbi.nlm.nih.gov/pubmed/16121521

Lemongrass *The Soothing Spice*

Softly scented graceful lemongrass (*Cymbopogon citratus*) is native to Sri Lanka and South India and is now widely cultivated in the tropical areas of the Americas and Asia. In many countries, such as Brazil, a centuries-old traditional medicinal drink called *abafado* is a popular remedy for anxiety that is enjoyed several times a day. Fold and bruise some fresh lemongrass leaves then plunge them into boiling water, steep for 10–15 minutes and pour into a cup. I like to add a little freshly grated ginger and coconut sugar, too. The delicately scented lemongrass steam gives you pause to stop and enjoy, and this soothing tea calms jangled nerves and will help you focus your scattered thoughts – a bit like reorganizing your brain's to-do list.

A tufted grassy perennial with a tangle of fresh pale yellow-green leaves and rhizome-type bulbs, the hardy lemongrass grows easily in tropical to sub-tropical climes throughout the world, from Australia to the Americas, the Pacific Isles to the Caribbean and even in garden pots in Cornwall.

Traditional lemongrass health benefits are numerous and promising. Ancient Thai remedies use lemongrass to treat gastrointestinal disorders and fevers and it is also believed to increase circulation.

In other cultures, it is used as an analgesic pain reliever, an antifungal and antiseptic and as a remedy to treat nervousness. A cup of lemongrass tea every four hours is recommended to reduce fevers. Many studies show the plant sterols in lemongrass can be effective to block the absorption of dietary cholesterol.

The light playful scent of this spice pairs perfectly with broths (see the Waygu Beef Carpaccio with Green Tea Noodles, Lemongrass and Ginger on page 246) and it is commonly used in teas and curries, too. It is also suitable for poultry, fish and seafood and is an important ingredient in Thai and Vietnamese cuisine.

Lemongrass is available dried and preserved but I recommend you buy and use fresh lemongrass if possible. (Or buy a whole lemongrass plant: it will happily grow in a plant pot and will add a little bit of the tropics to your garden or balcony.) It is usually sold in bunches – look for firm stalks – and, if you buy more than you need, you can freeze it, tightly wrapped in a zipped plastic freezer bag. When adding it to liquid, either mince the bulb into little wheels or bruise and bash the entire bulb to release the oils and then add to your recipe. As with bay leaf, unless you chop it into tiny bits, it is best to remove the stalks before serving.

'Lemongrass has been traditionally used as a tea and in aromatherapy. As a rich source of volatile oils, it contains citral, which serves as an antioxidant by turning on the body's key detoxifying enzyme, glutathione S-transferase, which can defend cells from damage by free radicals. Free radicals are a factor in most chronic diseases such as atherosclerosis.

In addition to containing B vitamins (folate, thiamin, pyridoxine and pathothenic acid) and minerals (zinc, calcium, iron, copper, magnesium and manganese), lemongrass is noted beyond its citrus scent as a multifaceted folk therapy as well as a modern science opportunity in both animal and human studies. Historically, it has sought to reduce gastrointestinal symptoms, depress the central nervous system and to promote sedation. Whereas animal studies have suggested beneficial activity as anti-inflammatory, anticancer, antiallergic and antianxiety nutrient, small human studies have shown assistance with other modalities to address chronic periodontitis and oral thrush (fungal infection) in HIV-positive patients. Although it was not as strong as antifungal pharmaceuticals, it showed antifungal properties against pityriasis versicolour—a common fungal skin infection of the upper and lower torso. Early studies demonstrate that the brief inhalation of the essential oil may accelerate the recovery of anxiety as compared to controls.

(*Safety note:* as a topical oil, lemongrass can cause skin irritation in some individuals when used in cosmetics, perfumes and as a massage oil.)'

Param Dedhia, MD

CORNISH SAFFRON POPOVERS
WITH SWEET SAFFRON BUTTER

Inspired by the classic British Yorkshire pudding, 'popovers' are baked in a similar fashion and are often made with cheese. Using traditional Cornish saffron bread ingredients, here is a recipe for quick-as-you-can popovers that are great for afternoon tea or an after-dinner bit of something sweet and surprising using this most alluring and expensive spice.

MAKES 24 MINI OR 10–12 STANDARD-SIZED POPOVERS

⅛ tsp saffron strands, lightly toasted

2 tbsp orange juice

zest of ½ orange

125g (4½oz./1 cup) plain (all-purpose) flour

1 tsp sea salt

240ml (1 cup) full-fat (whole), milk warmed to 38°C (100°F)

4 large whole eggs, beaten

1 tbsp grapeseed oil

For the sweet saffron butter:

⅛ tsp saffron threads, lightly toasted

3 tbsp granulated sugar

100g (3½oz./scant ½ cup) softened butter

½ tsp lime zest

½ tsp ground cardamom seeds

large pinch salt

2 tbsp currants plumped with 1 tbsp water or brandy

To make the sweet saffron butter, rub the toasted saffron threads into the sugar until combined. Put into a small bowl with all the remaining ingredients and whisk by hand or with a mixer until smooth and creamy. Cover and chill until needed.

To make the popovers, crumble the toasted saffron and dissolve in the orange juice. Set aside.

Mix the flour and salt together in a bowl. Add the warm milk a little at a time. Whisk until smooth, then add 80ml (⅓ cup) of cold water and the saffron orange juice, whisking until bubbly. Incorporate the beaten eggs, transfer to a jug, cover and chill for 30 minutes or up to a day.

When ready to bake, preheat the oven to 240°C (475°F/gas mark 9). Brush mini- or standard-sized muffin cups with oil and put them on a baking tray. Place in the oven on the lower shelf until smoking hot.

Rewhisk the chilled batter, then carefully remove the trays from the oven, pour the batter into the hot tins to about three quarters full and return them to the oven. Do not the oven door while they are cooking or they will not rise.

Bake mini popovers for 8–10 minutes, standard-sized ones for about 20 miniutes, then reduce the temperature to 200°C (400°F/gas mark 6) and bake for a further 8–10 minutes until brown, crisp and risen.

Serve the popovers warm with the sweet saffron butter.

CHICKPEA SALAD
WITH MINT VINAIGRETTE
Francesco Carli

'Delightful, simple, cooling and packed with easily digestible legume protein from the chickpeas, this salad is easily doubled and a cinch to prepare for picnics, parties and lunchboxes. Peppermint, which is higher in cooling menthol flavour than spearmint, releases an intense freshness to the senses when consumed and has excellent properties to assist digestion and fight infection. The last-minute addition of sweet, soothing, softly textured mango to the dish adds a sublime richness to this simple Brazilian-style salad.' FC

SERVES 4

2 tbsp olive oil	125g (4½oz.) cherry tomatoes, halved
2 tbsp lemon juice	½ cucumber, seeded and chopped
1 tsp lemon zest, or to taste	½ red (bell) pepper, seeded and chopped
1 tbsp apple cider vinegar	60g (2¼oz./½ medium) onion, chopped
3 garlic cloves, minced	30 peppermint leaves, chopped
400g (14oz.) can chickpeas, drained	100g (3½oz.) mango flesh, diced

In a medium bowl, mix together the olive oil, lemon juice and zest, vinegar, garlic and salt and pepper to taste.

Toss together the chickpeas, tomatoes, cucumber, (bell) pepper, onion and peppermint leaves. Check the seasoning and correct if necessary. Finally stir in the diced mango.

Serve immediately or cover and refrigerate for a while before serving.

BRIDGE STREET ROASTED PUMPKIN RAVIOLI
WITH PIÑON SAGE PESTO

These ravioli filling ingredients not only taste delicious but the acid–alkali balancing maple syrup, restorative garlic, spicy warming ginger and the prairie-pine, mind-clearing flavour of sage have added health benefits.

SERVES 6

For the filling:

120ml (½ cup) double (heavy) cream
350g (12oz.) roasted pumpkin or butternut squash flesh
175g (6oz/1½ cups) Turmeric Melted Onions (see page 146)
40g (1½oz./3 tbsp) butter
2 tbsp maple syrup or brown sugar
1 tbsp roasted garlic purée (2 cloves)
1½ tsp freshly grated ginger
1 tsp ground turmeric
large pinch each ground cinnamon, allspice and fenugreek
½ tsp kosher salt, or to taste

¼ tsp fresh cracked pepper, or to taste
1–2 tsp fresh lemon juice, or to taste
225g (8oz./1 cup) ricotta

For the ravioli dough:

2 whole eggs plus 1 yolk
2 tsp extra virgin olive oil
175g (6oz./1⅓ cups) bread flour
85g (3oz./⅓ cup) semolina
1½ tsp salt

To finish:

3 tbsp toasted pepitas (pumpkin seeds)

To make the filling, simmer the cream in a saucepan over medium heat, then add the squash, onions, butter, sugar, garlic purée and spices. Season to taste with salt, pepper and lemon juice. Purée with a stick blender until smooth. Fold in the ricotta by hand until well combined. Cover and chill until just ready to make the ravioli.

To make the ravioli dough, whisk the eggs and oil in a small bowl. In a medium bowl, stir together the bread flour, semolina and salt. Make a well in the centre, add the egg and oil mixture and stir to combine. Add 1 tablespoon of water, knead and shape into a pad. Cover with cling film (plastic wrap) and chill for 30 minutes.

On a lightly floured surface roll out the dough, then roll through a pasta machine to #5 thickness or roll out using a rolling pin to 5mm (¼in.) thick. Cut into two equal-sized sheets. Dot spoonfuls of the filling 3cm (1¼in.) apart on one pasta sheet. Run a wet finger around each spoonful of filling, then lay the second sheet on top. Seal each ravioli from the centre outwards to push out any air, then, using the dull edge of cutter, press around the filling to seal. Using a cutter one size larger, cut through the ravioli, transfer to a lightly floured tray and chill.

Gently drop the ravioli into a pan of simmering salted water a few at a time and cook to al dente. Drain well, arrange on a serving plate and spoon the pesto over. Garnish with a few toasted pepitas (pumpkin seeds) and serve.

PIÑON SAGE PESTO

MAKES ABOUT 480ml (2 CUPS)

50g (1¾oz.) cashew nuts
50g (1¾oz.) piñon (pine nuts)
20g (¾oz./⅔ cup) sage leaves, roughly chopped
15g (½oz./½ cup) basil leaves
2 tbsp parsley leaves

4 garlic cloves, peeled and chopped
squeeze of lemon juice
240ml (1 cup) extra virgin olive oil or pumpkin seed oil
55g (2oz./⅓ cup) grated Parmesan
salt, pepper and ground chipotle chilli or smoked pepper, to taste

Put the nuts, sage, basil, parsley, garlic and lemon juice in the bowl of a food processor with an S blade and pulse to chop. Scrape down the sides of the bowl, then, with the motor running, drizzle in the oil in a steady trickle until combined to form a green paste. Spoon the pesto into a medium-sized bowl and gently stir in the grated Parmesan. Season with salt, pepper and ground chipotle chili or smoked pepper to taste.

SWEET POTATO AGRODOLCE

Agrodolce is a traditional Italian sweet-and-sour sauce. This version, served with sweet potatoes, is packed with brain-food-anthocyanin-loaded cherries and spices and finished with a generous handful of the familiar, fragrant, antioxidant-rich basil leaf.

SERVES 4-6

3 tbsp dried cherries, roughly chopped

350g (12oz.) red sweet potatoes, kumara or yams, peeled and cut into 1cm (½in.) pieces

3 tbsp pumpkin seed, extra virgin olive or grapeseed oil

2 tsp cumin seeds, toasted and ground

60ml (¼ cup) balsamic or orange vincotto vinegar

2 jalapeño chilies, seeded and thinly sliced in rings

½ tsp ground turmeric

2 tbsp honey

2 medium-sized red onions (about 450g/1lb.), thinly sliced

2 rosemary sprigs

2 thyme sprigs

1 garlic clove, thinly sliced

20g (¾oz./¾ cup tightly packed) fresh basil leaves, plus extra for garnishing, torn

Preheat the oven to 200°C (400°F/gas mark 6).

Put the dried cherries into a small bowl, cover with hot water and leave to soften for 10 minutes. Drain and set aside.

Put the sweet potatoes in a bowl and toss with 2 tablespoons of the oil, the cumin and some salt, then spread out evenly on a baking tray. Roast, tossing occasionally, until golden brown and fork tender, 17–20 minutes. Remove from the oven, leave on the tray and set aside to cool.

In a small saucepan, mix the drained cherries with the vinegar, jalapeños, turmeric and honey and season with salt. Cook, stirring, until the sauce reduces to a thin syrup, about 5 minutes.

Heat the remaining 1 tablespoon of oil in a large pan over medium–high heat. Add the onions, rosemary and thyme and sauté until golden brown. Add the garlic, cook for about 3 minutes more, then add the cherry mix and reduce.

Gently fold in the sweet potatoes. Add the basil then gently toss again. Spoon onto a platter or individual serving plates. Garnish with extra torn basil leaves and serve immediately.

VEGETARIAN 'BURNING LOVE'
WITH BROWN BUTTER AND SAGE
Mette Helbak

'"Burning love" is a Danish classic comfort food dish of mashed potatoes with fried bacon and onions on top. This is a vegetarian version with lots of different vegetables, where the umami comes from sage brown butter and mushrooms.' MH

SERVES 4 AS A MAIN COURSE

For the mash:

500g (1lb. 2oz.) celeriac, peeled and coarsely chopped

500g (1lb. 2oz.) potatoes, peeled and coarsely chopped

50g (1¾oz./½ stick) butter, cut into cubes

2 tbsp coarsely chopped sage

2 tbsp coarsely chopped basil

a little bit of the water used for boiling celery and potatoes

For the brown butter:

85g (3oz.) butter

leaves of 5 sage sprigs

For the 'love':

150g (5½oz.) mushrooms

4 onions, diced

200g (7oz.) carrots, cut into cubes

200g (7oz.) parsley root, cut into cubes

200g (7oz.) Brussels sprouts, cut into quarters or halves

1 tsp salt

To make the mash, put the celeriac and potato into a pan, cover with water and boil for 20 minutes or until tender. Drain, reserving about 240ml (1 cup) of the liquid. Add the butter, sage and basil and mash with a whisk. Season with salt and add the reserved liquid a little at a time until the mash is soft and creamy.

To make the brown butter, melt the butter in a small saucepan and let it slowly turn brown over medium heat for 10–15 minutes. When it smells of roasted hazelnuts, it is done. Remove from the heat and add the sage.

To make the 'love', cut or tear the mushrooms apart into smaller pieces and fry them in a dry, hot frying pan for 3–4 minutes. Turn down the heat to medium and add the rest of the vegetables and a couple of tablespoons of the brown butter. Cook until the vegetables are turning brown and a little soft, about 4–5 minutes.

Serve the fried vegetables and brown butter on top of the mash.

SAGE, CITRUS ZEST

WAIMATE CORN FRITTERS AND MUSSELS
WITH SAGE-RUBBED BACON AND SMOKED-TOMATO AIOLI

One of the oldest farming communities in New Zealand, Waimate North grows luscious sweetcorn and hosts the country's oldest agricultural show, the Bay of Islands Pastoral and Industrial Show. Pungent and aromatic sage often appears dusty, fuzzy and grey, but don't be fooled: it is packed with mind-clearing compounds and can help relieve sore throats, too!

SERVES 4

4–6 rashers streaky or back bacon

1 tsp rubbed sage

¾ tsp sage honey

½ tsp chipotle powder

4–8 green-lip mussels, steamed in shells

baby greens, to serve

For the smoked-tomato aioli:

1 large egg yolk

1 garlic clove, minced

pinch sea salt

zest and juice of 1 lemon

2 tsp honey

20g (¾oz./¼ cup) semi-dried smoked tomatoes, finely chopped

120ml (½ cup) grapeseed oil

For the fritters:

500g (1lb 2oz./3 cups) fresh, raw or defrosted corn kernels

3 large eggs

1 tbsp finely chopped chives

¼ tsp hot chili sauce

1 tsp dried, rubbed sage

½ tsp baking soda

70g (2½oz./scant ½ cup) rice flour

85g (3oz./½ cup) chopped courgette (zucchini)

a little vegetable oil, to fry

Preheat the oven to 160°C (325°F/gas mark 3).

To make the aioli, in a small bowl or using a stick blender, whisk the egg yolk with the garlic, salt, lemon zest and juice, honey and tomatoes until well blended. Continue to whisk while drizzling in the oil in a slow, steady stream until the sauce begins to come together and thicken. If too thick, whisk in an additional teaspoon of water until well combined. Cover and chill for up to 2 days until ready to use.

Lay the bacon rashers on a parchment-lined baking tray. In a small bowl, mix the sage, honey and chipotle powder to a paste with a pinch of salt. Brush onto the bacon, then cover with another piece of parchment and top with another tray to keep the bacon flat. Bake for about 12 minutes until browned and crispy. Set aside.

To make the batter for the gluten-free fritters, cover the corn with boiling water, let it stand for 3 minutes then drain well. Put half the corn in a food processor with the eggs and chives and blend to a chunky purée. Add the hot chili sauce, sage, baking soda, rice flour, a pinch of salt and a few grinds of pepper, then pulse to form a thick batter. Stir in the reserved corn and the courgette (zucchini).

Heat a little oil in a heavy pan and cook in batches over medium heat, pouring about 3 tablespoons of batter for each fritter. Cook until golden brown and cooked through, about 3–4 minutes each side. Add oil to pan between batches if needed.

Place a fritter in the centre of each plate, top with a little aioli then repeat twice more. Arrange two mussels, sage, a piece of bacon broken in two and a little more sauce on the fritters. Scatter with baby greens and serve immediately.

DOVES BAY BOUILLABAISSE
WITH SPICY RED PEPPER ROUILLE

This classic French dish is transported to the southern hemisphere with the freshest of New Zealand's fish and shellfish. In the far north, where snapper is plentiful, the fishermen will often smoke their catch, infusing it with an intoxicating smoky sweetness that adds an amazing depth of flavour to this dish. The addition of kawakawa pepper to the stock creates a gentle spicy undertone to the soup that is heightened by the subtle, smoky heat of the paprika-scented red pepper rouille that is served alongside.

SERVES 8

For the smoked snapper stock:
bones of 2 smoked snapper or other smoked fish
2 onions, unpeeled, cut in quarters
3 carrots, cut in large chunks
1 celery stalk
small handful parsley
1 bay leaf
4 kawakawa or 6 wild pepper leaves, torn in pieces
8 peppercorns
½ lemon, cut in half

For the rouille:
1 red (bell) pepper, roasted (see page 24), peeled, seeded and roughly chopped
2 garlic cloves, roughly chopped
1 slice white bread, torn into pieces
1 egg yolk
1 tbsp Dijon mustard
juice of 1 lemon

¼ tsp smoked paprika or chipotle powder
120ml (½ cup) extra virgin olive oil
16 slices baguette, to serve

For the bouillabaisse:
4 medium new potatoes, cubed
2 large onions, cut into large dice
1 litre (4¼ cups) smoked snapper stock (see above)
240ml (1 cup) dry white wine
8 Roma (plum) tomatoes, peeled, seeded and cut into large dice
12 saffron threads
2 kawakawa pepper leaves or 4 wild pepper leaves, torn
350g (12oz.) scallops
350g (12oz.) whole king prawns (jumbo shrimp), peeled
225g (8oz.) smoked snapper, flaked (2 cups flaked)
1 large lobster tail, shelled and sliced
16 mussels, washed and beards removed
20g (¾oz./⅓ cup) chopped parsley, to garnish
8 thyme sprigs, leaves picked, to garnish

First make the stock. Put all the ingredients in a stock pot, add water to cover and bring to a very low simmer. Simmer for 2 hours, then cool and strain.

To make the rouille, put the red (bell) pepper, garlic, bread, egg yolk, mustard, lemon juice and paprika or chipotle powder in a food processor with an S blade and purée until smooth. With the machine running, slowly drizzle in the oil until the mixture becomes thick and smooth. Season to taste and set aside.

For the bouillabaisse, pour 700ml (3 cups) of salted water into a 1-litre (1-quart) pan and bring to the boil. Reduce to a simmer and add the potatoes and half the onion. Cook for 10 minutes, or until fork tender, then drain. Transfer the potatoes and onions to a large chopping board and spread out to cool.

Heat the grill (broiler) to high and arrange the baguette slices on a grill (broiler) pan. Grill (broil) until lightly golden, turning the slices halfway through. Set aside.

Put the stock, wine, saffron, pepper leaves, tomatoes, potatoes and all the onions into a large stock pot over medium heat. Bring to a gentle simmer, then add the fish and shellfish and cook gently for 2–3 minutes until the mussels have opened. Discard any that remain closed. Season to taste.

Preheat the grill (broiler) to high. Spread the toasted baguette slices with the rouille and place under the grill (broiler) until golden and bubbling. Ladle the bouillabaisse into individual serving bowls and garnish with parsley and thyme. Serve each bowl with two slices of the spicy rouille-topped bread.

RED MULLET POACHED IN SAFFRON BROTH
WITH KABOSU LEMON AND AMARETTO
Anne-Sophie Pic

Colourful, healthful and fragrant, with steaming Kabousu lemon-and-saffron-butter sauce,
this fish 'portrait' is a stunning work of art and flavour.

SERVES 10

10 x 150–200g (5½–7oz.) red mullet, or pink snapper
or sea bass
olive oil, for searing fish and brushing
Maldon salt, to finish

For the Kabosu lemon butter:
55g (1¾oz./½ stick) salted butter, at room temperature
55g (1¾oz./½ stick) unsalted butter, at room temperature
zest of 2 Kabosu lemons

For the pickles:
300g (10½oz.) baby red beetroot
90ml (6 tbsp) white balsamic vinegar
85g (3oz./scant ½ cup) sugar

For the garnish:
2 small parsnips (or 5 mini celeriac)
30g (1oz./2 tbsp) salted butter
100g (3½oz.) daikon (or Korean radish or celeriac) shavings
3 pieces of mini (or 'Golden Ball') turnip
100g (3½oz.) celeriac, peeled and chopped
100ml (scant ½ cup) milk

For the sauce:
5 saffron threads
½ tsp dried lemongrass
zest of ½ lemon
Kabosu lemon butter (see above)
30ml (2 tbsp) amaretto

To make the Kabosu butter, mix the butters together with the Kabosu lemon zest.

For the beetroot pickles, cut the beetroot into 50 wedges, reserving a tiny slice of red beetroot to cut into matchsticks, as pictured, for finishing. Arrange the wedges, separating the colours into sous-vide bags. Bring the balsamic vinegar and sugar to the boil then pour an equal amount over the wedges in bags and cool completely. Vacuum-seal the bags and set the sous-vide cooker at position 3. Leave to steam for 1½ hours. Alternatively, put the wedges in separate pans, pour over the boiling marinade and simmer gently until fork tender.

For the garnish, peel the parsnips and blanch them in salted water, then roast them in a beurre noisette (brown butter) until lightly and evenly coloured. Chill, then cut them into 1 x 4cm (½ x 1½in.) matchsticks.

Using a mandoline, cut the daikon 1mm thick then trim using a 4.5cm (1¾in.) diameter pastry (cookie) cutter. Peel and turn the mini turnips to give them a rounded shape. Cook them in butter then cut them in quarters.

Cook the celeriac in the seasoned milk, drain and purée, then immediately whisk in the Kabosu lemon butter, adjusting the seasoning with Kabosu lemon zest and salt if necessary.

For the sauce, heat 100ml (scant ½ cup) of water to 75°C (165°F), infuse the saffron, lemongrass and lemon zest for 15 minutes, then taste and infuse for a further 5 minutes if necessary. Strain through a muslin (cheesecloth) strainer then whisk in the Kabosu butter. Add the amaretto and adjust the seasoning as necessary.

Descale and clean the red mullet then lift and debone the fillets. Sear the fillets, skin-side down, on a griddle in a little olive oil. Cook the fillets evenly, remove them from the griddle, turn them over, check they are cooked, then brush a little olive oil on the skin side.

To serve, butter the daikon, parsnips and turnip. Arrange parsnip sticks next to each other and lay two daikon petals and a quarter of mini turnip on top. Add two dots of celeriac purée on either side. Add two red mullet fillets with a little Maldon salt on the skin side then place five alternating coloured wedges of beetroot in between the fish fillets. Carefully pour the sauce around the sides of each bowl to just cover the bottom. Serve immediately.

ROASTED FREE-RANGE QUAIL
WITH SAFFRON RISOTTO
Simone Cerea

'One of the most well-known dishes in Italy is the Risotto alla Milanese, It is also one of my favourites, originating in Milan, an area close to where I come from. The aroma and colour of the saffron is distinctive and enhances the simplicity of the dish. More complexity is delivered through the complementary flavours of the quail and the saltiness of the pancetta, which reminds me of family Sunday lunches. Dolcetto is a variety of black Italian wine grape, like Nebiolo from the Piedmont region. "Lardo di Colonnata" is the smooth, pure back fat of pigs aged in marble troughs with herbs and spices. These pigs are raised on a diet of chestnuts and acorns, near the town of Colonnata in northwestern Italy.' SC

SERVES 4

For the saffron risotto:
2 tbsp olive oil
5g (⅛oz.) finely chopped white onion
140g (5oz./⅔ cup) carnaroli rice
1 tbsp dry white wine
350ml (1½ cups) boiling chicken stock
pinch saffron powder
20g (¾oz./4 tsp) unsalted butter
20g (¾oz./1¾ tbsp) grated Parmesan

For the chicken mousse:
100g (3½oz.) chicken breast
10g (¼oz.) Lardo di Colonnata
2 tsp double (heavy) cream
2 tsp milk
5 pistachios, skin removed, lightly toasted and chopped
½ date, skin and seeds removed, finely chopped
2 amaretti biscuits, crumbled
1 sage leaf, finely chopped

For the bacon-wrapped quail:
4 whole free-range quail (semi-boned) (about 85g/3oz. each)
chicken mousse (see above)
20g (¾oz./4 tsp) butter
4 sage leaves
8 thin slices Pancetta Steccata

For the butternut squash:
200g (7oz.) butternut squash, peeled and cut into rings 2cm (¾in.) thick
1 garlic clove, chopped
1 fresh thyme sprig
20g (¾oz./4 tsp) butter
1 tbsp olive oil

For the mulled-wine reduction:
475ml (2 cups) Dolcetto d'Alba
1½ cinnamon sticks
4 cloves
1 star anise
3 juniper berries, cracked
⅓ orange, sliced
2 tbsp brown sugar
15g (½oz./1 tbsp) butter

To garnish:
2 tsp olive oil
16–20 individual Brussels sprout leaves
pinch saffron flowers (optional)

To make the saffron risotto, heat up a pan, add the olive oil and fry the onions until lightly golden. Add the rice and let the rice toast for 3 minutes.

Add the white wine and reduce completely before gradually pouring in the boiling chicken stock. Keep boiling until the grains are al dente, about 18 minutes. Add the saffron powder about 15 minutes into the cooking. Just before the rice is ready, remove the pan from the heat and add the butter and Parmesan. (Removing from heat will prevent the cheese from splitting.) Season with salt and pepper to taste.

Meanwhile, prepare the bacon-wrapped quail. Start by making the chicken mousse. Remove the skin from chicken breast and blend it in a food processor with the Lardo di Colonnata, adding cream and milk at the last minute to get a soft mixture. Stir in the remaining ingredients using a spatula and season with salt and pepper to taste.

Preheat the oven to 190°C (375°F/gas mark 5).

Turn the whole quail with thighs facing up and cut along the backbone. Remove the carcass by cutting around the bone, but preserve the legs and wings. Season with salt and pepper and place the mousse in the middle, keeping the skin on the outside. Recompose the quail as a whole and secure using a toothpick. Brush butter on the skin and hold the quail in place by wrapping it in foil. Bake in the oven for approximately 8 minutes, or until the skin turns golden brown.

Remove the quail from the oven, place a sage leaf on top of each one and wrap with two slices of pancetta steccata. Return the quail to the oven and cook for a further 4 minutes.

Remove and leave to rest for 5 minutes before serving. Reduce the oven temperature to 180°C (350°F/gas mark 4).

Put the butternut squash rings in a baking tray, scatter over the garlic and thyme, dot with butter and drizzle over the olive oil. Bake in the oven for 10 minutes until the squash rings have turned golden brown.

To make the mulled-wine reduction, mix all the ingredients except the butter together in a saucepan and let it simmer until the wine is reduced by a fifth of the total volume. Whisk in the butter before serving to achieve the right consistency.

Meanwhile, add 2 teaspoons of oil to a hot sauté pan and quickly flash-fry the Brussels sprout leaves for about 10 seconds – they should retain their crunchiness. Drain on kitchen paper and set aside for serving.

To serve, arrange a large serving spoonful of warm risotto on each of four plates, then top with the quail. Arrange the butternut squash to the side, scatter with the Brussels sprouts leaves and the saffron flowers (if using), then drizzle the mulled-wine sauce over all. Serve immediately.

Illustrated on pages 238–9

TURKISH LAMB STEW

John Gregory-Smith

'This humble stew is packed full of smoky flavours from the pepper paste and Turkish pepper flakes. Dry mint adds another dimension that mellows into the rich sauce as it cooks slowly. Marinating the lamb overnight in yogurt, pepper paste and spices tenderizes the meat, ensuring that it is beautifully soft, and gives it an extra depth of flavour. This is a simple trick that I use for any similar stew or casserole.' JGS

SERVES 4

600g (1lb. 5oz.) lamb leg, cut into 2.5cm (1in.) cubes	**For the marinade:**
4 tbsp olive oil	4 tbsp Greek-style yogurt
2 onions, thinly sliced	3 garlic cloves, crushed
3 Turkish green (bell) peppers, seeded and thinly sliced	2 tbsp mild Turkish red pepper paste
400g (14oz.) can chopped tomatoes	2 tbsp tomato purée
2 tbsp Turkish red pepper paste	2 tsp Turkish (Aleppo) pepper flakes
2 tbsp tomato purée	1 tsp dried mint
1 tsp Turkish (Aleppo) pepper flakes	½ tsp ground cinnamon
1 tsp dried mint	
cousous and a green salad, to serve (optional)	

Put all the ingredients for the marinade into a mixing bowl. Add a good pinch of salt and mix together. Add the lamb and mix well so it all gets completely coated. Cover and marinate overnight in the fridge.

Remove the lamb from the fridge to come to room temperature.

Meanwhile, heat the oil in a casserole over a medium heat and add the onions and (bell) peppers. Cook, stirring occasionally, for 6–8 minutes or until lovely and golden.

Add the tomatoes, red pepper paste, tomato purée, Turkish pepper flakes, dried mint and a good pinch of salt and pepper. Pour in 100ml (scant ½ cup) of boiling water and mix together. Add the lamb and mix well. Cover, reduce the heat to low and cook, stirring occasionally, for 1½–2 hours or until the lamb is beautifully tender, removing the lid for the last 30 minutes of cooking so that the sauce can reduce.

Serve immediately with couscous and a green salad.

LEMONGRASS, BASIL, GINGER, CITRUS ZEST

LEMONGRASS PORK PEARLS
WITH MANGO RELISH

Graceful lemongrass soothes the body and mind with its plant-sterol-rich oil, citral. It adds a luscious fragrance and flavour to this light, fresh, spicy dish, which is a go-to for cocktail parties – it's fun to make your own 'foldovers' – as well as making a delicious main course. If you like, you could serve it with little bowls of toasted chopped peanuts or almonds and additional mint to sprinkle on top.

SERVES 2 AS A MAIN OR UP TO 6 AS A SHARING PLATTER

For the pork pearls:
450g (1lb.) minced (ground) pork
3 large garlic cloves, minced (about 2 tbsp)
1 bunch (10g/¼oz./¼ cup) thinly sliced chives
1 stalk (10g/¼oz.) lemongrass, tough outer layers removed, lower 15cm (6in.) of tender bulb finely chopped
1 tbsp freshly grated ginger
1 tsp fish sauce (e.g. *nuoc mam* or *nam pla*)
1 tsp Sriracha sauce (hot Thai chilli sauce)
½ tsp sesame oil
1½ tsp palm or brown sugar
¾ tsp salt
½ tsp pepper

For the relish:
1 medium avocado, peeled, pitted and diced
½ small mango, peeled, pitted and diced
¼ small jicama or Asian pear, peeled, cored and diced
1 or 2 jalapeños, sliced in rings

juice and zest of 1 lime
juice of 1 passion fruit (strain seeds optional)
1 tbsp chopped coriander (cilantro) leaves
1 tbsp chopped Thai basil leaves
½ tsp Sriracha sauce (hot Thai chilli sauce)

For the sauce:
2 tbsp passion fruit juice and 2 tbsp water
2 lemongrass stalks
2 tsp fish sauce
1 tbsp toasted sesame seeds
1 tbsp sugar
½ tsp salt

To serve:
90g (3¼oz.) buckwheat soba noodles, cooked and tossed with 2 tsp oil
55g (2oz.) carrot, grated (about 1 cup grated)
12–16 lettuce leaves, e.g. butter or Little Gem lettuce
15g (½oz./½ cup) coriander (cilantro) leaves

To make the pork pearls, put all the ingredients into a large bowl and, using your hands, mix together, then form the mixture into 5g (⅛oz.) balls. Arrange the 'pearls' on a plate, cover and refrigerate for at least 30 minutes, until firm.

Preheat a pan to medium–high and add a little oil. Cook the pork pearls, swirling the pan until browned all over, about 3–4 minutes.

To make the relish, gently combine the avocado, mango, jicama, jalapeño, lime juice, passion fruit juice, coriander (cilantro), basil and Sriracha in a bowl. Cover and refrigerate until ready to serve.

To make the sauce, whisk all the ingredients together in a small mixing bowl. Season with more vinegar or sugar, depending on your preference.

To serve, arrange the noodles, carrot, lettuce leaves and coriander (cilantro) leaves on a serving platter. To eat, spoon some noodles into a leaf, top with the pork pearls, relish, coriander (cilantro) leaves and sauce. Fold over the lettuce leaf to enclose and have a bite!

WAGYU BEEF CARPACCIO
WITH GREEN TEA NOODLES, LEMONGRASS AND GINGER

A simple, quick, light dish – from fridge to bowl in 15 minutes. The scent of lemongrass as the broth is poured over the beef, noodles and vegetables soothes and calms the mind and soul and may even help to lower 'bad' cholesterol.

SERVES 4

200g (7oz.) Wagyu sirloin or other sirloin beef

1–2 tsp white miso paste

200g (7oz.) green tea or buckwheat soba noodles

½ tsp fresh wasabi or 1 tsp wasabi paste, or to taste

350ml (1½ cup) vegetable stock

2 or 3 lemongrass stalks, thinly sliced

1 x 30g (1oz.) piece ginger, peeled and sliced into matchsticks

200g (7oz.) choy sum ('Chinese flowering cabbage') or bok choy

150g (5½oz.) firm tofu, cut into cubes

10–12 chives cut in matchsticks, for garnish

In advance, freeze the beef, tightly wrapped in plastic.

Take the beef out of the freezer and slice, while still firm, into 8–12 thin strips. Using the back of a spoon or your thumb, spread the beef strips with miso paste on one side, then set aside on a small plate.

Boil 1 litre (4¼ cups) of water in a saucepan, then add the noodles and simmer for 4–5 minutes. Drain the noodles into a colander under running cold water, drain, then tip into a small mixing bowl and stir in the wasabi to combine. Set aside.

Warm the vegetable stock in the same pan with the lemongrass and ginger. Add the choy sum and simmer for 2 minutes.

Divide and mound the noodles into four bowls. Using a slotted spoon, remove the choy sum and ginger from the broth and arrange on top of the noodles. Pour the broth into individual pitchers or teapots. Arrange the beef on top of the noodles, miso side-up, scatter with tofu and chives. Pour hot broth over all, inhale the lemongrass-ginger-miso steam to savour, and enjoy it slowly.

CINNAMON BASIL ICE CREAM
Mindy Segal

'This ice cream was inspired by some beautifully roasted peaches that I bought one year at the farmers' market for a special dessert. I decided that it needed a little of the garden in the ice cream I served them with so I steeped fresh basil in my cinnamon ice cream. Eureka – delicious! It's also good served with poached berries. Indonesian (Ceylon) cinnamon is a milder, softer flavoured cinnamon also known as true cinnamon. Cassia cinnamon is also fine to use but as the flavour is stronger, the basil-cinnamon balance will have a stronger cinnamon taste when using the cassia variety.' MS

MAKES 1 LITRE (1 QUART)

4–6 fresh Indonesian cinnamon sticks
475ml (2 cups) double (heavy) cream
475ml (2 cups) full-fat (whole) milk
13 large egg yolks
225g (8oz./1 cup) cane sugar

leaves from 1 bunch (70g/2½oz.) cinnamon basil, regular basil or Thai basil, finely chopped
½ tsp fresh ground cinnamon
pinch sea salt
¼ tsp pure vanilla extract

Put the cinnamon sticks on a baking tray and toast in the oven until hot to touch.

Meanwhile, in a heavy-bottomed pan, heat the cream and milk to a simmer.

Remove the cinnamon sticks from the oven and crush into pieces. Put the pieces into the warm milk and cream mixture and leave to steep for 1 hour.

Combine the egg yolks and sugar in a 2-litre (2-quart) bowl, whisk thoroughly and set aside.

Strain the cinnamon sticks from the milk and cream mixture and discard them. Return the liquid to the pan and bring to the boil, then pour the liquid over the eggs and sugar, mixing thoroughly.

Pour back into the pan and cook over medium–low heat, stirring constantly until the custard coats the back of a spoon (nappe). Pour the hot custard into a bowl and set over an ice bath.

Steep the chopped basil in the hot custard until cool. Add the ground cinnamon and salt and mix thoroughly.

When cool, strain the custard through a fine mesh strainer then whisk in the vanilla extract.

Freeze the custard in an ice-cream maker, following the manufacturer's instructions.

The Contributing Chefs

José Andrés, who has been named one of *Time* magazine's '100 Most Influential People' and awarded 'Outstanding Chef' by the James Beard Foundation, is an internationally recognized culinary innovator, author, educator, television personality, humanitarian and chef/owner of ThinkFoodGroup. A pioneer of Spanish tapas in the US, he is also known for his avant-garde cuisine. Andrés' award-winning group of restaurants includes locations in Washington D.C., Miami, Puerto Rico, Las Vegas, Los Angeles and Mexico City. In 2012, Andrés formed World Central Kitchen, an NPO that uses the power of food to empower communities and strengthen economies. *thinkfoodgroup.com*
Recipe on page 193.

Lidia Bastianich is an Emmy Award-winning public television host, best-selling cookbook author, restaurateur and owner of a flourishing food and entertainment business. She is the chef/owner of four acclaimed New York City restaurants (Felidia, Becco, Esca and Del Posto) as well as Lidia's Pittsburgh and Lidia's Kansas City, with her daughter Tanya. She is also founder and president of entertainment company Tavola Productions, has a line of pastas and all-natural sauces called LIDIA'S and is co-owner of Eataly, the largest artisanal Italian food-and-wine marketplace in New York City, Chicago and São Paolo, Brazil. *lidiasitaly.com*
Recipe on page 196.

April Bloomfield is the executive chef and co-owner with Ken Friedman of the Michelin-starred restaurants The Spotted Pig and The Breslin Bar & Dining Room in addition to The John Dory Oyster Bar, Salvation Taco, Tosca Café and Salvation Burger. She is also the author of two cookbooks, *A Girl and Her Pig* and *A Girl and Her Greens*. A native of Birmingham, England, April began her culinary studies at Birmingham College and went on to hone her craft through cook positions in various kitchens throughout London and Northern Ireland, including Kensington Place, Bibendum and The River Café. *Instagram & Twitter: @AprilBloomfield*
Photo credit: Melanie Dunea
Recipe on page 78.

Neil Brazier's quirky outlook is reflected in a very inventive but approachable menu. Neil travelled extensively throughout the UK, America and Asia, working in various Michelin-star-rated restaurants and elite country house hotels, before returning to New Zealand as an executive chef for some of New Zealand's finest eateries and lodges, including the award-winning Kauri Cliffs in the Bay of Islands. Currently Peter Gordon's Executive Chef at The Sugar Club and Belotta, Neil draws inspiration from the various cultures he has experienced and combines them to create food that is as unique as it is elegant. *facebook.com/neil.brazier1*
Recipe on page 83.

Francesco Carli arrived in Rio de Janeiro from his native Italy more than 20 years ago and has since remained in Brazil, where he has become renowned for quality Italian cuisine. He has written several books and won many awards. During his tenure as Executive Chef responsible for all the restaurants within the Belmond Copacabana Palace in Rio de Janeiro, its Hotel Cipriani Restaurant was elected by the American magazine *Hotel* as one of the top ten hotel restaurants in the world. Francesco is currently Head Chef at the Country Club of Ipanema in Rio de Janeiro. *linkedin.com/in/francesco-carli-59b09480*
Recipe on page 224.

Simone Cerea's culinary journey began with a chance meeting with a cruise-ship chef who sparked a passion for cooking in him. Born and raised in Bergamo, Italy, he was mentored by the esteemed Italian chef and restaurateur Angelo Paracucchi. His culinary approach is as simple and straightforward as his love for quality ingredients, allowing the natural flavours to flourish in the dish. With more than three decades of experience and a 15-year tenure with Four Seasons Hotels and Resorts – he is currently Executive Chef at Regent Singapore – Simone's greatest satisfaction still comes from an empty plate and a satisfied smile from a diner. *regenthotels.com/EN/Singapore*
Recipe on pages 240–1.

Anne Conness' unique blend of creativity and drive have forged a career path that has taken her from painting to television production to cooking, and now, as co-owner and chef of Sausal, to creating a soul-satisfying Nuevo Rancho Cuisine. Sausal opened in September 2015 in El Segundo, California, to much critical acclaim. With a Mexican-inspired menu that pays homage to the history of Alta California cooking, Conness, along with Pastry Chef Natasha MacAller, brings that rich history forward with a new type of modern-rustic cooking they refer to as Nuevo Rancho Cuisine.
Instagram: @sausalelsegundo
Recipe on page 40.

Suzanne Goin's six LA restaurants (Lucques, a.o.c., Tavern, The Larder at Maple Drive, The Larder at Burton Way and the new Larder at Tavern at the Tom Bradley International Terminal at LAX) reflect her passion for seasonal cooking. Her artistry has earned her numerous accolades, including the coveted 'Outstanding Chef of the Year' in 2016. In December 2013, Suzanne and her business partner Caroline Styne launched The Larder Baking Company, a wholesale operation for breads and bakery goods developed with master baker Nathan Dakdouk. Goin is the author of two award-winning cookbooks, *Sunday Suppers at Lucques* and *The a.o.c. cookbook*.
Instagram: @suzannegoin
Recipe on page 30.

Peter Gordon was born in Whanganui, New Zealand, and collated his first cookbook aged just four. At 18 he moved to Melbourne where he lived for five years, training and working as a chef in various restaurants. Eventually his spirit of adventure and culinary curiosity led him to travel through Asia for a year, from Indonesia to India. This life-changing experience was to become a major influence on his culinary style, and he went on to earn an international reputation as the 'godfather' of fusion cuisine. Peter lives in Hackney, London, and has restaurants in both Auckland and London.
Instagram: @chefpetergordon
Recipe on page 150.

John Gregory-Smith is a chef and food writer who specializes in Turkish cuisine. He is passionate about Turkey, having explored the country extensively over the last ten years, and regularly hosts Turkish pop-ups and secret supper clubs in London. *Turkish Delights*, John's third book, follows the success of *Mighty Spice Cookbook* and *Mighty Spice Express*. John is also a presenter, who has appeared in the UK and US and who hosted *The Telegraph*'s Fabulous Foodies 2015. He has written for, and his recipes have been widely featured in, numerous UK publications, including *GQ*, *Sainsbury's Magazine*, *The Times* and the *Daily Mail*.
Instagram: @johngs
Recipe on page 242.

Mette Helbak is a Danish chef, food stylist and food writer with a love for creating beauty and great taste with vegetables, and she focuses on them both at her restaurants in Copenhagen and in her cookbooks. She began her career in food writing about other chefs' kitchen skills as a food critic and restaurant-guide editor, but wanted to create a restaurant where super-simple food cooked using the best seasonal ingredients fresh from local farmers would be presented at its best. Her restaurant, Stedsans, located inside the greenhouse of Scandinavia's first rooftop farm, ØsterGRO, is that dream come true.
Instagram & Twitter: @mettehelbak
Recipe on page 230.

Raghavan Iyer is a cookbook author, culinary educator, spokesperson, consultant to numerous national and international clients and host of Emmy Award-winning documentary *Asian Flavors*. From 2014 to 2015, he was President of The International Association of Culinary Professionals. He is the author of several cookbooks, including *660 Curries*, a companion video series of which won him the James Beard Award of Excellence in 2016, and has gained several other awards, notably the International Association of Culinary Professional's Award of Excellence for Cooking Teacher of the Year (2004).
raghavaniyer.com
Recipe on page 188.

Sarah Johnson was born and raised in California. Upon graduating from university, she moved to Berkeley to work at Alice Water's acclaimed Chez Panisse Restaurant. It was during that time that Sarah found her life's passion for cooking. This led her to travel through Europe, visiting kitchens in Ireland then Italy. Upon returning to California, Sarah continued her training in pastry at Chez Panisse and in 2014 she accepted the position of Senior Pastry Chef at Skye Gyngell's Spring Restaurant. Today Sarah collaborates with Skye and the biodynamic farm Fern Verrow to create dishes that are fresh, innovative and celebrate the fruits of the season.
Instagram: @johnson_sarita
Recipe on pages 168–9.

Judy Joo is a chef and host of the new and hugely successful cooking and travel show, *Korean Food Made Simple* (Food Network, worldwide). Her book of the same title was published in May 2016. After studying at the French Culinary Institute and working as a recipe developer for, and contributor to, *Saveur* magazine, American-born Judy moved to London to work at renowned restaurant Gordon Ramsay. A regular face on the Food Network/Cooking Channel, Judy made a name for herself as the only female Iron Chef UK. She has written for and been featured in numerous publications worldwide. Judy looks to her Korean heritage to add Eastern flavours and spices to her dishes.
judyjoo.com
Recipe on page 200.

Michael Kempf has been Head Chef at Facil in Berlin, Germany, since 2003. That year, he received his first Michelin star, at the age of only 26. More awards followed, including Up-and-Coming Chef of the Year from Gault Millau in 2010, and in 2013, he was honoured with his second Michelin star. Chef Kempf's cuisine is an exercise in elegant simplicity, combining exquisitely prepared main ingredients with fresh, unexpected accompaniments and focusing on light, modern preparations of vegetables and aromatic sauces. His love of fresh, healthy cuisine is more than just professional interest: in his free time, he is a long-distance runner.
facil.de
Recipe on page 75.

François Kwaku-Dongo was raised on the Ivory Coast but moved to New York in 1981 to study Literature. He worked in NYC restaurants while attending school, was bitten by the gourmet-cuisine bug and within a few years became sous chef at Remi in NYC, where he met Wolfgang Puck. He moved to LA and within 10 years was voted one of the best upcoming young chefs and became executive chef of Wolfgang's flagship restaurant Spago Hollywood. In addition to frequent TV and radio appearances, he has featured in various print media. François is currently Executive Chef at David's Soundview Catering in Stamford, Connecticut.
Instagram: @fkdongo
Recipe on page 116.

Christine Manfield is one of Australia's most celebrated chefs and a writer of several successful books, including *Dessert Divas, Tasting India, Fire, Spice, Stir, Paramount Cooking* and *Paramount Desserts*. One of Australia's leading culinary ambassadors, her professional life as restaurateur has included three groundbreaking, award-winning restaurants: Paramount (Sydney, 1993–2000), East@West (London, 2003–5) and Universal (Sydney, 2007–13). Her range of spice pastes and condiments, the Christine Manfield Spice Collection, is widely available at retail stores throughout Australia.
Instagram: @christinemanfieldchef
Recipe on page 114.

Anne-Sophie Pic is the only French woman to have been awarded three Michelin stars. She has also received numerous other awards and distinctions, including being named by Veuve Clicquot as 'World's Best Female Chef' in 2011. Her story is that both of an illustrious lineage of chefs and of a self-taught young woman who graduated from business school. This career path has enabled her to create an intuitive and exciting cuisine that is characterized by its innovative mixing of flavours and the constant search for complexity and aromatic intensity, which is revealed with finesse in her dishes.
Instagram & Twitter: @annesophiepic
Recipe on page 236.

Rachel Pol is a pastry chef, chef-owner of Tomato restaurant in Panama and hosts the Panama cooking TV show *Soy Rachel, Soy Foodie*. She also caters for the city's most exclusive events and is a consultant to hotels and restaurants and a regular guest chef and speaker at culinary events and conferences. Rachel is currently making and branding her own chocolate from bean to bar, using Panamanian organic cacao beans, promoting fair trade for local growers. Her project will educate about the sustainable use of the land and create educational centres for children in these communities.
Instagram & Twitter: @rachelfoodie
Recipe on page 110.

Mindy Segal specializes in contemporary American cuisine, placing a modern twist on traditional classics. Segal was awarded the prestigious James Beard Foundation award for Outstanding Pastry Chef in the Country in 2012. Her Chicago restaurant, Hot Chocolate, is the culmination of 25+ years of dedication to her craft. Her bestselling cookbook *Cookie Love* was released in 2015. Mindy has appeared on *The Today Show*, *The Martha Stewart Show*, *The Food Network* and in *Food & Wine*, *Bon Appétit* and *The New York Times*.
Instagram & Twitter: @mindysegal
Recipe on page 248.

Cyrus Todiwala, OBE, 2014 'BBC Food Personality of the Year', cooks, teaches and runs three successful restaurants: Mr Todiwala's Kitchen, Café Spice Namaste and Assado. He has also teamed up with Scottish Chef Tony Singh in the hit BBC2 series *The Incredible Spice Men*, is a regular on *Saturday Kitchen*, has authored six cookbooks and appears regularly at top food festivals around the world. He is Fellow of the Royal Academy of Culinary Arts and the Master Chefs of Great Britain and one of only a handful of British Asian chefs with an entry in *Who's Who*.
Twitter: @ctodiwala
Recipe on pages 36–7.

The Contributing Medical Doctors

Param Dedhia, MD, serves as a passionate internal medicine, integrative medicine and sleep medicine physician at Canyon Ranch in Tucson, Arizona. From lectures to one-on-one consultations, Param brings the science of medicine to the experience of individuals, helping them to live more healthily. His medical practice and lecturing explores the connections between nutrition, exercise, stress and sleep to attain optimal health.
Linkedin.com/in/param-dedhia-0066235

John La Puma, MD, is a board-certified internist, professionally trained chef and author of *ChefMD's Big Book of Culinary Medicine* and *The Realage Diet*. His current research focuses on improving the symptoms of aging and optimizing personal medical health with culinary and nature prescriptions. He is based in Santa Barbara, CA.
Linkedin & Twitter: @johnlapuma

Geeta Maker-Clark, MD, is a Clinical Assistant Professor, Coordinator of Integrative Medical Education and Director of the Culinary Medicine curriculum at the Pritzker School of Medicine, University of Chicago. She relies heavily on the use of food as medicine in her approach to healing, as well as herbs, botanicals, breathwork, conventional medicines and healing practitioners in the community.
drgeetamakerclark.com

Linda Shiue, MD, is a board-certified internal medicine physician and chef who believes that the best medicine is prevention, based on healthy food and a healthy lifestyle. She is the Director of Culinary Medicine at The Permanente Medical Group in San Francisco, CA, where, in addition to treating patients in the clinic, she also teaches healthy cooking as a building block of health. Her recipes and writing have appeared in numerous publications, including several cookbooks.
facebook.com/thedoctorsspicebox

Eleni Tsiompanou, MD, PGDip, MSc Nutritional Medicine, is an Integrative Physician trained in modern Nutritional Medicine and Ayurvedic Nutrition. She is also a practising Consultant Physician in Palliative Medicine. She is the founder of the Health Being Institute, where nutrition, physical activity, psychological and spiritual interventions as well as modern medical approaches are used to prevent and treat disease and improve health and wellbeing. Dr Eleni provides regular evidence-based training on diet and nutrition to doctors, nurses and other healthcare professionals.
healthbeing.co.uk / Twitter: @DrEleni

Luigi Fontana, MD, PhD, is Professor of Medicine at Washington University, where he is co-director of the Longevity Research Program, and at the University of Brescia, Italy.

Richard Lee, MD, is Medical Director of the Integrative and Supportive Oncology Program at the UH Seidman Cancer Center and Visiting Associate Professor at CWRU School of Medicine in Cleveland, OH.

Margaret Papoutsis, DO, Raw Dips (SN) (NT), MBANT, CNHC, is a registered osteopath and nutritional therapist. At her London practice, she successfully integrates nutrition, exercise and other complementary therapies within her osteopathic treatment recommendations.
margaretpapoutsis.co.uk

INDEX

THE AUTHOR

NATASHA MACALLER spent 30 years as a professional ballerina performing with New York's prestigious Joffrey Ballet and Boston Ballet, finishing her exhilarating career in the Broadway and Los Angeles productions of *The Phantom of The Opera*. Turning her artistic spirit to the kitchen, she now channels the same passion, diligence and precision that made her a successful dancer into her love of creative cooking. She divides her time between Los Angeles, London and New Zealand, where she teaches cookery courses and writes. She's also a highly sought-after restaurant consultant.

Spice Health Heroes, her second cookbook, blossomed from her passion for the distinctive, varied spices she cooks with while travelling and consulting. Her first book, *Vanilla Table* (Jacqui Small, UK), was published in 2015. Some 33 widely applauded international chefs contributed recipes. The book attracted great acclaim, resulting in television appearances and dazzling reviews in blogs, newspapers and magazines. *dancingchef.net / Instagram: @dancingchefnatasha*

ACKNOWLEDGEMENTS

Thank you for your generous contributions:
Spice Health Heroes was photographed in New Zealand and ingredients donated by: Wayne Fraser, owner thespicetrader.co.nz; Fenton Wood of Coppers follypurewasabi.co.nz; meats by Greylynnbutchers.co.nz; Cate Bacon, owner, theflipside.co.nz, organic saffron; Alexa Bell and Sandra Goodwin, owners flourflower.co; The Old Packhouse Market, theoldpackhousemarket.co.nz. Props supplied by: Collis Studio collis.co.nz; Republic Home www.republichome.com; Father Rabbit fatherrabbit.com; The Props Department thepropsdepartment.co.nz.

To you all with huge thanks for your support, help and humour:

Wendy & Dr. Graham Dobson, Sherry Yard, Rochelle Huppin, Jim Dodge, Elaine Skeete, Anna Seechran, Penny Subbotin, and Krystal Burtrum for your talented translations from German to English!
Testers and tasters: Tami MacAller, Sally MacAller, Matilda Lee, Ben Chevre, Neil Brazier, Alexa Bell, Roy Goodwin, Sue Lyon, Marita Hewitt, bread-pudding queen Merran Kenworthy and Kathy Kordalis.
Special thanks for your advice and assistance: John La Puma MD, Seth Crosby MD, Tim S. Harlan MD, Elmo Agatep MD, Rachelle Bross PhD, Lucy Dahill, Becky Cortese, Peter Gordon, Rosalinda Monroy, Sue Knight and Janice Wald Henderson.

Many thanks to my very patient, tireless editors, Anne McDowall and Fritha Saunders, Maggie Town for the beautiful design and Manja for the stunning-as-ever photographs.
Jacqui, thank you for the spark – and I'm still hoping to taste your world-famous curry!
And finally, thank you to each and every one of my inspiring contributing chefs and doctors; thank you for helping *Spice Health Heroes* come to life!

SUPPLIERS

UK
thespiceworks.co.uk
tfcsupermarkets.com
spicemountain.co.uk
boroughmarket.org.uk
thespiceshop.co.uk
thespicery.com

USA
thespicehouse.com
rareteacellar.com
spicestationsilverlake.com
worldspice.com
savoryspiceshop.com
laboiteny.com

CANADA
silkroadspices.ca/about-silk-road

FRANCE
anne-sophie-pic.com/boutique/epicerie
epices-roellinger.com

AUSTRALIA
herbies.com.au
harrisfarm.com.au
thespicelibrary.com.au

SPICE BOOKS AND WEBSITES

Cumin, Camels, and Caravans Gary Paul Nabhan
Culinary Herbs & Spices of the World Ben-Erik Van Wyk
The Flavour Thesaurus Niki Segnit
Healing Spices Bharat B. Aggarwal, PhD
Pepper Marjorie Shaffer
Food In History Reay Tannahill
World Spice At Home Amanda Bevill and Julie Kramis Hearne
The Spice Routes Chris and Carolyn Caldicott
The Oxford Companion to Food Alan Davidson and Tom Jaine
On Food and Cooking Harold McGee
The Modern Preserver Kylee Newton

drweil.com Dr. Andrew Weil, MD, FACP
drlowdog.com Dr. Tieraona LowDog MD
drlibby.com Auz/NZ Dr. Libby Weaver, nutritional biochemist
ncbi.nlm.nih.gov/books/NBK92774/Herbs and Spices in Cancer Prevention and Treatment